CRACOVIA
MINORIS POLONIAE METROPOLIS.
F
H
G
D
N
VISTVLA FL. REGNVM DIVIDENS.

COPERNICUS AND HIS WORLD

COPERNICUS
and his World

HERMANN KESTEN

ILLUSTRATED BY

HUGO STEINER-PRAG

ROY PUBLISHERS • NEW YORK

IN U.S.A. FIRST PUBLISHED MARCH 1945

SECOND PRINTING DECEMBER 1945

IN GREAT BRITAIN FIRST PUBLISHED OCTOBER 1945

SECOND EDITION FEBRUARY 1946

Translated by E. B. ASHTON *and* NORBERT GUTERMAN

PRINTED IN THE UNITED STATES OF AMERICA

CONTENTS

PAGE

Preface—The Celestial Revolution vii-ix

CHAPTER

BOOK ONE—HIS TOWN AND HIS CENTURY

1. Calendar-makers and Biographers 3
2. The Man of All Centuries 8
3. Poland's Greatest Son 11
4. Lost Youth 15
5. The Town of Torun 17
6. The Well-Known Time of Flowering 20
7. Our Life Is a Business 28
8. The Demiurge 43

BOOK TWO—YEARS OF STUDY AND TRAVEL

9. Copernicus in Cracow 55
10. The Foreigners 60
11. The Young Canon 70
12. Savonarola 73
13. The Astronomers of Vienna and Bologna 88
14. The Astrologers 95
15. The Beggar of Bologna 101
16. Student Life at Bologna 104
17. Rome—Ferrara—Padua 108

BOOK THREE—FAVORITE AND REBEL

18. My Uncle, Bishop Watzelrode 115
19. A Case of Nepotism, or: Directions to Servants 123
20. Life with a Bishop 128
21. Life, Part Two 131
22. The Brother's Death 135
23. Queen Bona 138

BOOK FOUR—THE ASTRONOMER

24. "For Mathematicians Only!" 151
25. A Humorist Condemns the Ptolemaic System 156

CHAPTER PAGE

26. The Long Way: From Ptolemy to Copernicus 161
27. The Copernican Theory 167
28. The Book of Revolutions 175

BOOK FIVE—L'UOMO UNIVERSALE

29. The Reform of the Calendar 193
30. The Pamphlet Against the Nuremberger 196
31. " 'Tis War, Alas, 'Tis War!" 201
32. Good Money 219
33. Some Tremendous Trifles 225
34. And Fame? . . . And the Great Works? 234
35. The New Aesculapius 239
36. The Prodigious Reader 246

BOOK SIX—THE TRUTH AND THE OBSCURANTS

37. The New Pythagoras 251
38. Bishop Dantiscus 254
39. Luther and Melanchthon 261
40. The Obscurants 266
41. The Disciple 274
42. "In Praise of Prussia" 286
43. The Republic of Letters 290
44. Funeral Song 308

BOOK SEVEN—THE SLOW TRIUMPH

45. The Readers 315
46. Giordano Bruno 323
47. Tycho de Brahe 333
48. Johannes Kepler 346
49. Galileo Galilei 362

EPILOGUE

The Great Triumph 402

Preface

THE CELESTIAL REVOLUTION

THE mightiest human in a thousand years was a Polish astronomer. Being fond of order, he began the fiercest revolution—that of science. Although he wrote about the moon and the stars, no author has dealt mankind and its false pride a heavier blow.

He was peaceful and pious, a quiet man without great power, great titles or wealth, an astronomer, a humanist who observed, calculated and thought. Yet no Genghis Khan or Napoleon, no Emperor or Pope has changed the course of mankind more radically than the canon of Torun, Nicolaus Copernicus.

For four hundred years our world system has borne his name. Every child learns today that the earth turns, and moves around the sun, yet Copernicus hesitated for thirty-six years before daring to print this observation. In his time it was dangerous to say aloud that the earth moves. Indeed it was the most impudent statement ever printed.

On account of it the Church proscribed Copernicus' book, the very title of which contained revolutions. On account of it Galileo was jailed and forced to recant and Giordano Bruno was burned at the stake. Great men were afraid to follow his simple thought.

Not until the nineteenth century did the Church strike the works of Galileo, Kepler and Copernicus from its Index of banned books. Martin Luther, the rebellious monk of Wittenberg, scoffed at the revolutionary canon of Torun—"the new astrologer who would prove that the earth moves, not the sky and the firmament, sun and moon . . . The fool would like to reverse the whole art of astronomy! But it says in the Holy Writ that Joshua bade the sun stand still, not the earth!" And Philip Melanchthon, the *Praeceptor Germaniae,* invoked the law against the Polish astronomer's spiritual license.

"Our eyes bear witness against Copernicus," he exclaimed. "Sensual perception speaks against him, the authority of the Bible speaks against him, and the one-thousand-year consensus of learned men. Therefore he is absurd."

But today there are more pious Copernicans than pious Lutherans, or Mohammedans, or Jews.

Copernicus was lucky and he was wise. Singly he defied the world, the Church and the Emperor, the reigning authors of his century (God and Aristotle and Ptolemaeus), visual evidence, learned prejudice and nude ignorance. He seemed the most impudent man in a thousand years. How else was he to conquer, unarmed save with his reason?

Goethe wrote, "Of all discoveries and opinions, none may have exerted a greater effort on the human spirit than the doctrine of Copernicus. The world had scarcely become known as round and complete in itself when it was asked to waive the tremendous privilege of being the center of the universe. Never, perhaps, was a greater demand made on mankind—for by this admission so many things vanished in mist and smoke! What became of our Eden, our world of innocence, piety and poetry; the testimony of the senses; the conviction of a poetic-religious faith? No wonder his contemporaries did not wish to let all this go and offered every possible resistance to a doctrine which in its converts authorized and demanded a freedom of view and greatness of thought so far unknown, indeed not even dreamed of."

No religion or revolution has conquered so universally as that of Copernicus and his successors. Copernicus alone freed human thought. All our thinking rests on his results; science begins with him; civilization, through him and Kepler and Galileo and Newton, has made greater strides in three hundred years than it had in three thousand. And if now Einstein writes that the simple, universally plain Copernican idea that the earth rotates on its axis and moves around the sun has not remained untouched by scientific progress; if he writes that perhaps this great discovery which could be fully appreciated only from the physicist's point of view, might under certain, seemingly impossible conditions, become irrelevant—still, without the theory of Copernicus there never would have been an Einstein theory.

Copernicus was lucky. Tycho de Brahe, dying in exile, asked whether he had not lived in vain. Kepler gave his three great laws to the world and was persecuted; Galileo in his old age ended as a prisoner of the Inquisition; Bruno died at the stake; Columbus presented the Catholic Kings of Spain with a new world, and, by way of reward, was brought back from America in irons. Columbus died in poverty and despair, and a minor explorer and writer of amusing travel accounts, one Amerigo Vespucci, named the continent; Socrates was poisoned; Spinoza was expelled from the Jewish community; and Einstein, because of his theory, from the German community.

Copernicus lived to the age of seventy and died at peace with himself and the world. In his last hour, his hands held the first copy of the book which he had dedicated to the Pope, the book which started the great war between science and religion. Throughout his life he had *otium cum dignitate,* honorable leisure, and never a worry about his daily bread. He enjoyed the beauty of the stars; he saw the little world and the great one and gazed deeply into the infinite; he had friends in Rome and Wittenberg as well as at home, in Poland. He believed that he was the first in the modern world to see truth with his own eyes—greatest joy of any mortal—and he had reason, and a kind heart.

And he had wisdom. He may have quoted the ancients: "That which pleases the people I do not understand; that which I understand does not please them. We stand apart."

Instead of talking with the masses, he spoke to none but the wise—as Pythagoras advocated earlier and Goethe later. Instead of fame he sought truth. It was by truth that he wished to live after his death.

In Poland, at night, an old man stands on his tower gazing at the stars. He observes and calculates their courses, and considers the infinite.

The true enigma of the world is the concern of a dozen men . . . The billions of men live like children. Until the time of Copernicus we were told that the earth was standing still, and we believed it. Copernicus taught that the earth was moving, and we believe it. But the difference changes countless lives.

A glance at the stars, four thousand or four hundred years ago—that is the beginning and the end of wisdom.

BOOK ONE

HIS TOWN & HIS CENTURY

1

CALENDAR-MAKERS AND BIOGRAPHERS

"I am perjured most."
SHAKESPEARE, Sonnets

"The Calendar-makers make the calendars, but God makes the weather."
ZINCGREFF, Apophthegmata (1631)

NICOLAUS COPERNICUS was born at Torun on February 19, 1473, at 4:48 P.M.

For the minute precision of this intelligence, as minute as the accuracy of a modern stop-watch, we are indebted to two astronomical books and one historical calendar compiled by several stargazers. The old astronomers—who almost always were astrologers as well, for lack of either intellect or money—took a special delight in casting their colleagues' horoscopes. Each read the other's dire future in the stars.

The astrologer Garceus put the birth of Copernicus at 4:30 P.M. of February 10, 1473; according to him, this particular planetary moment bestowed "ingeniosity."

"Nothing else?" asked Lichtenberg, adding, "Garceus was born in Brandenburg on December 13, 1530, at twenty-eight minutes after thirteen o'clock; what the planets said then we are not told." Alexander von Humboldt, who scaled Chimborasso and described the "Cosmos," regarded all astrologers as professional twisters of fact; but Gassendi, called "the seventeenth century's most famous libertine" because he did not believe in God, is shown by his "Life of Copernicus" to have believed the astrologers.

This is the trouble with calendar-makers and biographers. Overly conscientious in details which only show the abstruseness of human life, they are silent on the world-shaking facts of history. Michael Maestlin, Kepler's famous teacher; the anti-Copernican Peucer who espoused Melanchthon's daughter as well as his prejudices; Professor Mulerius of

Groningen who edited the third printing of the "Revolutions"; Gassendi the atheistic biographer of Copernicus; and finally an Italian astrologer—all have apprised us with uncanny precision of the false minute of Copernicus' birth. None of them has told us when he first saw the earth moving.

Manor books, court and academic records, church registers, a few letters, a few notes and prefatory remarks by his first disciple, Rheticus, and above all Copernicus' own book, *De revolutionibus orbium coelestium*—these are the main sources of the few documented data and details about the first half of his life. The youth of great men is full of picturesque detail. The nurse of the sculptor Michelangelo was the wife of a stone-cutter. An eagle kissed the lips of young Leonardo da Vinci. Goethe, at four or five years of age, threw his mother's porcelain out of the window, desiring applause. Petrarca loved Laura. Dante loved Beatrice. And Copernicus?

He is said to have painted his own portrait, in Cracow. What a pity he did not write an autobiography.

Of course, the author's spirit may be discerned in his book about the "Revolutions." But this revolutionary book is inaccessible and, like most world-shaking books, would bore the layman. Although it has seen five printings in four hundred years (at Nuremberg in 1543, Basel in 1566, Amsterdam in 1617, Warsaw in 1854 and Torun in 1873) and has been translated into the German, Polish, French and Italian languages, the work of the man who set the courses of stars, and of mankind, aright was never printed in English. You cannot go to the nearest book shop and buy it. There are only scattered copies of it, buried in libraries. The book has changed our view of the world, and the world's history. It abounds in noteworthy, poetic details of great beauty and world-historic importance, but few people still read it and it is out of date and out of print. Yet Goethe called its author the greatest man of our era.

There is the star called Aldebaran, "that brilliant star in the Hyades." Copernicus saw it on the night of March 9, 1497, at Bologna. Dominicus Maria di Novara, his friend and teacher, stood next to him. The eyes of both men were raised to the sky. And there, both saw the moon darken Aldebaran. It was a moment of epochal significance. A glance at the stars in Bologna, on the night of March 9, 1497, imparted a more forceful impulse to the justification of mankind than a hundred wars.

Despite the dearth of biographical sources and the virtual inaccessibility of his book, the Latin text of the "Revolutions" reveals the whole Copernicus. In it, we see a profoundly read and cautiously daring man: a man with acute calculations and miserable instruments, with world-wide views and life-long errors, with boundless pride in being an astronomer, unique and grandiose assurance and satanic power of antithesis, with conventional mistakes and a supremely original idea. We meet the whole curious blend of all great men of incongruous traits that are characteristic in this canon who dedicates his Church-wrecking thesis to the Pope, in this man who is brave enough to speak his mind about the sun but not about Ptolemy or Aristotle. It is not surprising that Copernicus did not bluntly state his views on Aristotle: he did not wish to be burned alive. (Nowadays, people are put to death by governments for less important reasons.)

Naturally, the most courageous man of modern times lacked the courage to admit that he was an innovator. What did he quote, to justify himself before the head of Christendom? Half-admitted or apocryphal hypotheses framed by heathens in Antiquity. And for what? For a hypothesis of his own? No, for Truth, which is the only Divine thing on earth if there is a God—and a truth.

Did Copernicus fail to see that he was pushing the dear Lord out into the infinite void? Giordano Bruno saw it, and said it, and was burned for it.

Is it not strange to see how Copernicus, constantly stressing the greatness of the Egyptian astronomer, Ptolemy, never ceasing to quote his observations and star tables, stripped of his authority this very Ptolemy who had been famous for 1400 years? Is it not painful and significant to see the man who corrected a two-thousand-year-old error, falling into great errors of his own and perhaps devoting the last thirty years of his precious life to an error? Yet patriarchal and at the same time Promethean was Copernicus' lifelong habit of lifting his eyes to the stars, to which his book so amply testifies. Does this lifelong view of the sun, the moon and the stars which enlightened him and us, not outweigh the narrative value of twenty adventures and a youthful love for a German Gretchen or a Polish Zosia?

And besides—do we not know more? We know his century. We know his contemporaries. We know the great man's opinions. Let us listen to him:

"From among the great number of arts and sciences by which the human spirit elevates itself," he writes in the Introduction to the First Book of his Revolutions, "according to my conviction, those should be most highly valued and zealously cultivated which deal with things most sublime and most deserving of study. To these belongs that science which concerns itself with the marvelous revolutions in the universe, with the course of the planets, their size, distance, risings and settings: in brief, which explains the whole structure of the universe. What is there more beautiful than the heavens, which indeed comprise all beauty? This is shown even by its Roman names, *caelum* and *mundus:* the Romans called it *mundus* to denote its purity and beauty and *caelum* to denote its sublimity. A great many philosophers, because of its lofty grandeur named it the visible god.

"Thus if the hierarchy of the sciences is determined according to their subject matter, that science is by far the noblest which some call astronomy, others astrology, but which many of the ancients term the completion of mathematics. For this queen of the sciences which is most worthy of the attention of free men is based on almost all the branches of mathematics. Arithmetic, geometry, optics, geodetics, mechanics and whatever other branches there may be, are all in the service of astronomy. And while it is a characteristic of all the sciences that they turn the spirit of man away from vices and direct it to better things, astronomy can do this in a particularly high degree, quite apart from the incredible keen pleasure it gives. For who would not, while constantly studying the universe so clearly arranged in the most beautiful order and directed by divine wisdom—who would not, through the constant contemplation of this, I might almost say through intercourse with it, be induced to do everything good and to admire the Architect who created all this, in whom there is the highest bliss and in whom all good reaches its summit?

"The inspired psalmist would not sing that he is enraptured by God's creation and that he rejoices in the work of His hands, if he, like all men, were not moved by the sight of this Creation to the contemplation of the Supreme Good. To what extent astronomy is conducive to the good and edification of the community, not to mention its innumerable advantages for the individual, Plato expressed well when he declared in the seventh book of The Laws that men must devote themselves to its study so that time might be ordered by the sequence of days, months and years, and the festivities and sacrifices, which give the state life and vitality might be fixed; and if anyone, he adds, thinks that this science is not necessary for one who wants to learn any other of the noblest sciences, he is greatly mistaken. According to Plato he would be far from receiving the name of a godlike man, who did not regard the knowledge of the sun, the moon and the other stars as necessary.

"However, this more divine than human science, which investigates the sublimest things, is not free from difficulties, chiefly because most of those who have undertaken to study it are not in agreement concerning principles and assumptions, which the Greeks call hypotheses, and consequently do not base their assertions on the same computations; and also because it has been impossible to compute with certainty and know with exactitude the course of the planets and the revolution of the stars without the passage of some time and after many preceding observations through which that knowledge was so to speak transmitted from mouth to mouth and thus to posterity. For although Claudius Ptolemaeus the Alexandrian, who in his admirable understanding and exactitude far surpasses the others, with the help of more than four-hundred-years-old observations brought this science almost to its perfection, so that nothing seemed to remain that he had not touched upon; yet we see many things which do not tally with what should have taken place according to his theory, and this is because certain other motions were discovered later that were unknown to him. That is why Plutarch says: 'up until now the motion of the stars has triumphed over the insight of the mathematicians.'

". . . It is well known, I think, that various opinions have been expressed on the solar year, so that many despaired of being able to compute it exactly. The same is true of stars.

"However, in order not to create the impression that under the pretext of this difficulty, I seek to conceal my fear of work, I shall, with the help of God, without whom we can do nothing, attempt a detailed discussion of this subject. For the number of auxiliary means for the study of the heavens is increasing with the passage of time and with our distance from the founders of this science. What I have recently discovered can be compared with their discoveries. Finally I admit openly that I teach many things differently from my predecessors, although we owe them a great debt for having been the first to undertake these investigations."

2

THE MAN OF ALL CENTURIES

Is it then so great a secret, what God and mankind and the world are?
No! But none like to hear it; so it rests concealed.
(GOETHE, Maxims in Verses)

NICOLAUS COPERNICUS, who rose against twenty centuries of pious nonsense as the Christian Church's most dangerous, because most hidden apostate—this "prodigal son" was, of course, more than any other, the proper heir of his time.

And like all times, his time was Janus-faced. The century of the humanists was also that of the astrologers. The age of the Reformers was also that of the Inquisitors. The death-defying discoverers were at that time sailing to all continents, against all elements, and unprejudiced artists of life were trampling on all good customs. It was the period in which men found the printing press and the philosopher's stone, in which they used the compass and the magic root. Then the printer was also a conjuror; the sailor, an alchemist. Copernicus, the revolutionary astronomer, was a medievally reactionary physician.

Soldiers of fortune, such as Cortez and Pizarro, took a handful of armed men to Mexico and Peru and gained empires. At home such a man was most likely a peasant, an appendage to his master's estate, a movable implement, cheaper than a head of cattle; or, if he rebelled and fought in the Peasant Wars, he was termed a rebel arsonist and quartered, under the law. Beyond the seas he was termed *conquistador* and appointed governor or viceroy.

It was the time of the Renaissance; the century of the Reformation.

Today, millions of superstitious Christians, myriads of scientists appear benighted beside Copernicus, the only seeing one. In retrospect, it might even seem as though the Babylonians had recorded the cycles and times of the stars for him alone. But his contemporaries did not know his name. A few canons knew of him, a few hundred peasants and townspeople, his bishop, a neighboring bishop and a small prince in the vicinity, in addition to a few calendar-makers, mathematicians and astronomers, a Cardinal in Rome, a Pope and a few hundred educated people who mostly laughed at him, such as Luther at Wittenberg or Rector Gnapheus of Elbing. Yet Nicolaus Copernicus became the immortal initiator of our era.

How much has happened, how many wars and inquisitions and invasions, to keep him from becoming a forgotten martyr! Where are there not causes and effects, facts and consequences? When Europe's nations, in the Christian centuries, went to war against the gaily polygamous Turks for God's sake (and for cinnamon and pepper), the Holy Land as well as Byzantium were lost, but many an erudite Greek was driven to Venice, to Rome and Florence—and there, from the folds of their long, gold-embroidered purple garments, the light-minded little Greeks shook many Oriental perfumes and Greek manuscripts containing the verses of Euripides, the jokes of Aristophanes, the wisdom of Socrates. Good immigrants have a way of giving far more to their unwilling host countries than they receive. Most Florentines and Romans laughed at the Byzantines. A few learned Greek. One of them taught it to Copernicus. Thus he read Plato, and found the famous passages in "Timaios" and in the "Republic"; he read Plutarch, and learned that Anaximander thought of the earth as "a smooth, stony pillar" and that Aristarchos of Samos had taught that it was moving; he read Cicero, to the effect that the earth was insignificant in the infinite universe. He learned from Cicero and Diogenes Laertius that Pythagoras had held the view that the earth was round and the most perfect forms were the globe and the circle. Many Pythagoreans, he discovered, had taught that the earth was revolving on its own axis, and some even contended that it moved round the sun which was standing still. Mostly, Copernicus found these views only half-expressed or opposed—because for many centuries it was politically dangerous to publish your opinion about the stars.

And the exploits of Ferdinand and Isabella, the first, so-called "Catholic" rulers of Spain, who, in the same year in which Columbus discovered the new world, burned pseudo-Christians on the pyres of the Inquisition expelled the Jews and slaughtered many Moors in Granada, Toledo, Seville; and the flight of Spanish Jews through the countries of Europe, spreading their knowledge and that of the Moors everywhere—cannot this mixture of barbarism and enlightenment be held to refer to Copernicus? Can we not conceive of a course of education planned for the great astronomer by those very stars which had at last grown tired of being publicly charged with pursuing the little earth and even influencing the inconsequential destinies of its insect population—mankind?

For whom did Columbus discover America? For whom did Luther reform the faith of the North-Germans? In whose interest did Poland's "Golden Age" dawn, under the Sigismunds? Did all this happen for Copernicus, for him whose fame the heavens tell—for the man of all centuries?

Great men seem to rise like comets from the jungles of the world, enlightening their whole era. This error in perspective only reveals the enormity of intellectual achievements. For a great man to see and finally express the truth which everyone ought to have read in the sky, two thousand years must prepare his education. In the end he appears, sees, knows and speaks out, is laughed at and, for the moment at least, proves to be right.

The beginning of a revolution seems just as absurd as the consummated revolution seems trivial.

3

POLAND'S GREATEST SON

> *"Poland is Catholic."*
> Polish adage
> *". . . policy, that heretic."*
> SHAKESPEARE, Sonnets

COPERNICUS was born in Poland, died in Poland, lived in Poland. The Poles hail him as Poland's greatest son.

Many Germans also claim him for their fatherland. It is not the most inglorious imperialism to want to worship the great men of other countries as your own. How many nations have made a Jew their Saviour? And besides, the Germans, settled in the center of Europe and always known as excellent spiritual brokers and cultural mediators, have done much to honor the works of Copernicus.

Fundamentally, this whole war over Copernicus is like every war, a moral absurdity. It merely proves that those who wage it, are incapable of solving their conflicts peaceably. What does the squabble of nationalities mean in view of the infinite? And what is it about? About the heliocentric theory, or about the right to put up monuments?

Great men are the property of the whole world. (The astronomers pay no attention to wars, not even to total war; these little sons of the sun are accustomed to such astronomical distances and periods that a difference of one thousand miles, or one thousand years, strikes them as a mere microscopically trivial miscalculation.) And in the days of Copernicus there were no nations in the modern sense—just as there may be none again.

The Kingdom of Poland, united with the Grand Duchy of Lithuania, was the greatest realm in Eastern Europe. In the era of Polish imperialism it reached from the Carpathian Mountains to the banks of the Dvina, and compassed the great plains crossed by the Vistula, the Njemen and the Dvina, the Dnjester and the Dnieper. It reached from Danzig, Poznan and Cracow to Lwow, Kiev and Vilna, from the Baltic to the Black Sea. This realm embraced the Kingdom of Poland, the Grand Duchy of Lithuania, the domains of Prussia, Masovia, Samogitia, Kiev, Volhynia, Podolia, Podlasia and Livonia. Furthermore, the King of Poland was sovereign over Courland, East Prussia, and Moldavia. Thus, there were Great Poles and Little Poles living under this King, Lithuanians and Russians, white Ruthenians and Ukrainians, Cossacks and Tartars, Germans, Moldavians, Wallachians, Gypsies, Letts, Jews, Armenians, Catholics, Greek Catholics, Lutherans, Calvinists, Anabaptists, Unitarians and Muslims. There were separatist Lithuanians, Moldavians and Prussians, the monks and knights of the Teutonic Order, and a multitude of aliens and emigrants. If we consider for a moment the national allegiance of Copernicus—a "problem" which caused a great deal of ink to spurt on either side—what principles are to guide us?

Copernicus, born at Torun in West Prussia, occasionally called Prussia his native country. But after 1466, West Prussia was again a Polish province, and Copernicus was born in 1473—seven years later. His sovereign was indubitable the King of Poland.

His father's family probably came from Silesia, and may have come to Cracow in about 1350. His mother's family hailed from Torun. His grandfather sided with the King of Poland against the Teutonic Order; his uncle Tilman von Allen was twice Polish burggrave of Torun, his uncle, Bishop Watzelrode, a good friend and counsellor of Polish kings. His father, Mikolaj Kopernik, came from Cracow, the ancient capital of Poland. Of his sisters, one was Mother Superior of a Polish convent, the other was married and lived in Cracow. Copernicus himself and his brother Andreas studied in Cracow and became Varmian canons under the overlordship of the Polish King. Once, Copernicus sent the King a memorandum against the Teutonic Order in which he called the German knights "robbers" *(latrones),* and in the war against the Order he was on Poland's side. All this is cited in favor of his Polish allegiance by the champions of the Polish thesis.

The advocates of the German thesis write his name "Niklas Koppernigk"—with two p's, because the Polish language knows no double consonants—and from this spelling they deduce his German descent. They further point out that there were many German immigrants and colonists in Poland, especially in the cities, including Cracow, and maintain that German was his mother tongue.

Presumably Copernicus was bilingual, as are members of all frontier populations; and spelling was no evidence in those times, for instead of one authentic way of doing it there were dozens. You wrote as you pleased then, even proper names. The court clerks and chroniclers of Cracow, Torun and Allenstein, the correspondents of Copernicus, his friends and he himself spelled the name in every possible way.

Moreover, Copernicus chose a new name for himself—and wrote this self-made name, too, quite arbitrarily. The young savant latinized his name, to make it easier on the ears and tongues of savants all over the world.

In every country, the humanists wrote in Latin. They scorned the multicolored names of the profane mob; they avoided the language of the people with its smell of earth and handicraft. They formed the international republic of science, and fought their pompous wars with the pen—with ink streaming, rather than blood. They were ahead of their time and of many times: a true scientist did not know a fatherland, any more than the dear Lord. A humanist would read the works of the old Greeks and Romans to find out what the world was really like. He denied the existence of a violet if it was not described in Pliny. However, these humanists were not only the pious sons of Antiquity but also the impudent fathers of the revolution. By his new name, while basing himself on Antiquity, a humanist seemed to say: With me the new world begins!

Deserted by etymology, the followers of the two national theses turned genealogists and found what they were seeking. Essays were written about Koppernigks and Koperniks. Among those exhumed by the philologist and file-diggers were a tower guard of Cracow, a cordwainer of Lwow and a porter at a public bath. One man became known to posterity because he had run up debts; another as the second husband of a lady who dragged him to court and compelled him to hand her first husband's dowry over to her third.

Darker centuries mistook the father of Copernicus for a peasant, baker or blacksmith, but now, since the more enlightened nineteenth century, we know that he was in the copper business. Court records are still extant which show that in Danzig, on the Saturday before Epiphany of the year 1448, he brought suit for thirty-eight hundredweight of hard copper valued at eighty-six marks and sixteen pfennigs.

Besides in the year 1454 the townsmen of Danzig gave the father of Copernicus one thousand Hungarian gold gulden for the Cardinal of Cracow. They preferred to become Polish, like the other towns and the Estates of Prussia, than to have the Teutonic Knights lord it over them any longer; and with their one thousand Hungarian gold gulden in his pocket, the good Danzigers thought the Cardinal would deem them better Catholics than the German knights. Be that as it may, Copernicus Senior was a man who could be trusted with one thousand Hungarian gold gulden as well as a Polish patriot, willing to bribe a Cardinal.

It is uncertain at what time and for what reason he moved from Cracow to Torun. In Torun he married Miss Barbara Watzelrode. Her father was a merchant of Torun, an urban and rural property owner, a jury foreman, at one time a confidant of rebels, at another a *vehme* judge, and on several occasions a partisan of the Polish King. He married a gay widow, whose mode of living was criticized when her son, Lucas, became a bishop. But since the Prussian provincial councillors rose as one man in her defense, we have it on the highest authority that the grandmother of Copernicus was "a pearl among the women in the city of Torun."

One of the merchant's daughters married Tilman von Allen, who was Polish burggrave and mayor of Torun; the other married the copper trader Mikolaj who had migrated from Cracow, and bore him four children. She remains among the least known mothers of modern genius.

The great man in the family was of course her brother Lucas, the Prince Bishop of Varmia and uncle of Copernicus. This uncle was important in the history of Poland and of his nephew. Not until one or two hundred years after the successful uncle's death did the nephew become better known than the Bishop. Most contemporaries, judging soberly, as contemporaries mostly do, thought the Bishop far more remarkable than a canon with an insipid theory.

We shall hear more of this good man, to whom the world owes much for having made his nephew's studies long and his life an easy one.

4

LOST YOUTH

"Faibles amusements d'une douleur si grande . . ."
RACINE, Berenice

"What have you done, friend, with your younger days?"
PAUL VERLAINE

GRANDFATHER Watzelrode left to the parents of Copernicus:

the house in St. Anne's Alley, in which they lived;
another corner building with two sheds;
18 gulden rent out of town and in the village of Mocker;
the vineyard in the Little Cloister;
3 acres of land and a meadow;
19 gulden rent at Conradswalde, on 9¼ acres of land,
and sufficient silver, gold and chattels.

Evidently, Nicolaus Copernicus spent his youth in comfortably bourgeois circumstances, in the house in St. Anne's Alley, in the vineyard in the Little Cloister, on his father's meadows and fields and amid implements of gold and silver.

His father, after the grandfather's death, became a juror at Torun and lived for nineteen more years. He was a gentleman who bought real estate and brought law suits, as we know from the Torun judicial records, and he was a guardian of widows—in those shrewd times guardians were appointed for widows as well as orphans. Once, we are informed, the senior Kopernik went on a trip to Breslau. And once he became a Tertiary Brother of the Polish Dominicans—i.e., in exchange for absolution of his own sins, he was supposed, to denounce those of his neighbors to the spies of the Inquisition.

The father of Copernicus died. About his mother we hear nothing. Good Uncle Watzelrode—a canon by that time—turned his nephews

Nicolaus and Andreas and the older of his nieces over to that great mutual aid society, the Church. The girl became a Mother Superior; Andreas died of leprosy. Their sister "married Bartel Gertner of Cracow and begat five children with him." Of four brothers and sisters, three lived in celibacy. The family came down in the world. A niece of Copernicus married a Prussian army drummer.

Nobody has left word for us about the youth of Copernicus. At ten he lost his father; at nineteen he went to the University of Cracow.

For a century, there were only a few scattered notes about him extant, and those were incorrect. Rheticus, the first disciple, is said to have written a brief biography during the master's lifetime; Bishop Giese, in a letter, advised his young friend to have his "elegant" *vita* printed in one volume with the great work of Copernicus, the *vita* to serve as an introduction. The project did not materialize. This life-story of Copernicus by one who for two years lived in his house and with his friends, who studied the master's "Revolutions" and turned them over to a printer at Nuremberg, has been lost.

Copernicus died in 1543. In 1654, in Paris, in the appendix to his biography of Tycho de Brahe, Gassendi published brief biographies of three older astronomers: Peurbach, Regiomontanus and Copernicus. Thus, for a long time, one-third of an appendix to a French biography of Tycho de Brahe, the world-famous opponent of the Copernican theory, was the main source of information on the life of a man whom many a great European regarded as the very greatest of them all. Bergson called modern science the daughter of astronomy; yet to find out anything about Copernicus, the father of modern science, one must read the biography of his erring opponent.

Tycho de Brahe, while frowning on Ptolemy's system as too complicated, also rejected the new one of "great Copernicus," the follower of Aristarchos of Samos—although in Tycho's opinion nothing in it conflicted with the principles of mathematics. According to him, the Copernican system conflicted with the principles of physics because the heavy, clumsy earth could not be capable of movement. Besides it impugned the authority of Holy Writ. Nothing was left to Tycho de Brahe but to work out his own astronomical system, in accord with mathematical and physical principles, yet not subject to theological censorship. "As though inspired," he hit upon a system, according to which the earth was the center of the universe.

Then too, the King of Denmark, Tycho de Brahe's protector and benefactor, was opposed to innovations.

5

THE TOWN OF TORUN

"Ah, il n'y a plus d'enfants!"
MOLIÈRE, Le malade Imaginaire

TORUN was called the Queen of the Vistula. The town is situated on the right bank of the thousand-yard-wide river. Copernicus spent his childhood there, and perhaps his school years, in the parochial school of St. John's Church. Possibly, however, he went to the Cathedral school at Kulm. The point is still debated.

In his day Torun numbered about twenty thousand souls. Two-thirds of the population lived outside the walls. When the enemy came, he killed these suburbanites first, abducted their daughters and raped their wives. Living there, of course, were only those artisans who were too noisy, such as the blacksmiths, or the saltpeter boilers and others whose trade involved fire hazards. And the poor, naturally, for the poor are both noisy and a cause of fire hazards. They lived in perhaps thirty streets, some of them paved. They had six churches for worshipping God by themselves, and two chapels; and for their sins they had a court of their own.

We know the picture of medieval towns. The largest houses were owned by the dear Lord. The towns were fortresses rather than places of abode; built not so much for the pleasure of living with others as for fear of them. Accordingly, men surrounded their lives and their towns with walls, towers, moats, bastions, drawbridges and sentries. The communal buildings, such as council and slaughter houses, were of stone and built to last a thousand years. Dwellings were of wood, loam, straw and cane, without chimneys, with smoke and the devil exiting by any odd hole. When a fire started, the townsmen dallied with small buckets and whole cities were laid in ashes. Pavements and gutters were later triumphs of civilization.

The townsmen lived as in the country, in one building with their wives, children, asses, chickens, pigs and help, male and female. The household further included horses, cats, dogs, dwarfs, evil spirits, little men and saints. Neighbors peered through each other's windows and into each other's pots; the alleys were too moist, too dark, too narrow, and so were the rooms; merchandise and vats were stored in the hallway, and men were seldom run over but frequently stabbed.

The well-to-do citizens of Torun lived in the old inner town. The house in which Copernicus was born stood on the corner of Baker's and St. Anne's Alleys. The houses there were low, some of them gabled; the corner house was three-storied, narrow, with three outside windows on each floor—unpretentious, but close to the landings on the Vistula. The children visited the ships which came in from strange rivers and from the sea. They played on the river banks and made friends with shippers and sailors. In the evenings they sat on the bank and felt the wind blow from far away.

The house at Torun may still stand. A merchant who purchased it in 1849 had modern tastes and altered the façade. (In 1939, an electrician named Juchnicki lived in the house.)

An hour out of town, the family owned a vineyard on a hill by the Vistula, next to the convent. Torun's men of wealth built their summer residences among meadows and fields and drank Prussian wine from their vineyards, of which, according to the tax records, there were twenty-five on the sunny hills. The nuns in the adjoining convent watered their flowers, picked medicinal herbs, prayed and gave the children little wooden crosses. In the blue distance were the spires of Torun, the hills to the east and the wide plains of Poland. On the wide, quiet river a boatman called out, as he rowed past.

The great sailing vessels of the Hansa came in from points as far off as Bruges or Bergen, Lubeck or Stralsund or the city of London. They sailed in convoy, escorted by armed frigates to protect them from the dreaded pirates' league of the Brothers of St. Vitalia. From Poland and Hungary, fleets of rafts came carrying pitch and honey, tar and wax. On the way back, up-river, the ships took salt and salt herring, cloth and silk and spices shipped from the Orient via Venice and Bruges. A merchant of Torun came halfway around the world. A wealthy merchant of Torun frequently paid more in taxes than the entire nobility of Kulmerland.

For a hundred years the Toruners ruled Prussian trade. They drilled their armed guards in their guild house, with Grandfather Watzelrode and Uncle Tilman von Allen as captains. The Toruners concluded trade pacts with great nations. Their town was the link connecting Poland, Hungary and Western Europe. They imported foreign merchandise and views from Venice and Novgorod, Nuremberg, Bruges and Bergen. They had houses in London. In Denmark they had fishing rights and judges of their own.

Like Danzig, Elbing and Cracow, Torun was a member of the Hansa, the great Northern European league which originated in Flanders and flourished from the thirteenth to the seventeenth century. At first its members were individual merchants, then free cities by the sea and in the interior. As many as ninety cities thus augmented their commerce and protected it from arbitrarily high tolls and from the depredations of pirates. The Hansa, supernational and powerful, built roads and canals, subdued the Kings of Sweden, Norway and Denmark by armed force, gave crowns and took them away. In its towns civil rights were first enforced, the rights of the free individual independent of tyrants and local boundaries. In them, free merchants and seafarers laid the foundation of a supernational Europe and a uniform civilization.

Rheticus, in his "Encomium on Prussia," called Torun "formerly famed for commerce; now sufficiently, for its great son, my lord preceptor."

6

THE WELL-KNOWN TIME OF FLOWERING

"O tempora! o mores!"
CICERO, against Catilina

"Of all the various ways in which the imagination has distorted truth, there is none that has worked so much harm as an exaggerated respect for past ages."
HENRY THOMAS BUCKLE, History of Civilization

"Das Jahrhundert
Ist meinem Ideal nicht reif. Ich lebe
Ein Bürger derer, welche kommen
werden."
SCHILLER, Don Carlos

"THEREFORE," Copernicus wrote in his *Commentariolus,* "thirty-four cycles are altogether sufficient to explain the entire structure of the world."

At that time Ulrich von Hutten, one of the few laughing Germans, exclaimed, "O century! O sciences! It is a joy to live . . . Studies thrive, minds are stirring; take the rope, barbarism, and prepare to be banished!" previous to dying of syphilis, inch by inch. "Times are evil," declared Andreae, a Lutheran theologian. Erasmus of Rotterdam criticized Hutten and the whole "new, bold, impudent generation," and Luther could see only "this vain hog's life . . ." Erasmus wrote: "Never was so wild an age as ours."

So violent was the conflict between the views held by some authors of this well-known European time of flowering, which was later called the time of the Renaissance and of the Reformation. Copernicus was bold enough to explain the structure of the world with a few cycles; but after due consideration of his interesting time he waited for about thirty-six years before he made public his thirty-four cycles—more than a year for each one of them. Any time is the most interesting of all times; but his was curious indeed.

Dante, Boccaccio and Petrarca, three Italian men of letters, were the first modern teachers of Europe. They discovered Antiquity. And in metaphysics, politics, ethics as well as in the natural sciences and mathematics, the scions of the Middle Ages threw off the chains of the Church and of its pan-theological imperialism.

The universities, especially the theological university of Paris, were bastions of the Church and nurseries of theology. There scholastics debated with scholastics, dogmatists with dogmatists. They did not cultivate classical literature and wrote bad Latin. Yet a Frenchman swore to the fact that even mathematics had started its march of triumph through Europe from the University of Paris, led by Heinrich von Langenstein and above all by Johannes Gerson, Doctor Christianissimus, chancellor of the University of Paris and strong man of the Council of Constance, who in 1383 came to Vienna and there prepared the ground for the great astronomers, Peurbach and Regiomontanus, the trailblazers for Columbus and Copernicus.

Thus, the Frenchman maintained, the Germans would not have invented the printing press and gunpowder and modern navigation without the aid of the mathematicians from Paris; the geographical and astronomical discoveries of Portuguese and Spaniards and Italians and Poles would not have been made; today, poor Europe still would have to do without America, potatoes and tobacco, and the very sun would still turn round the earth.

Why not? In our time, in which all is claimed and all denied, what is the value of a thesis? The Germans themselves are already beginning to doubt that they invented gunpowder. A Dutchman is said to have printed books before Gutenberg. Who discovered the compass? Was not Columbus an Aragonese Jew without the slightest idea of navigation, a Jewish poet, unfamiliar with the world, who had the Cubans mixed up with the Japanese? And Copernicus was ignominiously shown up a mere hundred years later, when his pupil Kepler declared that his thirty-four cycles were really not cycles at all, they were only ellipses.

Curious time! Carefree as birds of passage, the footloose humanists wandered from town to town, from country to country, and became idealists and rebels in the school of Antiquity. Thunderers like Brutus, flatterers like Horace, they took the gods of the Romans and Greeks into the Gothic cathedrals and mixed many civilizations. "By mixture we came into the world," they said and turned Europe into a chain of cafés. They were called "poets" and rose against the scholastics in the name of common sense. Like pepper, cinnamon or other imported articles of profitable trade from town to town, the humanists and new, foreign preachers turned up in all merchant cities and brought their new attitudes, their brazen ways of speech and a whole new era.

A German contemporary sighed: "All the beer halls are now chockfull of useless preachers. The ministerial squabble is getting to be the only national interest." It caused Erasmus, the sage of Rotterdam, to exclaim, "I am sick of Germany!"

The saints of that time had criminal traits, and the murderers were art patrons. One Pope mixed the famous "white powder"; another stormed walls and moats. The Emperor built his world empire, abdicated and became a monk. The masters of that time have never been surpassed in either art or follies. Michelangelo lay on his back on a scaffolding, with a torch in his left hand, and to the last, loveliest, most perfect detail painted what no man would ever see in the dark corner—"God sees it," he said. Leonardo, on the other hand, never finished anything he started; he left incomparably great works uncompleted; he made inventions and concealed them in the cryptograms of his hidden sketchbooks. The great names of the Renaissance became eternal symbols. Castiglione became the word for courtliness; Torquemada or Cortez meant blood-thirst; Ferdinand the Catholic came to symbolize a crowned criminal; Charles V, cynicism; Aretino or the Roman Curia, venality; Machiavelli, literary worship of power; Henry VIII, a Bluebeard on the throne. Who was so bold as Columbus and Copernicus? Who so brave as Bayard, or the Indian bishop Las Casas? Who could equal Luther or Rabelais in abuse? Were not Raphael the handsomest of painters and Alexander VI the most depraved of family men? Each was perfect of his kind, a model for a thousand years. It was a time of demigods and Calibans, a complex, wonderful time.

Customs grew more refined even in the North of Europe. Certain German court regulations forbade a gentleman to do his needs in front of the womenfolk and generally to befoul rooms, corridors and stairs with urine and other filth, to throw bones about him at table, pour beer into another's face or lay hands on the ladies under the table. A German summarized the situation: "There is too much eating. There is too much drinking. Lewd, leaping and cavorting women gather in the towns." And at the country dances the girls were "thrown over" by their partners, so that you saw "everything."

Various authorities prohibited the drinking of toasts, swearing, even whoring. "The authorities lie sick abed and want to cure others." Uninhibited preachers, determined to do their all, visited the brothels—to preach. In the public baths, naked youths bathed with their girls in the same tubs. You wined and dined there; there were lutists, flutists, trained poodles, giantesses and dwarfs, and professional fools. You were massaged by the bath porters. You laughed and loved there. Poggio described a Swiss spa, where officers consoled abbesses, diplomats shared their table with "light damsels" who shared their beds with canons, while rich merchants studied far into the night with adolescent monks.

In some places the public baths as well as public license were forbidden. Love under God's own sky was deemed unfitting. Poor procuresses were buried alive; bawds or brothelkeepers were left to carry on for payment of a weekly rental to the ruling prince. Thus does the law protect the poor from vice, and the rich from annoyance.

"The later the time, the more Epicurean the people." Business in "fair merchandise" was thriving all over Europe. A Leipzig cultural historian reported with local pride that highest prices had been paid for Saxon girls. Reformers inveighed against the bathhouses, so people ceased to bathe.

"The world is not growing old now," Luther chided and wrote another lampoon. Everybody wrote lampoons and had them printed. As soon as paper was made out of rags, the printing press was invented. Men printed books, but aside from the Bible, in which God slanders them and they slander God, they printed chiefly lampoons. They even talked lampoons. The pamphleteers spread like the plague. The plague was called simply, "It dies."

"Now they sit together in bathhouses here and there, and talk heretically against God and Emperor," people complained at the time and padlocked the bathhouses. Physicians, too, inveighed against the bathhouses—wishing to cure souls rather than bodies, for they were monks. They prayed with the patients. Shepherds, hangmen, barbers and "wise women" cured diseases. The saints were specialists. St. Dionys of Paris cured the "French disease." St. Roch, St. Quirin and St. Sebastian were called against the plague, St. Levi against podagra, St. Blasius against sore throats, and the virgin Nothburga in cases of pregnancy. It was not till later that the "Fourteen Saints Deliverers" acquired their great popularity.

A cleric such as Copernicus, who studied medicine at Padua and practiced it in Varmia, was barred from surgical practice by professional dignity. For surgery you had the barbers. They were "dishonorable" and pulled teeth, cut corns, massaged and performed operations. The cleric or trained physician healed by means of astrology, alchemy and theology. He began by commending a patient to the dear Lord and praying with him; then he examined the constellation of the planets, recommended the philosopher's stone, compounded remedies such as thieves' fingers with pulverized unicorn, cats' dung and sulphur, purged the patient, bled him and left him to live or be buried—just as today. Neither was it a pleasure to be sick in those days.

A gentleman from the second century A.D., Galen, the "Father of the Church from Pergamon," furnished the prescription. An Arab philosopher from Bokhara, Avicenna, who practiced medicine about the year 1000, provided the methods. In the lecture hall of a university the professor would sit on the platform and read a chapter from Galen; standing beneath him, the "demonstrator," a doctor, pointed with a stick to the organs under discussion; on the floor, ignorant barbers carried the corpse. No professor handled a knife.

Paracelsus, the founder of more recent pharmacological doctrines, was not born in Switzerland until a year after the discovery of America. Copernicus still faithfully employed the panaceas and "sovereign remedies" of Antiquity or the Middle Ages. His "Revolutions" came out in 1543, the year in which Cardano became professor of medicine at Padua—Cardano who wrote in his autobiography: "Among the greatest and rarest natural occurrences I count the fact that I was born in the century in which the whole *orbis terrarum* was discovered, while the ancients knew only one-third of it." In the same year 1543, at Basel, Vesalius, the founder of modern anatomy, published the revolutionary book, *De humani corporis fabrica*. Thus the discovery of America and of the universe was rounded out by the discovery of man and of his body.

Grateful humanity seemed to have but one purpose: to punish the discoverers. Paracelsus died in 1541 in disrepute, regarded as an adept of the devil. Cardano, in his seventieth year, was cast into a dungeon at Bologna by the Inquisition, as an unbeliever. Vesalius, the personal physician of Emperor Charles V and King Philip II of Spain, was sentenced to death by the Spanish Inquisition, but the "Great Inquisitor," who was a tool in Philip's hands—commuted the doctor's sentence to a pilgrimage to the Holy Sepulchre and Mount Sinai. Vesalius embarked in order to save his life and promptly drowned at sea, dying by water rather than by fire.

Michael Servet, like Columbus a maraño or forcibly baptized Jew from Aragon, discovered the minor blood circulation, and at Calvin's instance, was burned at Geneva ten years after the death of Copernicus. He lived only to the age of forty-two. As late as 1628, a storm of indignation rose in London and Paris when William Harvey hesitantly revealed his knowledge of the entire blood circulation, in his "Anatomical Treatise on the Movement of the Heart and of the Blood in Animals." It led Harvey to remark that it was far better to seek wisdom quietly in your own house than to publish hastily the results of research which cost much toil and sweat and thereby call forth storms that deprive you of tranquillity and the peace of your future.

Are not such feelings, expressed in the seventeenth century, based on the same knowledge of men and of the world as those harbored by Copernicus in the sixteenth century?

This very peril of Truth—which often stands on but two feet against the million-footed beast—appears to be its most reliable quality. It is because of such disproportionate vexations, such incessant struggles against apparently unrelated prejudices and foes, that the majestic story of the human spirit strikes us as so grotesque. The fact that men are persecuted merely for explaining the courses of blood and the stars seems so absurd that pessimists are driven to regard absurdity as the sole law of mankind. The two desires for knowledge and for virtue (viewed as one and the same by Socrates and by the Bible), by which mankind stays alive, seem suicidal to their champions: both world interpreters and world reformers are of the stuff of martyrs.

For a thousand years the Catholic Church had tried to give life a meaning, and mankind a uniform faith based upon revelation and orthodoxy. As it always happens when truth is intent on setting up a dictatorship, the dictatorship was accomplished and the truth suppressed. Now the Reformers, both within and without the Catholic Church, wanted either to restore the old truth or to proclaim a new one which went back, of course, to even older truths—for most revolutions are mere re-excavations.

The humanists, supernational as all that is great, still differed regionally. In Italy, in particular, they tended to a thoughtful enjoyment of the world within an aesthetic, neo-pagan culture based on the Greek ideal of *kallokagathia,* the union of beauty and virtue, the Hellenistic joy felt in all perfectly beautiful forms in poetry and drama, in paintings, statues, temples, palaces, gardens and the human body. The humanists of Northern Europe, on the other hand, were aiming at a sound formal education and at the purification of life, at a Divine permeation of everyday existence by means of a reform of the faith and a re-establishment of original Christianity.

Led by Gerhard Groote, the "Brothers of the Common Life" (who toward the end of the fourteenth century had founded a school at Deventer in Holland, which soon acquired influence all over Europe) demanded that laymen should read the Word of God in their native tongues. Realizing the importance of language, they knew that the old languages were the keys to the treasure troves of the European spirit, and that a man's style not only reflects his mind and his morals but retroactively reforms and educates him. Is it only the just who will find the language of justice? And can justice long be spoken without being practiced? They strove for a classic Latin and taught Greek, although science interested them only in so far as it led to a sanctification of life.

Out of this school of the Brothers of the Common Life came Erasmus of Rotterdam. This European sage of the sixteenth century was a witty man of the world, a philologically schooled journalist, a conscientious translator and a great satirist. As a philologist, he went strolling about the New Testament. His Latin translation of the Greek text started a revolution. Many revolutions have begun with translations: the French Revolution profited by the translations of Hobbes, Locke and Hume; the Russian, by that of Karl Marx; the Fascist, by the translation of Sorel; the American, by the translation of Rousseau. The history of most modern national literatures begins with translations. For contemporaries do not necessarily share the same civilization; nations live in different cultural epochs; even within each nation, different stages of civilization exist at the same time. This is why the nations often wake up as from a bad dream, when a quick translator reveals to them how wonderfully far other nations have gone.

The philologists are dangerous radicals: they go to the sources. The thinking philologist learns to scorn false authorities and finally all authorities. Thus Vesalius arrived at his anatomical discoveries because the humanists went back to Hippocrates; the ancient physician's errors brought him to nature. Thus Peurbach and Regiomontanus went back to the original texts of the antique authors because the humanists had cleaned the corrupted ones. Regiomontanus found and preserved the work of Ptolemy in Greek; it was not until Copernicus had read the Greek that he found the courage to upset him.

The road to nature led via the Greeks. From the perusal of the ancients one came to the dissection of corpses. While monks were the sole teachers, the world resembled a convent behind walls.

The humanists, disciples of those worldly Hellenes who were born to see, learned to see for themselves. The jurists ceased to ask God in His heaven, their own instinct or the common people what might be right and wrong. They leafed through Justinian and read the Corpus Iuris. The theologians, disillusioned by the scholastics and Fathers of the Church, ceased to gaze into their own hearts or at the stars and instead read the Bible in the original text, "God's own Word in its own language." They printed the Greek text of the New Testament and the Hebrew text of the Old, compared both with the authorized translation and pointed

TORUN
NICOLAUS COPERNICUS
ST

mann Giese and Moritz Ferber, canons at Frauenburg. This was no more than customary in Varmia where a few patrician families of Torun and Danzig traded the prebends among themselves. Bishop Ferber made four nephews Varmian canons; Bishop Dantiscus, three nephews; Bishop Hosius, two nephews.

Copernicus was out of luck at the first vacancy. The cathedral cantor, whose death had freed a position, had died in the wrong month. For there existed a sort of death lottery, between the Bishop and the Holy Father: the successor of a canon dying in an even month was named by the Bishop, and the successor of one dying in an odd month, by the Pope. As late as the seventeenth century Professor Broscius of Cracow—who pilfered many Copernican documents from the Frauenburg archives—was in possession of letters from the youthful Copernicus, complaining that jealousy had cost him the good canonicate.

In the summer of 1496 Copernicus had left for Italy; but in the very next year Canon Czannow obligingly died, and Copernicus got his canonicate.

For the first ten years of his new splendor, his name appears but twice in the Frauenburg records. In 1499 he acquired an allod, a country house, and in July, 1501, he asked his colleagues in the Chapter for a new leave of absence, for studying purposes, his first such leave of three years having expired. Copernicus spent these ten years in the merriest way, at Italian universities and in Rome. He moved, so there was movement—as Luther said of himself with equal justification.

A Varmian canon was well off. The Bishop owned temporal property amounting to about eighty square miles, and almost one-third of this—to wit, the three separate districts of Frauenburg, Mehlsack and Allenstein—was left to the Frauenburg Cathedral Chapter. In their districts, the canons had sovereign rights, as had the Bishop in the whole of Varmia. They had jurisdiction over everything. They distributed the fiefs, determined the services, rents and taxes; they were the judges and chief magistrates. Under feudal law, they leased the church lands to the peasants and farm tenants. They appointed both municipal and rural officials, and had the patronage over the parishes, and the fishing and hunting rights.

Varmia was a blessed fertile country with a mixed population. The proceeds from the rich possessions of the Cathedral Chapter were divided directly among the sixteen canons. The income of a single canon was considerable; aside from natural services for the maintenance of his house, it amounted to about nine thousand dollars a year, rent-free.

Of all the bishops in Prussia, the Varmian bishop was the most independent. He was a prince in Prussia and chairman of the Prussian diets. After the Second Peace of Torun, in 1466, Varmia was Polish crown-land.

The canons had become very worldly in time. Many bore arms and went riding about the country. The statutes obliged each to keep at least two servants and three horses. Beside an allotted free residence on Cathedral Hill, the *curia,* each received a farm in the vicinity of the cathedral. Their duties were easy. They had to "be in residence" at the cathedral, on peril of losing their income; but as the ecclesiastical life grew increasingly soft, presence for half a year and sometimes even complete absence were deemed sufficient. The canons also were to observe daily morning and evening devotions—*horas canonicas*—and read the soul masses, particularly on the death anniversaries of the great donors and benefactors of the cathedral; the distribution of the allods, farms, etc., followed immediately upon the final prayers on the anniversaries of the richest donors—and those who were late, or left too soon, got nothing. In addition, the canons were to advise the Bishop, take part in Chapter meetings and carry out special missions for the Chapter or the Bishop.

Anybody could become a canon. No theological education was needed, no religious interest required. In the days of Copernicus it happened that hardly one presbyter knew how to conduct the altar service. All who could evade ordination, with its added duties, did so.

Otherwise, the Varmian Cathedral Chapter was a place for cultured people. Every new canon lacking an academic degree was obliged, after one year's residence at the cathedral, to go for three years to a university, while he continued to receive his income. In fact, one lazy canon by the name of Heinrich Snellenberg, who loafed during his studies, lost his income upon his return for the express reason of his laziness.

At no time in his life did Copernicus know material worries. From his twenty-fourth year on he lived on prebends and sinecures, on the sweat of toiling peasants. So narrow-minded is our kind, or so inconsistent, that even the noblest calmly bears the inherited injustice peculiar to his age.

Copernicus rectified the astronomical error of mankind. How was he to see the social injustice of being a canon?

12

SAVONAROLA

"Jeglichen Schwärmer schlagt mir ans Kreuz im dreissigsten Jahre! Kennt er nur einmal die Welt, wird der Betrog'ne der Schelm."

GOETHE, Venezianische Epigramme

COPERNICUS came to Italy for the demise of the fifteenth century. "On commençait à penser comme nous pensons aujourd'hui: on n'était plus barbare"—men began to think as we think today, and were no longer barbarians.

How joyful life was for a young man of twenty-three, inquisitive and world-intoxicated, unworried and strangely free from the common impatience of all uncommon minds! What a joy to wander under the olive trees of Campagna, through the lemon groves near Padua, among the palaces of Bologna and the twittering ladies at the court of Ferrara; or to sit in an *osteria* with a goblet of wine, with bearded humanists, virtual inkwells of learning and citation-spouting dictionaries of all arts and sciences, and to dispute with them about the precedence of Aristotle or Plato or about the august plan of God who created the universe as a benefice of mankind, according to the rules of feudal law—who made lambs to be roasted, and carp for the Polish sauce. What a great joy to live, to learn Greek from the "beggar of Bologna," to look up at the stars with your revered, somewhat queer teacher, the great astrologer Maria di Novara! What a bright, laughing pleasure to collect manuscripts of ancient sages; to visit dancing girls; to listen, in the palaces of erudite Roman courtesans and prelates, to a mysteriously sweet song or a dialogue from Plautus! What an intoxicating ten-year span of study in Italy!

Copernicus was in Rome in the great year of Christianity's rejoicing, for the Easter festival of 1500. He met the vast flood of pilgrims from all over Europe and saw the horrible *paterfamilias,* Pope Alexander VI (bullnecked Rodrigo with the unceasing laugh), sitting in St. Peter's chair.

The Holy Father was fondling his favorite gigolo when Cesare Borgia, the Holy Father's son, came in and thrust a dagger into the gigolo's bowels; vainly the boy sought to hide under the Papal cloak; his blood spattered on the Papal cheeks; on the next day the gigolo's corpse swam in the Tiber beside a dead girl, one of Alexander's paramours.

Did Nicolaus Copernicus enjoy the sweet questionable pleasures of the first declining years of an incomparably great era? Did he yield to the seductive and dubious charm of the young days of decadence? Did he lie in the arms of one of Raphael's sensually grave madonnas? Or in the arms of a lady painted by Leonardo?

At Florence, Copernicus saw the diminutive, thundering, dubious saint, Savonarola, terrorize a metropolis until the roaring, lascivious, criminal giant on St. Peter's throne shut the tiny prophet's mouth with smoke and fire. At Bologna, Copernicus was the pupil of a great astronomer who had to make his living as a charlatan, uttering the ridiculous prophecies of a duly appointed calendar astrologer. In Rome Copernicus may have seen Michelangelo burrow into the ground like a gravedigger, in order to unearth the images of the dead, smooth "devils," the sunken marble statues of the eternally laughing Greek gods. Once he came upon a statue which he himself had copied from the ancients. Thousands of collectors and fakers were digging in the ground, filling hundreds of palaces and museums.

Copernicus' arrival in Italy coincided with the rise of the great French disease, the new merry plague. Charles VIII, the glory-mad young King of France, had just ridden through all of Italy with his noble Sir Bayard, the *chevalier sans peur et sans reproche.* Later Copernicus saw the other Pope, Julius II, who always entered the breach in the wall of a beleaguered fortress ahead of his soldiers, but who also called Bramante and Michelangelo to Rome, to build St. Peter's Church for him, and who called Raphael.

In Italy Copernicus could see every way of governing men: kingdoms in the south, theocracy at Rome, and in the north republics, princes and condottieri in their conquered principalities. Copernicus saw them all, these laughing Italians who no longer believed in God and the devil—atheists in the Vatican and saints on the highway, political derelicts offering themselves for sale, venal generals, adulterous monks, baby-killing nuns, painters of genius, architects aping Antiquity, poison-mongering collectors and blackmailing pamphleteers, fourteen-year-old cardinals and seventy-year-old despoilers of virgins.

this preacher. "Wonder words," his disciple Fra Domenico Buonvincini called his sermons. The crowd wept, screamed, howled, hung on his lips. After his sermons women threw their jewels away and tore their silk dresses; a usurer gave up three thousand ducats; the clerk who took down his speeches (we possess ten volumes of his sermons) interrupted his text: "Here, tears and emotion prevented me from writing further."

Savonarola preached. He preached against the century. Against the corruption of Italy. But the scourge of God, the barbarian, was already on his way across the Alps, to kill, burn and ravage. "They will lead our tyrants into captivity like bears, with iron rings through their noses. In vain you will wish to flee to the right and to the left—the scourge of God will appear on all sides; on all sides there will be darkness. You will find no place to hide your head. Darkness here, darkness there, all the world in tumult, earth and heaven, sun and moon." He cursed and cursed, and suddenly he would call: "Mercy! Mercy, oh God! In the name of the blood of Christ!"

And the crowd would call: "Mercy! Mercy, oh God! In the name of the blood of Christ!"

Savonarola said that an inner fire was burning his bones and forcing him to preach. The Turkish Sultan, Bajazet, asked the ambassador of Florence to send him the speeches of this famous preacher, so that they might be translated into the Turkish language.

In 1491 Savonarola was elected prior of the monastery of St. Mark's. He wrote to a prior in Pisa: "We are willing to have the simplest convents, to wear rough garb, eat and drink simply like the saints, live in cells without a single luxury, in silent contemplation." He founded a school of Oriental languages in the monastery, so that one might read Greek and Hebrew and receive the Holy Scriptures in the original tongue. Florentine laymen also went to this monastic school.

He attacked the Medici and Pope Alexander VI. Both tried in vain to buy him. When Lorenzo lay dying, he called Savonarola; he did not know any other pious man. In 1493 Savonarola was called to Bologna, to preach there. After his return he was appointed Vicar-General of Tuscany. He was the most powerful man in Florence. Lorenzo de' Medici was dead; his son Piero was banished; Charles VIII invaded Italy—without Savonarola, Guicciardini wrote, there would have been conflicts, revolution, proscriptions, perhaps a return of the Medicis as a last resort accompanied by general slaughter, and finally the ruin of the city.

Savonarola governed without a legal title. Varillas wrote in his Florentine Anecdotes: "Due to his talents, he acted with more authority than if he had been a sovereign; the public councils followed his advice; he was the arbiter of domestic conflicts and matrimonial disputes; there was no appeal from his verdict nor a postponement of sentence." He proclaimed Christ King of Florence and called on every citizen to develop himself in the Christian virtues: love thy neighbor, try to understand him, help him.

He established a council to make laws and appoint officials. He released debtors and founded an interest-free loan bank for the poor. He introduced the Consilio Grande in which every citizen, rich or poor, had the same voice. By majority vote, artisans reached the highest public positions. The nobility raged.

Gabriel Naudé, one of his earliest biographers, said: "By the sound of his voice he could make the Florentines do anything."

Gay Florence became a wailing convent. The taverns were closed, the butchers ruined by too many new fast days; ruined, the butchers walked about the streets with prayer books.

Burlamachi said: "They gather, about thirty of them, men and women together, and choose an agreeable place in the city or before the gates. There they hear Mass and receive Holy Communion and spend the day singing psalms. They flock round a picture of the child Jesus and pray and weep. They listen to a moral sermon and carry madonnas in the procession."

Savonarola, not satisfied with converting the gayest city in Italy, wanted to reform the whole Church and chastise the Pope. He dispatched a call for a Council to all great potentates. And he went about turning Florence into an empire of God on earth, an example for the world. He wanted to restore the Church's original simplicity and purity. He lashed out at the venality of the Papacy, but he was a devout Catholic and did not doubt fundamental dogma.

Alexander VI offered to make him Archbishop of Florence—or even Cardinal. Savonarola, in his next sermon, prophesied that for having spurned the red Cardinal's hat he soon would receive the hat granted to the saints and martyrs, reddened by his own blood. In 1495 the Pope called him to Rome, and upon his refusal forbade him to preach. In his Lenten sermon, the seer of Florence had prophesied—great misery, of course, like all Lenten preachers—and of course he was soon proved right.

The Franciscan, always angry at the *domini canes,* sent him a competitor. A Franciscan began to predict even greater evils. But when Charles VIII came to Italy in 1494, a week after Piero's expulsion, "like a new Cyrus, armed by the Lord with the sword of vengeance," no one counted save Savonarola, the prophet. (He had not only prophesied Charles VIII but personally called him.)

Savonarola had democratic tendencies and theocratic ideals. His watchword was: "Jesus Christus Rex populi florentini S.P.Q. decreto creatus."

He spoke at the bier of his friend, Pico della Mirandola. This cabalist and neo-Platonic with the Talmudic philosophic knowledge of a rabbi, a teacher of Hebrew long before Reuchlin, recognized the truth and science of all ages. Against the one-sided pride of the humanists, who acknowledged only Rome and Hellas, he declared: "We shall live forever, not in the schools of the casuists but in the circle of the sages, where neither Andromache's mother nor Niobe's sons are discussed but the more profound grounds of things divine and human. He who approaches there will see that the barbarians also had the spirit, not on their lips but in their hearts." This great Pico della Mirandola was now reproached by his friend Savonarola, in his funeral sermon, with having failed to take holy orders despite an inner voice coming from God. Therefore he, Savonarola, had asked God to chastise the friend—though of course he had not wished his death.

In the dispute between the adherents of Plato and those of Aristotle, Savonarola sided against both. He preached: "The only good which Plato and Aristotle produced were the many arguments they put forth and which can be used against heretics. They and other philosophers are in hell nevertheless. An old woman knows more about faith than Plato. It would benefit the faith if many otherwise seemingly useful books were destroyed. In times when there were not so many books and not so many ratiocinations and disputes, faith grew faster than it has grown since."

For moral reasons he wished to banish Catullus and Ovid, Tibullus and Terence from the schools. In addition to Homer, Virgil and Cicero one was to read St. Jerome and St. Augustine. In fact, only a few people were to learn the sciences; in general, science was noxious. The tradition of human knowledge ought not to perish, however—especially so that a few giants of science might crush the chief heretics and their sophisms. For the rest, instruction in religion, Christian living and grammar would suffice. As in the good old days, monks would again administer all knowledge and they, the "most knowing and saintly ones," were to rule empires and cities.

To the astrologers he was as opposed as his friend Pico della Mirandola, who regarded astrology as virtually the root of all godlessness and immorality. The astrologer who deduced everything from the stars, good as well as ill fortune, ought to worship the planets as gods; it was he who laid the foundation for every superstition, with chiromancers, geomancers and necromancers all relying on astrology to choose their proper hours. Savonarola wanted to burn the astrologers at the stake.

He held autos-da-fé for books and works of art, and turned the servants and members of families into stoolpigeons for purposes of a higher morality, trailblazing for Calvin and worse tyrants. He organized a kind of Hitler Youth—Florentine boys who entered private houses, took beautiful things and good books out of them by force and carried them to the pyre. When courageous people in some houses thrashed the boys, the adolescent holy citizenry was given an adult escort, a sort of S.S. troop.

When starvation reigned in the Florentine realm and the peasants came to Florence, half-dead, and lay exhausted about the streets, Savonarola had them fed by his adherents. At carnival processions he sent the children out with flowers in their hair, dressed in white and carrying red crosses, to demand gifts, part of which he had distributed among the bashful poor. In 1496 he ordered a great procession, and just as the crowd filled all streets a messenger with a green branch came riding up as by prearrangement, to report the arrival of an expected grain ship—*ecce propheta!*

On Christmas, 1496, Savonarola brought more than thirteen hundred boys and girls up to eighteen years of age together in Santa Maria del Fiore and imparted Holy Communion to the lot. The people burst into tears. *Ecce innocentia!*

About that time the Pope had thrice exhorted him to stop preaching. Michelangelo wrote to his brother that in Rome everybody was talking of Savonarola and calling him a filthy heretic; it would be best if he came to Rome in person, then they would make him a saint. True, recently five heretics had been hung, but this should discourage no one!

On the last carnival days of the years 1496 and 1497 and 1498, the great autos-da-fé took place on the Piazza della Signoria. Did Copernicus travel to Florence from Bologna, to look at this fiery world reformer and his fiery deeds?

A tiered pyramid was erected there, the kind on which the bodies of Roman Emperors had once been burned. Spread out at the bottom lay masks, false beards and fancy dress. Above them lay the books of Latin and Italian poets, of Pulci, Boccaccio, Petrarca, precious parchment prints, manuscripts with lovely miniatures, jewelry, toilet articles, mirrors, veils, perfumes; higher up lay lutes, harps, chess boards, tric-tracs, playing cards; at the very top lay paintings, especially of beautiful women, of beauties partly ancient, partly living. The painters Baccio della Porta and Lorenzo di Credi brought their immoral paintings in person.

In 1497 a merchant from Venice was present and offered to pay the

Signoria of Florence twenty thousand gold thalers for the pyramid. They had him portrayed at once and the portrait laid on the rest. Fire was set to the stake. The Signoria came out on the balcony. There were singing, trumpeting and ringing of bells; there were cries: "Viva Christo il re di Firenze! Viva Maria la regina!" Later the crowd moved on to the Piazza San Marco and danced in three rings round the square—in the center the monks of St. Mark's, alternating with choir boys; in the second circle young clerics and laymen; in the outermost circle old men, townspeople and priests crowned with olive branches. Since time immemorial bliss has been thought of as dancing. Did Copernicus see this dance of the barbarians?

Many Florentines were asking each other: "Have we become Goths or Vandals?" Savonarola himself talked of "festivals of the higher madness"—*maggior pazzia.*

Two parties evolved in Florence, the Piagnoni or Howlers (so-called because they howled during Savonarola's sermons) and the Arrabiati or Madmen (because they raged against Savonarola's reforms). The former, also called the "Whites," were the people's party; the "Grays" consisted of aristocrats yearning for the return of the Medici. Several notables were arrested at the time, for political reasons; they were charged with desiring to restore Piero de' Medici. Henceforth, Savonarola could no longer go out without an armed guard.

Machiavelli wrote:

"Fra Girolamo was excommunicated, or better, he was forbidden to preach. He had been silent from last summer to February, but now he was again beginning to preach, during the merriment of the carnival. His sermons were very forceful and all directed against the Church. The Pope and the whole Roman court felt so offended thereby, that they sent new *breves* to him and to the Signoria.

"He preached again because the new Signoria was to be chosen, and he already smelled the stake. For the city, learning of his disobedience to the Pope and greatly fed up with his prophecies which contained nothing but misery, began to turn against him. This was why he wished to put off his evil fate . . .

"Some time before the King of France died, signs of epilepsy were observed on him, and though this malady was not the cause of his death it contributed greatly to it. It was March; the Brother was preaching, and the Pope was hurling excommunications. The divided city voted unevenly. At the Signors' entry, in March, very serious Papal *breves* immediately arrived; there were many consultations. At first the Signoria was divided, and this led to the great dispute.

"On April the 8th, 1498, Charles VIII died of a stroke, and on the same day, in Florence, the Brother was involved in an event deserving detailed mention . . ."

Alexander VI who loved life, loved works of art, loved books, loved beautiful nude women and pictures of beautiful nude women, an ever-laughing old man who liked best to watch dancers and—unlike Savonarola who would turn the gay city of Florence into a gloomy theocracy—was just about to turn the Roman theocracy into an all-too-temporal Italian kingdom for his son, Cesare Borgia—Alexander VI, in the fair month of May, 1497, laid the great ban of the Church on the over-bold prior of St. Mark's monastery in Florence.

"Nowadays," Savonarola replied, "you get four excommunications for a penny. Everybody can buy them and use them against an enemy." It sounds as unabashed as though coming from Luther.

Savonarola said: "A *breve* came from Rome calling me a son of hell. I—so-called—keep neither gigolos nor concubines but preach the faith of Christ. Whoever listens to my teachings does not spend his days on deeds of darkness, but confesses, receives Holy Communion and lives an upright life. I fight to elevate the Church; you, to disperse it. Patience! The time will come when the basket will have to be opened (to reveal the corruption of Rome). One turn of the key, and such a stench will come out that it will poison all Christendom."

Cardinal Piccolomini informed Savonarola that five thousand gold ducats would change the Pope's mind, but Savonarola disdained this method. In his letter to the great potentate he wrote: "I swear that this man is neither Pope nor Christian. He does not believe in God."

Meanwhile the plague came to Florence. Savonarola dismissed seventy of his monks and locked himself in the convent with the remaining forty. "We are more than forty, and the citizens care for our needs and see that we lack nothing. Since we do not go out, they bring everything to us." Savonarola said he had remained in Florence to comfort the stricken. His enemies said he had locked himself in the convent for fear of catching the plague.

Machiavelli wrote in his letters to the Ten of the Balia:

"In the first days of this month the Brother was preaching when a man beating the drum started a great noise in the church. Swords were drawn; great tumult was about to break out but was quickly quelled. From Rome, the Brother was beset with *breves*. The Pope sent a certain Giovanni da Ghinazzano with these *breves* to the Signoria and to Brother Girolamo: to the Signoria, that it should stop the Brother's preaching; to him, for the same purpose and that he should appear before the Papal vicar, et al. Most of it had been requested by the opposition here. His party in turn strongly defended him. However, because of the heat, the plague and many other troubles, he did not preach this summer . . ."

The party strife, like the plague, entered every house. Parents beat their children; children denounced their parents. "Daily you heard threats and curses: a mother-in-law would drive her daughter-in-law out of her house, a husband would leave his wife; a woman wished secretly to warn the prophet of opposition waged against him by her husband."

Savonarola said: "I have worshipped the Lord in all sincerity. I only sought to follow in his footsteps: I prayed whole nights, gave up my peace, sacrificed health and life in the service of my neighbor. Now, it is impossible that the Lord should have deceived me . . ."

Then came the comedy of the ordeal. Savonarola and a Franciscan were to walk through the flames; the one remaining unhurt would have been protected, approved, distinguished by God. The Franciscan declared, "I shall certainly burn. But Savonarola will burn too. So the false prophet will be unmasked."

The Signoria appointed a commission of ten—five from each faction—to fix time and place of the ordeal. It was to occur on April 7, 1498, the day before Palm Sunday, on the square before the Palace. A cordon of armed men surrounded the piazza. Franciscans and Dominicans marched up in two hosts, the former silently, the latter singing. Most Florentines were disappointed when it was learned that Fra Buonvincini, Savonarola's disciple, would go through the flames in his stead.

Fra Buonvincini, led by Savonarola, appeared before the impatient throng with a blessed host in his hand. The host was to protect the Brother on his fiery stroll. The opponents protested. They said it was sacrilege.

The sky was covered; the clouds hung heavier and lower, Savonarola discussed the sacrilege with increasing fervor; finally the rainstorm broke, the flames were extinguished, in the downpour a new fire was not to be thought of. Savonarola called the rain a sign that God did not approve of this ordeal.

Why should not rain be a sign? But now most of the Florentines laughed about their prophet.

On the next morning, on Palm Sunday, while the Signoria decided to banish Savonarola, the Arrabiati and a howling mob stormed St. Mark's monastery. The monks opened fire from arquebuses and mortars. Five of the attackers were killed and three monks, Savonarola's brother among them. A fire was started; Savonarola was led off by men of the Signoria.

The people pushed him, laughingly demanded that he prophesy who were the pushers. They cried: "Doctor, help yourself!"

Alexander VI called the Dominican General and the Archbishop of Sorrento to try the heretic. He said, "This monk must be killed though he be another John the Baptist."

"Because of the costs," Machiavelli wrote in his letters, "and also because it was so desired here, the Pope waived Fra Girolamo's surrender to Rome but agreed to the Signors' asking His Holiness by letter to deign to send someone for the investigation. This was done . . ."

Savonarola was tortured; he confessed and immediately retracted his confession.

Savonarola was condemned.

In the fair month of May, 1498, Fra Girolamo Savonarola was first hanged and then burned on the Piazza della Signoria, together with Fra Domenico Buonvincini and Fra Silvestro Maruffi, the somnambulist, who had insisted on sharing Savonarola's fate. The three Brothers died silently, after being spat at and stoned by the rabble of both factions. Their ashes were strewn into the Arno. On the following day a letter came from the new King of France, Louis XII, forbidding Savonarola's execution.

Savonarola lived to be forty-six years of age. He had outlived his personal power, his compelling effect on the people even before his fall. Later, the martyr came back into fashion. Pico della Mirandola had a nephew who boasted of possessing a scrap of Savonarola's heart which could do miracles; the heart, it was said, did not burn. It had risen from the depths of the Arno and had been salvaged by worshippers. Botticelli painted Savonarola borne to Paradise by angels. Raphael in one of his canvases painted him beside Dante. Michelangelo admired him when he was dead. For the jubilee of 1500, medals with Savonarola's picture and a crown of rays were struck and sold to the pilgrims. Luther called him a martyr.

Guicciardini wrote:

"Never a monk was seen with such talent, with so much authority and influence. His very enemies had to admit his expertness in many sciences, especially in philosophy. For centuries none had been so adept in the Holy Scripture. No contemporary was so eloquent. His speech was never artificial or forced; it flowed simply and naturally from his lips, with unequaled authority.

"How am I to judge his life? There was no trace of greed or pleasure-seeking, neither weakness nor passion. He offered the example of a religious life; he was pious, charitable, obedient to the monastic rules, devout not merely on the surface but in his heart. In none of these points could his enemies discover the slightest fault in him, no matter how much they labored during the trial.

"He carried out a holy and admirable work with his moral reform. There never was so much virtue and piety in Florence as in his days, and the fall of virtue and compassion after his death affords us with the measure of the good that he accomplished. No more public gaming tables, little private gambling, the taverns closed, the women modestly dressed, the children leading a holy life. Led by Fra Buonvincini they went to church in groups, wore their hair cut short and abused and stoned drunkards, gamblers and immodestly dressed women.

"In short, the works of this great man were precious. Since some of his prophecies had been fulfilled, many people continued to believe in his Divine inspiration despite his excommunication, trial and death at the stake."

Thus far Guicciardini. And Copernicus? All Italy, all Europe was talking about this monk, of his attacks on the Holy Father, of his attempts to reform the Church, of his end on the gallows and in the fire. And Copernicus? Did he see this pyre lighted for a bold innovator?

13

THE ASTRONOMERS OF VIENNA AND BOLOGNA

> *"I have often stated that in my opinion the sky does not mix decisively in particular affairs. However, since I am being commanded . . ."*
>
> JOHANNES KEPLER (in a letter to Emperor Rudolph, 1606)

MÜLLER'S world-wide fame was said to have impressed young Copernicus so deeply that his greatest ambition was to become a second Müller.

In fact, he was rather impressed by the man, by this Johannes Müller who knew the skies better than any one before him—who was called to Rome by the Pope because of his fame. After his death legend made him bishop of Regensburg and buried him in the Pantheon because of his (astronomical) virtues. In his lifetime, Copernicus was never so famous as this Müller. After death, of course, the fame of Copernicus surpassed that of Müller a hundredfold; the bitter glory of the dead . . .

Regiomontanus-Müller was still in his thirties when the Pope called him to Rome to reform the Christian calendar. But Copernicus, in his dark province, at almost seventy got one reprimand after the other from his bishop, on account of his young housekeeper, with whom he allegedly—or even actually, perhaps. . . .

Müller was a great man, but who was he to be compared with Copernicus?

On the other hand Gassendi wrote that without Regiomontanus-Müller and his teacher Peurbach there might have been no Copernicus at all.

Peurbach and Regiomontanus are considered the restorers of astronomy in Christian Europe. Both died young—one at thirty-seven, the other at forty. The Austrian Georg Aunpekh (1423-1461, surnamed Peurbach after his birthplace) was at the age of thirty a famous humanist, and unpaid lecturer—the first, by the way, to give humanist lectures in Germany: he commented on Virgil, Horace and Juvenal at the University of Vienna. He tried to earn his bread by tutoring and astrology, but was compelled to borrow money and starve. Finally, his astrological hocus-pocus won him patrons including an Emperor, a King of Hungary and Bohemia, a Duke of Tyrol and a Bishop of Grosswardein.

In 1451 he began his astronomical observations. At Padua he lectured and met Cardinal Nicholas of Cusa who would gladly have taken him into his service. But instead Peurbach returned to Vienna where he gave the famous lectures on his "New Planetary Theory" in 1454. This theory had fifty-six Latin, one Italian, one Spanish, one Hebrew and four French editions. Unlike Ptolemy's theory in the Almagest, it does not start with observations, but explains the figures of the planetary motions. He attempted to re-establish the old hypothesis that the celestial spheres were concrete and material; but he was also the first Christian astronomer to use the most important contribution of the Arab astronomers: trigonometry. Peurbach and Regiomontanus first had the great notion to employ the sky as a timepiece. From its movements they deduced the true times of their observations. They invented this procedure because they lacked precise clocks, later, when the clocks grew better, it was used to test them.

Müller-Regiomontanus (1436-1476) was a child prodigy. A student at the University of Leipzig at the age of eleven, he was the author of a yearbook full of the most difficult astronomical computations, the motions of the planets, at the age of twelve—his manuscript still shows his childish hand. He came to Vienna as a fourteen-year-old boy in order to hear the great Peurbach, immediately computed the yearbook for 1451, and at the age of fifteen became court astrologer to Emperor Frederick III. He read in the stars the fate of the emperor's fiancée, Leonore of Portugal (incorrectly—but this was not realized until later).

This child prodigy earned legitimate world fame under his name Johannes Müller as the greatest astronomer of his century; posterity called him Regiomontanus or Königsberger after his birthplace of Königsberg, in Franconia, made a legend of him and gave him world fame for another reason, this time undeservedly, to wit, as the greatest astrologer of the Occident. Thus Müller under two different names acquired two different kinds of world fame in two different epochs.

Having begun as Peurbach's pupil, Regiomontanus became his assistant, friend and successor, and greater than his teacher.

The two astronomers manufactured crude instruments for the observation of the positions of the planets, and discovered divergences from the positions stated in the Alphonsine Tables.

Perpetually in need of money Peurbach computed yearbooks and tables of eclipses. When the celebrated Cardinal Bessarion was in Vienna, as Papal Nuncio, he called on Peurbach and invited him to Italy, to obtain the great astronomer's advice in translating the Greek original of Ptolemy's *Almagest*—the astronomical Bible which in Europe was known only in the Latin translation of an Arab edition of a Syrian translation. Bessarion was that honorable Greek and bishop of Nicaea who had accompanied the Byzantine Emperor to Ferrara, to help unite the Greek and Roman Churches at the Council, but was converted to the Roman Church instead, remained in Italy and helped to spread the literature of the ancient Greeks in Europe.

Finally, poor Peurbach obtained a paid commission from Cardinal Bessarion, to write a commentary on Ptolemy; but before he could complete the first six Books of the *Extract from the Almagest* or *Epitome,* he died. On his deathbed he asked his favorite pupil, Regiomontanus, to complete this work. The people of Vienna who let so many of their authors starve and toasted them after their death, buried him in St. Stephen's Cathedral.

After Peurbach's sudden death the Cardinal Bessarion took Müller to Italy and commissioned him to look for Greek manuscripts and to write his trigonometry. And Müller did both things and for seven years moved from city to city.

For four years Regiomontanus was professor of mathematics at the first Hungarian university newly founded at Presburg; he computed astronomical tables and bought books for the king who was a slave of astrology. (Martin Ilkusch, the court astrologer, later gave some books of Regiomontanus to the library of the University of Cracow.)

In the spring of 1471 Regiomontanus followed an invitation from his friend and pupil Bernhard Walther, a wealthy Nuremberg patrician, and settled in the Free City, the treasure-box of the German Reich, full of clockmakers, humanists, and, owing to its extensive trade relations, rich in scientific reports from all over the world. In the observatory which Walther had built for him on Rosengasse, Regiomontanus observed the comet of 1472. There, on Rosengasse, Regiomontanus set up a mechanic's shop, where the best astronomical instruments and compasses were manufactured. There, he founded a printing establishment. He planned to publish the most important mathematical, astronomical and physical works of antiquity and the Middle Ages, taking good care to avoid the innumerable errors contained in the old manuscripts, in sum: twenty-nine classical works, nine in new Latin translations and twenty-two of his own works. He printed only seven books, the first of which were his teacher Peurbach's new theory of the planets and trigonometrical tables as well as his own "Ephemerides." These tables, containing the daily positions of the planets, became widely known a few years later through the Nuremberg geographer Martin Behaim, who built the first globes, and won world-wide renown when they guided safely across the seas a number of great discoverers, such as Diaz, Columbus and Vasco da Gama. In 1474, Regiomontanus brought out the first German calendar. Finally, in July, 1475, he followed the Papal bid to Rome, to correct the calendar of Christendom, and died the year after, at the height of his activity.

Regiomontanus was a scholar with a passion for writing. He gave himself marks on his work, and praise or reprimands as the case might be. Thus he miscalculated one of the numberless problems he liked to send to scholars all over the world and castigated himself with the words: "You've been too hasty!" whereupon he completed his calculations, correctly this time, on a separate sheet of paper. He wrote down whatever occurred to him. And he constantly had new ideas.

In 1464 he wrote to Bianchini: "But I do not know whither my pen will run; it will use up all my paper if I don't stop it. One problem after another occurs to me, and there are so many beautiful ones that I hesitate as to which one I should submit to you." He would often notice at the end of a problem that he had forgotten something and would add a second or even third conclusion. There are 688 problems and theorems in his writings, and he worked out three to six solutions for many of them.

Mathematics was his hobby, astronomy his passion. He wanted to reform the whole science of the stars. In a letter to the Rector of the University of Erfurt he wrote that he could only regret that today people were called astronomers who had somehow learned to compute the orbits of the stars, who were astronomers at home in their study, but not under the open sky. In his own printing shop he did not publish any of the popular writings about comets or astrological almanacs. But his own almanacs, entirely free from astrological trimmings, were corrupted by the addition of such material only a few years after his death. It is true that these additions considerably increased the books' sales, because they dealt with the influence of the planets and signs of the zodiac on human destiny, the most favorable hour for bleeding, on rules of health, etc. In the end, only the astrological insertions were reprinted, under various titles such as "Brief concept of the natural art of astronomy by the world-famous Johannes Königsberger." These were later taken over in the "Great Book of the Planets" which appeared in innumerable editions until 1852. Annual prophecies under the name of Johann Königsberger were published until 1803.

Regiomontanus realized at an early date that the prophecies of the astrologers could not be correct as long as the planetary orbits were not known with greater exactitude. His observations in Vienna revealed discrepancies in his computations of the positions of Mars; despite his advance calculations he was unable to find Mercury; nor did his actual observations of Venus confirm his computations.

Maria Novara, Copernicus' teacher, refers to Regiomontanus as his teacher.

The *Extract from the Almagest,* by Peurbach and Regiomontanus, was used by Copernicus and Galileo.

The Nuremberg admirer of Regiomontanus, Georg Hartmann (1489-1564), a skillful constructor of sundials and globes, owned a note, allegedly torn out of a letter of Regiomontanus' which contained the following words: "it is necessary to revise somewhat the motion of the stars in view of the motion of the earth."

Hartmann preserved this note as a great treasure because he interpreted it as a proof of Regiomontanus' belief in the motion of the earth. What did the astronomer really mean by this phrase?

The people had made a wizard out of him: he was said to have created an iron fly which, rising from his hand, flew back to it at his command; he also had sent a wooden eagle out to greet the Emperor, and then let it fly ahead of him, into the city. Walther, who survived his master by twenty-eight years, published his own and Regiomontanus' observations one year after the death of Copernicus.

If Peurbach and Regiomontanus came to the attention of Copernicus only through their fame, their writings and the lectures, he heard about them at the Cracow university—and if he heard Brudzewski, the astronomer and mathematician of Cracow, speak in public only about Aristotle—his work with the "astrologer of Bologna," Maria di Novara, is twice attested by Rheticus.

In the *Narratio Prima,* published in 1540, Rheticus reported: "My teacher made observations with the utmost care at Bologna, where he was not so much the pupil as the assistant and witness of observations of the learned Dominicus Maria; at Rome, where about the year 1500, being twenty-seven years of age more or less, he lectured on mathematics before a large audience of students and a throng of great men and experts in this branch of knowledge; then here in Frauenburg, where he had leisure for his studies."

And again, in the preface to his "Ephemerides for 1551," Rheticus wrote: "He lived with Messer Maria of Bologna, whose calculations he knew exactly and at whose observations he assisted."

The fairest fame of this Maria, who died at fifty, in 1504, after twenty-one years as the "astrologer of Bologna" and professor at the university, rests on his disciple—Copernicus. Maria's writings have been lost, except for a few astrological almanacs which he was required to publish annually under orders of the university: a calendarium listed the moon phases and the positions of the planets, as well as the resulting "good" and "evil" days. But on March 9, 1497, Maria and Copernicus watched as Aldebaran, that "brilliant star in the Hyades," was eclipsed by the moon (*De revolutionibus orbium coelestium,* 4,27); it was the first astronomical observation which Copernicus exploited scientifically, to prove his theory of the lunar parallaxis.

It was Gassendi's belief that Maria and Copernicus were bound to attract each other because the "astrologer of Bologna" was also as Kepler described Copernicus, "free in mind and soul."

With two of his research results, Maria hoped to shatter the allegedly unshakable Ptolemaic system. The first was his erroneous discovery of a systematic increase in the latitudes of several places in southern Europe; the second was his true discovery of the decrease in the obliquity of the ecliptic from the days of Antiquity. Maria di Novara, spellbound by the new Platonism, sought to express the structure of the universe in terms of simple mathematical relations.

Georg Christoph Lichtenberg, the wittiest of mathematicians, wrote: "With this Maria, Copernicus emulated Regiomontanus's experience with Peurbach: the pupil soon turned into a friend and assistant. Maria's whim was to believe that the latitudes had noticeably changed since Ptolemy's day—that the one of Cadix, for instance, had increased by more than a full degree. He presented this opinion to Copernicus, and the teacher is said by Gassendi to have been overjoyed at the pupil's failure to dissent. This joy on the teacher's part, on such an occasion, rather honors the apprentice and his failure to dissent does not discredit him—even if it should have been more than a mere compliment, as I suspect.

"Quiet, strict, grave Copernicus was not the flattering sort, nor was he a volatile famous traveler, of whom such flying judgments may be noted. These men were living together and had talked this thing over. I think: perhaps his very eminent sense of order and simplicity in nature found the Ptolemaic confusion odious even then, so that he thought of improving it. In such a situation, any new opinion uttered by a famed and experienced man sounds well—if only because you hope perhaps to find a means of salvation in it, or else at least some support for the belief that one day you will throw all the rubbish away and start afresh."

Novara was a splendid *observing* astronomer. Libri, in his "Histoire des sciences mathematiques en Italie," lauds him for re-determining the positions of all stars listed in Ptolemy's "Almagest." Copernicus, in the original manuscript of the "Revolutions" (Vol. 3, Ch. 6—where the figures on the obliquity of the ecliptic from Ptolemy's time onward are compared), quoted the results of Peurbach, Regiomontanus and Maria di Novara side by side, although in the printed book Novara's figure was omitted and the text reads simply: "As regards our time, finally, we have by frequent observations during thirty years found about 23 degrees and 28 2/5 minutes, from which Georg Peurbach and Johannes Regiomontanus, who did not long precede us, differ but slightly."

For his daily bread, his position and his fame, of course, Maria—despite the bold courage he displayed against the astronomical prejudices of his colleagues and his era—was indebted throughout his life to a worse prejudice: astrology. As a rule, a revolutionary is an innovator in his field alone, and in all others is as reactionary as his century. Besides, a professor's pay was so small that an astronomer had to turn charlatan to eke out his income.

The astrological superstition, a popular pastime for many thousands of years, was at that time also of military, political, intellectual and religious importance. It was a science like any other, with scientific apparatus, and astronomical knowledge was employed by it to determine the positions of the planets. Aristotle's metaphysics provided the nature-philosophical contents for any one who would relate the course of the stars to his own fate.

Kepler, in his treatise on the stargazing superstition, wrote: "This Astrology may be a foolish damsel; but dear Lord, what would become of her mother, the highly sensible Astronomy, if she did not have this foolish daughter! After all, the world is a good deal more foolish . . ."

14

THE ASTROLOGERS

"A dying man in Pomerania to his pastor who was pestering him, 'To please you, I will believe in a resurrection—but you will see that nothing is going to come of it.' "

A dying man in Pomerania

"God! God! on what can mankind base a faith, by which they hope to be happy forever!"

GOTTHOLD EPHRAIM LESSING

"Glocester: *These late eclipses in the sun and moon portend no good to us. . . . 'Tis strange. (Exit.)*
Edmund: *This is the excellent foppery of the world, that when we are sick in fortune—often the surfeit of our own behavior—we make guilty of our disasters the sun, the moon and the stars: as if we were villains by necessity, fools by heavenly compulsion; knaves, thieves and treachers, by an enforced obedience of planetary influence; and all that we are evil in, by a divine thrusting on: an admirable evasion of whore-master man, to lay his goatish disposition to the charge of a star! My father compounded with my nativity was under Ursa major; so that it follows I am rough and lecherous. Tut, I should have been that I am, had the maidenliest star in the firmament twinkled on my bastardizing . . ."*

SHAKESPEARE, King Lear

SCIENCE, or rather Truth, had three great enemies in the century of Copernicus: faith, unbelief and superstition.

From the rubble of temples and manuscripts the humanists dug up the laughing reason of Greece and its grinning madness. They laughed at ancient superstition with the Athenian comedy-writers, and argued against it with the dignity of Roman philosophers. As they were copying the wisdom of the ancients, the dust of age-old folly clung to their fingers and stuck in their hair; along with mockery, they inherited its object.

Instead of God, the enlightened disciples of Antiquity and of the Arabs believed in the stars. Laughing at their priests, they bowed down before astrologers.

We know that both the philosophical fools, who like to see only themselves and the present, and the historical fools, who in the dust of libraries and ruins mean to gaze into the hearts of the dead, are sages in comparison with prophets and fortunetellers. For cash, the astrologers read from the relative position of the planets, to each other and to the signs of the zodiac, what their clients must do and expect. Sometimes, in foretelling the future, they actually determined it—for the clients made their decisions in accord with the prophecies, and in a manner likely to make them come true.

Copernicus dedicated the book of his life, his main work, "On the Revolutions," to Pope Paul III. Theoretically, this book put an end to astrology. Yet Mendoza reports about this same Pope: "The influence of the stars on the success of human activity was hardly questioned in this period. Paul III would call no important meeting of the Consistory and take no trip, without choosing his days and observing the constellation. An alliance with the King of France met with the objection that the Royal and Papal nativities did not conform. This Pope seems to have felt himself ringed by a thousand noxious influences: not merely the natural ones of the world, but also the supernatural ones of a stellar configuration; it was his purpose to *consider* duly the power of one as well as of the other, to shun its disfavor, utilize its favor, and skillfully steer to his goal between all the rocks menacing him on all sides."

This was the Pope whom Leopold von Ranke called, "A man full of talent and spirit, and penetrating intelligence, placed in the highest position!" But he was a plaything of the astrologers—like Wallenstein who had his Seni, his Kepler; like most of the kings of the time; like many cities who numbered among their officials such astrologers as Johann Reyer of Amorbach, who was employed in Frankfurt-on-Main as physician and astrologer. Reyer predicted bad weather to the Council, in writing, whenever he was out of town, and recommended a procession as an antidote.

The University of Cracow at times might lack professors of medicine and of astronomy, but it always had an astrologer. Children of the better families had their nativities cast. Goethe himself began his autobiography with the position of the planets at the moment of his birth. Cardano, in his autobiography *De propria vita,* wrote that his entire youth was spoiled for him by an astrologer's prediction that he would not live past his fortieth year—or his forty-fifth, at the most. He wrote this at the age of seventy-six, "otherwise still feeling tolerably happy," and still faithfully attributing an influence upon his talents and future fortunes to the stars which shone on his birth.

Astrologers were the great puppeteers of the century. The mighty of the earth jerked at their strings. From Paris and Toledo, their printed forecasts went all over Europe and frightened people nearly to death by predicting wars, comets, earthquakes, floods and epidemics. The astrologers evolved their own historical philosophy, their own theogony. According to them all religions originated from the conjunctions of Jupiter: Judaism from the one with Saturn. Mohammedanism from the one with Venus and Christianity from the one with Mercury. The conjunction of Jupiter with the moon, they believed, would bring the Anti-christ. Checco d'Ascoli, in casting the nativity of Jesus Christ, reached the correct conclusion that Christ had died on the cross; only, prophesying backward, he failed to foresee that the Florentines would burn him for it.

Geomantics, chiromantics and other wizards needed the astrologers' help, because of the constellations. Of course, people also believed in ordinary omens—such as a goose getting the pip, or a horse dropping a shoe—and there were magic formulas against everything, including evil magic. Meteors, comets, signs in the sky, cloud formations, the flight of the birds, images of the Virgin which winked or shed tears, prolonged rain: all that meant no good. (Any peasant was able to confirm that prolonged rain did no good.)

Poggio—the radical who would not believe in the inequality of men and scoffed at the nobility—was a believer in omens. "Near Como," Poggio reported, "four thousand dogs were seen in the evening, on the road to Germany; they were followed by a multitude of cattle; then came a host of armed men on foot and on horseback, partly headless, partly with heads scarcely visible, and finally a giant horseman followed by another herd of cattle." And on the coast of Dalmatia a triton appeared with beard and horns, a satyr of the sea, with the lower body of a fish, stealing girls away from the shore; he was finally overpowered by five strong washerwomen. Poggio did not doubt it; hadn't he seen the triton's wooden image at Ferrara?

The astrologers also read Virgil; the page they happened to open constituted an oracle. They were on the best of terms with specters and dead people. At that time people still lived with specters and with their dead—who would return, for instance, to steal children. The dead were conjured up and asked for their secrets, as if the dead, in any case, were shrewder than the living—as if death made every idiot wise.

Astrology had come from Babylon, from Greece and Rome and from the Arab countries. Thomas Aquinas had sanctioned it. No doctor would cure without astrology; and every limb obeyed a different star. The astrologers also foretold the weather, and some of them made it. It reassured people to believe in the stars. Everything was written in the stars. Everything was predetermined. A child's fate was to be read in the stars, as were the secrets of the future and the mysteries of the world. The faith in the stars gave the littlest man an importance equal to that which an Aryan of today derives from his anti-semitism.

True, Petrarca and the Italian novelists were laughing at the astrologers. Villani called astrology a vice, and what was worse, a vice inherited from the old Romans. Pico della Mirandola said that all immorality was due to the faith in the stars—why did the astrologer not worship the stars as gods? Guicciardini, the Florentine historian, praised the luck of the astrologers: they found credence if they told one truth among a hundred lies, while others lost all credit for one lie among a hundred truths.

Regiomontanus bitterly assailed the astrologer Johannes Stoffler. Tycho de Brahe—who was an astrologer himself, published prophecies and annually compiled prognostics for the Danish King—wanted to write a book entitled, "Against the Astrologers for Astrology" *(Contra Astrologos pro Astrologia)*. In his booklet about the New Star, he wrote: "The daring astrologers, the exquisite and subtle calculators who carry on their astronomy . . . behind the stove, that is to say in books and tables, but not in the sky itself. Many of them do not even know the stars—I shudder to note the fact—and this is how they consult them *(sic itur ad astra)*." And he derides the astrologers who are so mad as to state planetary positions exactly to the minute or the second, basing their statements on the Alphonsine Tables, or on the Prutenic ones (compiled by Reinhold, following Copernicus)—although the conjunction of Saturn and Jupiter in 1563 had found the Alphonsine Tables in error by a whole month, and even the Prutenic Tables could scarcely fix days precisely, much less minutes or seconds.

It was Copernicus who theoretically exterminated astrology, casting the earth from the center of the universe out into endlessness and dependency, and man into insignificance, and moreover, changing the sun from a planet into a star. And yet in the very first treatise, in which Copernicus was celebrated and his great work announced and explained to the world, astrological superstition celebrated one of its most splendid triumphs. Rheticus, in his *Narratio Prima,* in which he chiefly dealt with the contents of Book III of the "Revolutions," inserted an absurd astrological discourse: "On the dependency of the world's monarchies upon the movement of the above-mentioned eccentric circle."

"Now I will add a prophecy," Rheticus wrote there. "We see that all monarchies have started with the center of the eccentric circle located in some eminent point of this small cycle. Thus the Roman Empire became a monarchy when the sun's eccentricity was greatest, and with its decrease that Empire, senescent as it were, also grew weaker and weaker and finally perished entirely . . .

"But when the center of the eccentric circle will reach its mean distance on the opposite side—that time, we hope, will mark the arrival of our Lord Jesus Christ. For this was the point in which the center of the eccentric circle stood at the time of the Creation. This calculation does not differ much from the word of Elijah, who in Divine inspiration prophesied that the world would endure for only six thousand years; in this period of time, almost two cycles will have been completed.

"In truth, therefore, this small cycle is that wheel of fortune *(rota Fortunae),* by whose rotation the empires of the world originate and change. In this cycle, as it were, all the events of world history are enclosed . . ."

This discourse was addressed especially to Johann Schoner of Nuremberg—since the whole *Narratio Prima* was merely a letter which Rheticus promised to send to his teacher in Nuremberg, when he set out for Frauenburg, to call on Copernicus and study his theory. Schoner had authored a whole textbook of astrology. And his friend Melanchthon had tried systematically to determine the nature-philosophical bases of astrology and to unite this allegedly scientific astrology with a reasonable conception of the Christian faith. Melanchthon wanted to present astrology as one more proof of the glory of God.

In his mathematical and astronomical books Rheticus, the pupil and friend of Schoner and Melanchthon, made other avowals of his faith in astrology. But the most candid confession is found in this *Narratio Prima,* in which he proclaimed and explained the new doctrine of Copernicus. And he wrote this treatise in Copernicus' house, before the master's eyes.

What a crazy time! What an obscure existence of reason! Its very disciples were fools.

It appears, this great book of Copernicus—dealing the coup de grâce not to astrology alone but to entire false world systems, to scores of centuries, to churches and utopias—this anti-astrological work appears, is announced by an astrologer, Rheticus, in a treatise addressed to an astrologer, Schoner, and is dedicated to the plaything of the astrologers, to Pope Paul III, who at the same time is head of the Catholic Church and chief of the geocentric, anthropocentric religion!

Kästner, the witty epigrammatist, said in his "History of Mathematics": "One might think that he who takes the sun for a star, and lets the earth circle round it like other planets, could not think much of astrology, for which the sun must be a planet and everything must move around the earth. Still, Rheticus found in the path followed, according to Copernicus, by the center of the eccentric cycle of the earth, the real astrological 'wheel of fortune.' "

15

THE BEGGAR OF BOLOGNA

"They are but beggars that can count their worth."
SHAKESPEARE, Romeo and Juliet

"Der wahre Bettler ist
Doch einzig und allein der wahre König!"
LESSING, Nathan the Wise

IN ITALY Copernicus learned Greek. There were professors of Greek in Bologna and in Padua—Musurus in Padua, and Codrus in Bologna.

As a young man, for ten years, Antonius Urceus Codrus was tutor to a son of the Master of Forli. He lived in the palace, but in a room that was so dark that he left his oil lamp burning even in the daytime; studies, he said in drawing a maxim out of the darkness, had to smell of oil. Once, he went out and upon his return found the street full of people and smoke: half the palace had burned down. His room was a pile of cinders, his manuscript was burned, a precious book that he had borrowed was burned. He heard it all from the servants; in vain despair, he kept asking, "My manuscripts are burned too?" and they repeated, "Yes, the manuscripts too"; he queried further, "My books too?" "Yes, the books too." And so he planted himself before an image of the Virgin and cried out to her: "Hear what I tell you—I am not insane, I speak deliberately! If I should call on you to help one day, in the hour of my death, you need not listen and lift me up to your own for I wish to dwell with the devil through all eternity!"

After such blasphemy, to be sure, he hid out for six months with a woodchopper; not until after the Master of Forli had died did he move to Bologna, where he was given the chair of Greek grammar and kept it until his own death (in 1500).

Petrarca and Boccaccio had inspired the study of Greek; the fugitive Greek scientists had furthered it. Hellenism flourished in Florence, later in Venice. After 1520 the Greek emigrants died out; but in the meantime the humanists in Northern Europe had learned Greek and preserved the tradition: Erasmus of Rotterdam, the brothers Estienne (Henri Estienne died in the poorhouse at Lyon, having ruined himself for Greek manuscripts) and Guillaume Budé, who induced King Francis I of France to found the Collège de France.

Antonius Urceus owed his nickname, Codrus, to a witticism. Once, when a rich nobleman met him in the street and by way of greeting commended himself to Urceus, the humanist replied: "Great gods! How far we've come—Jupiter commends himself to the beggar!" (The Latin for "beggar" is *codrus.*)

He was short, thin, prematurely bald, always pale because he was ailing, with hollow eyes that made him appear dissipated, although his life was one of temperance. Politianus read his Greek epigrams to him; everywhere he had friends, such as the great Pico della Mirandola and the famed Venetian printer, Aldus Manutius. Doctors, professors and public officials came to his lectures. He was polyhistoric; a pupil said in his praise that he interpreted the whole of life—all arts, every science, the laws, poets, philosophers, physicians, mathematical works, the aphorisms of Hippocrates, the surgery of Heliodorus, Galen, whatever you wanted. But Codrus had thus extolled Homer: "Hearing and studying him, you will hear and study all the arts and sciences and all the knowledge of man."

He was unselfish. For years, he lectured on Greek without pay and had to tutor privately for a living. He was a bachelor and liked to complain of the children he did not have. "Unhappy Codrus, unwedded one!" But he consoled himself with his pupils, who loved him like a father.

A contemporary described him: sitting with the *Iliad* on his knees, skimming milk with his right while his left turned a spit in the fire.

He also interpreted the astronomy of the Greeks and lectured on Euclid and Archimedes. Copernicus probably seized his first opportunity to hear about Greek and Greek astronomy from a teacher who was so bold, so high above the prejudices of the time.

Then only a few Greek authors were translated, and fewer of them had appeared in print. There was even a dearth of grammars and good dictionaries. Codrus, therefore, did not teach many rules but at once proceeded to the perusal of the texts. In the winter term of 1499-1500 he was interpreting the Greek epistolographers, whom Aldus Manutius had printed in the spring of 1499 in a volume dedicated to his old schoolmate, Codrus, and recommended for his lectures. It was out of this book that Copernicus translated the epistles of Theophylactus Simocatta into Latin, and had them printed at Cracow with a dedication to his uncle, Bishop Watzelrode.

Codrus was a sceptic. He reviled the monks and the hierarchy, and mixed sacred matters with both his own and town gossip. He would talk edifyingly of Christ, after enumerating all the follies of the pagan religions, and continue: "But our theologians frequently totter, too, squabbling *de lana caprina* about the immaculate conception, the Anti-christ, sacraments, predestinations and some other things which ought to be passed over in silence rather than made the subjects of sermons."

He was superstitious and worried by auguries and prodigies. But when his students questioned him about the immortality of the soul, he coldly replied: "We do not know what happens after death, to man, his soul or his mind. Any speeches about the beyond are bogies for old women."

When he came to die, at the age of eighty-four, and his pupils tearfully asked for the conclusions of his wisdom, he gave them the appropriate pious speech and, pointing his finger upward, admonished them to fear God. "Especially," he said in a weak voice, "be sure to believe in immortality. Yes," he exclaimed, "and also in a retribution after death!" But on perceiving the long faces of his favorite pupils, hs hastened to add, "Pray that God make you like me," and sighed, to top it off: "How much virtue will be buried in my grave!"

Then he received the sacrament in the monastery of San Salvatore where he lay abed, and died.

In his last will, he commended his soul *or* his spirit to Almighty God. He laid great stress on the distinction; it was a philologist's final jest at the expense of the theologians, who at the time were quarreling about the meaning of a Greek word—whether it was to be translated "spirit" *or* "soul."

On his tombstone he directed that only two words be placed:

Codrus eram.

They meant: I was Codrus! Great Codrus—without comment.

They also meant: I was a beggar.

16

STUDENT LIFE AT BOLOGNA

No better life than student life,
As made by Bacchus and Gambrinus!
German Student Song

THE city of Bologna spent plenty on its university—as much as twenty thousand ducats, half the public revenue. And if the city was famous for its extravagance, the student of Bologna was famed for his gay life.

A student in Bologna did not die of boredom, what with academic festivals on the meadow before the Gate of San Manolo, with the daughters of the citizens of Bologna, with the fireworks on the Piazza di San Domenico, with singing through the whole day and half of the night, with music, wine, fencing and drinking bouts, disputations and discussions, at times pious pyres—and studies upon occasion. There was no end to the noise of fights and disputations. The wealthy students came with dogs, courtiers, servants and one or several mistresses. The beggar-students came with nothing but their nationality, and so they got to fighting over that, with Poles, Hungarians and Burgundians allied against the Germans, and the German students against Hungarians, Britons, Sicilians and Lombards. You smashed the candelabra in the mêlée, plundered at times, mutually drove cold steel into each other's bellies. Students quarreled with townsmen and slept with their wives. And then the endless squabbles of the philosophical schools, the Platonics and Aristotelics, the Thomists and Scotists, accompanied by the song of the guitars and the angry cries of the mules in the streets before sunup! You did not die of boredom, as a student in Bologna.

A young canon such as Copernicus—or his brother Andreas who came to Bologna two years later, also in order to study Canon Law—was rid of all clerical duties at Bologna. He lived in the most temporally cheerful manner with the temporal students, enjoyed himself without inhibitions and went about like any gentleman, wearing a sword and a bright hat. Only to Mass and on holidays he wore the scholar's garb as did the students of the Roman Law: a dark robe down to the ankles, and a hood.

Foreigners, by the way, were under strict supervision. Every stranger, for a time, had to obtain a pass at the gate of Bologna, to be allowed to leave the city again by another gate. But the foreign students were protected by the heads of their "nations." For the students, the Italians or *Citramontanes* as well as the foreigners or *Ultramontanes* (those come from beyond the Alps), were divided into fraternities according to their nationalities: there were seventeen Italian fraternities and eighteen from beyond the Alps, among them Gallia, Portugallia, Provincia, Anglia, Borgondia, Aragonia, Catalonia, Navaria, Alamania, Ungaria, Polonia, Boëmia, Flandrenses, et al.

The rectors were elected by the scholars and governed them. The heads of the "nations" administered the funds and the fraternity houses in which the students could live; they supervised the students and the statutes and received a percentage of each student's annual allowance, one Bolognese groschen for every mark. The registration fee at the university was twelve solidi.

In the "Annals of the highly famous Nation of the Germans" and in the "Matricula of the high and noble College of the Germans" of the year 1496, we find (on page 141 of the Annals, for instance) "Dominus Nicolaus Kopperlingk de Thorn" registered with nine grossets inscription fee.

This entry determines both the beginning of the studies and his field: at the time, the *Natio Germanorum* took in only law students. It took all those whose mother tongue was German—theoretically; for Bohemians, Moravians or Danes also liked to join the "German nation" at Bologna, because it enjoyed more privileges than others. For the sake of these privileges, rich young gentlemen even had their tutors and servants inscribed in the German nation. Annually at the beginning of the term, the beadles visited the students' quarters to ask for new arrivals, bringing the registration book with them; if the newcomers were members of the nobility, the procurator called in person.

Copernicus never excelled as a jurist. We do not know the names of his legal instructors. Besides, the professors shifted from one field to the other; they would change faculties and universities from term to term; sometimes, appointments were made only for one term. Humanism was a kind of itinerant trade; you lectured in learned societies and held private courses for the rich, and there were monastic universities and humanist societies arranging public disputations. Latin—less frequently

Greek—was the language of the day. In some places, the professors had to take an oath that they would not expound the same wisdom anywhere else. The salaries differed. The geniuses were as rare as certain books, which for this reason were tied to the desks with iron chains.

Copernicus may have lived in the house of the astrologer of Bologna, Maria di Novara. Underpaid professors like to take paying guests; it is known that Galilei was forced to take them. Other students lived with their tutors, or they rented apartments; the rent was fixed by a mixed commission of students and townsmen and no student was allowed to outbid the other; usually, the leases ran for three years. There also were many older students in Bologna, gentlemen of status and position, who came to Bologna for the love of science, to be students again.

We know—from a letter which Cathedral Dean Bernhard Sculteti, the Varmian plenipotentiary in Rome, wrote to Uncle Watzelrode, the Bishop of Varmia—that the two young canons Nicolaus and Andreas Copernicus had run up debts. And that though the two merry students drew not only their full income from the Cathedral Chapter of Frauenburg, as whose members they continued, but also got forty-five marks each as subsidy from their uncle, besides possible additional subsidies from the Chapter. And yet they had borrowed from the Varmian secretary Georg Pranghe, when he stayed over in Bologna on an official trip—in fact, Andreas had threatened to take foreign service, in Rome, if he did not get some money. However: "naked, they met the unclothed." Pranghe had no surplus money. But he approached Sculteti (who later, by the way, became Leo X's private chaplain and chamberlain) and Sculteti obtained a loan from a Roman bank for his young colleagues, at a high rate of interest, and guaranteed its repayment in four months.

Since he was a man of caution, however, he wrote to Uncle Watzelrode after only one month, asking for a speedy remittance of the amount to Poznan or Breslau—lest the Messrs. nephews might lose too much interest or, worse, the indorsers' credit might be impaired. "After the way of students," Sculteti wrote, "the Messrs. nephews have suffered great want of money . . ."

Copernicus remained four years in Bologna, from 1496 to 1500. An astronomical note in his own copy of the Alphonsine Tables states that he made an astronomical observation there as late as March 4, 1500. In early April, 1500, he probably traveled to Rome for Easter Week, and stayed for a whole year.

At Bologna he studied mathematics and astronomy and Greek grammar. At Bologna, in the year 1500, Messer Giorgio da Novara was burned alive in an open square for a few loose remarks or frank thoughts. What notions, on such occasion, were bound to strike a young man like Copernicus, who was about to overthrow the whole dogmatic structure of the Church!

To be sure, Doctor Gabrielle da Salò got off easier than Giorgio da Novara. The General of the Dominicans let this Salò off with a statement of repentance, although the doctor used to say: "Christ was not God but an ordinarily conceived son of Joseph and Mary; he has ruined the world with his cunning; he may have died on the cross for crimes committed; besides, his religion soon will come to an end . . ."

17

ROME—FERRARA—PADUA

I. *Roma aeterna*

> *"All that is loathsome and shameless is wafted into Rome from all over the world —and here is celebrated!"*
> TACITUS, Annals

THAT famous art lover and criminal, Pope Alexander VI, had invited Christendom to Rome, to celebrate the Year of Jubilee with him. He had issued the Bull of Jubilee for the great peace festival. He had rapped on St. Peter's door with a silver hammer, on Christmas Eve of 1499. On Easter Sunday, 1500, an alleged two hundred thousand Christians from all over the world (hardly seventy thousand lived in Rome) had knelt before the ever-cheerful Borgia, to receive his blessing.

In Rome, in the Year of Jubilee, Copernicus gave mathematical or astronomical lectures to a circle of scholars, scientists and, according to Rheticus, great men—probably in the manner of itinerant humanists, as was done by Conrad Celtes in Cracow, by Peurbach in Ferrara and by Regiomontanus in Padua.

In his "Revolutions" Copernicus reported on a lunar eclipse, which he had observed in Rome on November 6, 1500.

What else, and whom else, did he observe in Rome? The Borgia family? Bramante, Raphael, Michelangelo? The famed Roman courtesans, for whose mere conversation Montaigne paid as much gold as if he had slept with them? Or the humanists at the university? Or did he come to the house of the Luxemburger Goritz, a member of the Papal chancellery, where scientists, artists and poets gathered for academic discussions, and Erasmus, Reuchlin and Ulrich von Hutten were guests?

There was no dearth of entertainment in Rome. "No night passed without four or five murders; bishops and prelates were among the victims. On the morning of May 27, 1500, the Romans saw eighteen hanged from a gallows on the Angels' Bridge, among them the physician and the surgeon of the Lateran hospital, who had made a business of robbery and murder at dawn . . ." And the summer of 1500 saw the occurrence of "that tragic event committed by the Pope's son on his own brother-in-law, and no search seems to have been made for the guilty"—Reumont, the discreet Catholic historian of the Popes, is referring to Cesare Borgia's murder of the husband of his sister Lucretia.

In the summer of 1500, the three-year study leave of Copernicus had expired. Without any undue haste, he traveled to Frauenburg in the following year. On July 27, 1501, he and his brother Andreas appeared before the Chapter. "After mature deliberation," Andreas received a further study leave, having been "deemed fit to devote himself to studies." Nicolaus Copernicus had not even taken his law examination; he promised to study medicine, however, so that in future he might be of use to the very reverend head of the diocese (as well as to the gentlemen of the Chapter) as a physician. So he was granted two more years, mainly to study medicine.

Copernicus set out to study medicine—besides mathematics, astronomy, history of natural sciences, law, Greek and Latin. The alleged influence of the stars on health involved a link of medical and mathematical-astronomical studies. Most remedies were administered according to the planetary constellations. The audience of the astronomical lectures always contained a great many students of medicine. Many professors of astronomy had taken their doctor's degree in medicine.

The medieval Church did not favor the practice of the medical profession on the part of its clerics. They were forbidden to do any burning or cutting; surgical operations were considered evidence of hard heartedness, and under canonical rules disqualified their practitioner from ordination as priest. And though at the end of the Middle Ages internal medicine was almost wholly in the clerics' hands, some universities required every student of it to take an oath that he would never take up surgery. In the fifteenth century, however, the ecclesiastical prejudice against the medical art vanished. Besides, Copernicus had taken only the four lower orders upon entering the Chapter—and never took the higher ones.

Starowolsky, in his "Life of Copernicus," wrote: "In medicine, he was revered like a new Aesculapius."

Gassendi even related that Copernicus would treat the poor free of charge.

II. *Ferrara*

". . . to be able to do wrong in safety, however, you have to study law."
GEORG CHRISTOPH LICHTENBERG

"There's an old saying: A jurist, a bad Christian. It is the truth."
DR. MARTIN LUTHER

To be in time for the new term, Copernicus had to start out from Varmia in summer. He first went to Padua, where the medical art was in high repute. But he took his doctor's degree in Canon Law at Ferrara. There, as was customary, in the palace of the Archbishop, a nephew of Pope Alexander VI, the insignia of a *doctor decretorum* were solemnly handed to him before a notary and witnesses. The diploma reveals that Copernicus possessed another benefice by then, in Breslau; it identifies him as a "Varmian canon and scholasticus of the Collegiate Church of the Holy Cross in Breslau." He kept this Breslau prebend until shortly before his death.

Ferrara is said then to have been more populous than Rome. The court of the Estes has been immortalized by Ariosto and Tasso (and Goethe). There were great humanists at the university; in the house of Bianchi, the mathematician, Cardinal Bessarion, Peurbach and Regiomontanus had been guests. Maria and Codrus, the teachers of Copernicus at Bologna, had studied at Ferrara—as had Savonarola.

Lucretia Borgia had espoused the heir to the throne of Ferrara in 1502, at twenty-two years of age. Ariosto hailed her then as the "most beautiful virgin"—*pulcherrima virgo.* She kept the gayest court.

III. *Padua*

"Trust not the physician . . ."
SHAKESPEARE, Timon of Athens

"The priests cultivate the acre of God, and the doctors, God's acre."
LICHTENBERG

From Ferrara, Copernicus went back to Padua. For a long time, doubts persisted as to whether he actually studied at Padua; but in the past century, at Ferrara, his doctor's diploma of 1503 was found, which confirmed it: ". . . Nicolaus Copernicus of Prussia, who studied at Bologna and Padua . . ."

In Padua, which was part of the Republic of Venice, professors with less than six students had to pay a fine of ten lire for each lecture.

The School of Arts at Padua (in which Copernicus had to enroll, to study medicine) was headed by Pomponatius, a teacher of world-wide renown. He had published a book "On the Immortality of the Soul," which got him into the greatest trouble—because, while not denying the soul's immortality, he stated that it was not be proved either rationally or by the authority of all the writings of Aristotle and his pupils; in other books, he even attacked the worship accorded relics and went so far as to defend the individual's right to examine ecclesiastical dogmas.

All over Italy, Copernicus encountered such unprejudiced teachers, courageous rebels, reckless humanists, heretics and modernists.

There was no chair of anatomy at Padua. Dissection was practiced only to explain Galen, and as a commentary to Mondini's textbook. Once annually, there was a demonstration on a human corpse. There was a house for the anatomists; each had to pay three marcelli upon entering, as a contribution toward maintenance of the house, interment of the corpses, etc. The superintendents were two poor students who also took care of the instruments. By the end of February, at the latest, the rector had to supply two cadavers—one male, one female. The professor was assisted by two older students; no students with less than two terms behind them were admitted. An extraordinary professor would read a chapter from Mondini's textbook of anatomy; an ordinary professor would explain the text and then demonstrate on the corpse; the dissection proper had to be performed by surgeons. The other professors were not allowed to speak until the explanation of the textbook chapter as well as the demonstration was over.

One of the professors of theoretical medicine was Marcus Antonius della Torre, for whose anatomical studies—first made on horse cadavers, and then on human corpses—Leonardo da Vinci furnished drawings.

It is not known whether or not Copernicus received a medical diploma at Padua; it could neither add to his academic honors, nor did he need one to practice as a physician.

Copernicus returned home at the age of thirty-three. After some ten years of carefree student life in Italy, he returned with a universal education—a mathematician, a jurist, a physician, an astronomer, a humanist, a secret revolutionary. But at home, in Varmia, he was "the Bishop's nephew."

BOOK THREE

FAVORITE AND REBEL

18

MY UNCLE, BISHOP WATZELRODE

> *"Celui est bien mon oncle*
> *Qui le ventre me comble."*
> PROVERB

WHAT a change! Copernicus came from the paradise of arts and sciences, the eldorado of the joy of life and its enjoyment, from ever-greening orange groves and olive trees, Roman amphitheaters and courtesans, merry cardinals and pagan gods, and went back to the outermost rim of Sarmatia, to the Amber Coast with its foggy nights, savage Prussians and heathens of yesterday, its monks and Knights of the Teutonic Order, Tartar invasions and Polish schlachzitzes, its wolves and vojvods, the narrow life in towns of fifteen hundred souls, or castles where bears and foxes lived around the corner.

The field of the astronomer—the starry sky—is ill-plowed up there, in the gray North. All too often the nocturnal skies are starless; there are many fogs and long winters—snow and rain, rain and snow! And Christianity, which in each century and every corner of the world assumed the form of the new century and the new corner of the world, was Sarmatian up there; and humanism was Prussian.

True, the sun shines everywhere. And Copernicus himself was a Sarmatian, a Prussian. He had many friends. He had his uncle. And he had a good job—was he not a canon at Frauenburg? He had security. And what did he have besides?

Man does not feed on light. Was he fed on the shadow of light—on the spirit?

The nephew went to the episcopal castle of Heilsberg, ten miles from Frauenburg. The Cathedral Chapter granted the necessary furlough. Copernicus was to have been the Bishop's physician; he became his secretary and protégé, companion and counsellor, escort and assistant, potential successor and private scientist. For six years (1506-1512) he lived with hi uncle like a son. Not until after the uncle's death did Copernicus becom in fact what he had long been in name: a canon of a church by the Baltic Not until he was forty did he become free and independent—as far as th freedom went. It extended to the infinite reaches of the universe, not however, to the undisturbed possession of a young housekeeper. I sufficed for the boldest thoughts and calculations of mankind, but not fo the publication of a new—in fact, of the true astronomical theory.

Professionally, and concerning external position, Copernicus barely advanced beyond what had been his at twenty-four, because his uncle had thrown it into his lap: prebends and sinecures. He had an easy life with his uncle, and continued to learn even in the Bishop's house. For six years he had both opportunity and leisure to inspect the machinery of state and ecclesiastic politics, at the court of a prince of the Church.

There, from close up, he saw the eternal violent cures of history: the advancement of the whole species by forced motion; the giant strides of mankind—one forward and two back. He saw the fever of nations, the mutual fury of estates and classes. And the provincial hostility of those who speak different languages.

If you see just *one* condition of the world closely and precisely, you soon know many conditions as from within. You know the long illnesses of mankind, and its brief, sudden fits of health. The great, ordinary world! *Et quanti viri!* How easily and quickly men are made evil by politics and power. But even faster, even more easily spoiled are those who sit beside them, their closest aides and subordinates. Overnight, builders of humanity turn into apes of humanitarianism.

This universally educated canon and protégé might well have rotted and become a village Solon.

His uncle was a politician from inclination, rejoicing in intrigue—an ambitious individual who bore a hundred projects in his bosom. What! he did not want to become Archbishop! Sovereign of Prussia. Metropolitan. He took good care of his protégés roundabout, according to custom, and he probably wished to groom Nicolaus as heir of Varmia. Watzelrode, who played a great role in Prussia and Poland, intrigued with the same delight in Cracow and in Rome, in Torun and in Danzig. He was a friend of Polish Kings, and of the Italian humanist Callimachus. He was an energetic, active diplomat, no shepherd of souls. His, after all, was a century of politicians dressed as princes of the Church.

To his contemporaries he seemed one of the righteous. They praised his moral life. That the burgomaster of Braunsberg was his bastard did ot count. That he mixed in the dirty business of world politics did not ount.

He is said to have been a grim sort of man. No one ever saw him augh. He was proud and rigid, a merchant's son of Torun in Prussia vho had risen high. He was a Polish patriot like his ancestors. He hampioned the interests of Varmia like a temporal prince. He loathed he Teutonic Order and would have liked to see it transplanted to 'odolia or Wallachia, to fight Turks and Tartars. According to a chronler, the Knights of the Teutonic Order daily prayed to God for the lemise of this embodied Satan.

He could be tart. When the Frauenburg Cathedral Chapter, including is two nephews Nicolaus and Andreas, would not obey a ritual order f the Bishop's, he declared that even his own nephews had to bow or he vould throw them out of the Church.

For six years Copernicus lived with this strict uncle, worked for him, erved him, entertained him, accompanied him on trips about the diocese nd to Prussia and Poland, to Polish and Prussian diets such as those of Cracow or Petricow, to the assizes at Poznan or Torun, to King Sigisnund's coronation and to his wedding at Cracow, to Elbing, where Watzelrode wanted to found a university—a plan which failed because of the Elbingers' stupidity—and to Poznan, where the ambassadors of he Emperor, the King of Hungary and the Grand Master of the Teutonic Order gathered and Uncle Watzelrode was the ambassador of Poland's King.

But with all these goings-on, with all this commotion Copernicus enoyed the most beautiful leisure. He finished his translation of Simocatta from Greek into Latin, and made an excursion to Cracow from the Diet of Petricow to give it to the printer on June 2, 1509, observing an eclipse of the moon as well. And at Castle Heilsberg he had full leisure to write his book, to pursue his studies, to see, calculate and think. And this leisure of his nephew is to the lasting merit of the Bishop of Varmia, who by now would otherwise have been forgotten.

Naturally, Copernicus acquired some of his Bishop's political views and concerns—for instance, his dislike of the Teutonic Order. Order Marshal Wilhelm von Eisenberg, in writing a pasquill against Bishop Watzelrode which he distributed far and wide and even sent to the Bishop himself through the Council of Torun, did not exempt Copernicus, the Bishop's nephew, from his scorn, so at least reports Gassendi; the libel proper has since been lost.

Like his whole family, Watzelrode was pro-Polish from the start and

always remained so although once, on the occasion of his election
Bishop he had a quarrel with the Polish King. Watzelrode had lost h
father at fifteen and entered the University of Cracow at sixteen, w
Master of Arts at twenty-two, and sold one of his paternal estates to b
able to go to Bologna to study law, and soon, as Doctor of Canon La
became Canon of Frauenburg. He had acquired additional Polish ben
fices, "sat on the Polish Council and served Polish prelates"—but also, wi
a "pious maiden," made that boy whom he later made mayor of Braun
berg. When the Bishop of Varmia died, Watzelrode had been hurried
elected to succeed him, lest the King of Poland appoint his twenty-yea
old son, Prince Frederick who was already Bishop of Cracow, to be Bisho
of Varmia as well—and then Grand Master of the Teutonic Order to
if possible, as rumor had it. Watzelrode happened to be in Rome (pe
haps not altogether unintentionally) and had himself immediately co
secrated by the Pope; he made a fast entry into Frauenburg, seate
himself on the episcopal chair and received the homage of the Varmia
population (an occasion for all estates to quarrel over precedence, a
usual, with neither curses nor intrigues sparingly handled). To the Kin
of Poland, Watzelrode was thereafter just "this person" and not
reverend priest. In fact, the King (who after the second treaty of Toru
in 1466, claimed the right to choose the Varmian Bishops and now sa
himself cheated out of this privilege, by Watzelrode) vowed to crush th
Bishop if such revenge left him, the King of Poland, "reduced to his shirt.
And the Royal chancellor said that the devil had taken the last Varmia
Bishop, and soon would take the present one as well.

Death made the peace. King Casimir of Poland died. Within a week
his son Jan Albert wrote to his "beloved friend, *Bishop* Watzelrode,"
to ask for his vote in the impending royal election. He got the vote
and King and Bishop remained friends. Since Callimachus also was
friend of Watzelrode, and King Jan Albert's former Latin teacher ha
now become a royal adviser and friend, these three unequal friends joine
in a common policy with the ambitious goal of making Poland the firs
power in Europe.

The strongest link between them was their hatred of the Teutoni
Order, whose lands encircled Varmia on three sides. The Knights wer
the Bishopric's most dangerous neighbors and would have liked to pocke
it. They also were in constant strife with Poland; and Bishop Watzelrode's
plan to uproot the Order and transplant it to Wallachia delighted no
only the King but also Callimachus, whose favorite project and political
dream was Turkish policy—who wanted to get Europe and especially
Poland into war against the Turks. Watzelrode, the politician in holy

garb who would have liked best to be the temporal ruler of all Prussia and a Cardinal besides, branded political meddling on the part of an ecclesiastic order as profoundly unethical. Still, he really had a modern mind and hated, in the Knights, the absolute symbol of past centuries; he called them impudent idlers, who only came from the Reich to enjoy their sinecures intemperately.

What was this Order? "Who is the highly honored knight?"—*El Caballero de la triste Figura.* The Teutonic Knight had really come to be the "Knight of the sorry Figure."

In 1190, at the siege of Acre in the Holy Land, merchants of Bremen and Lübeck, on seeing the sick and wounded lie helplessly in the field, had stripped the sails off their ships, put up a tent in a near-by graveyard and carried the wounded there—partly to nurse them back to health and partly to bury them. They dedicated this field hospital to the Virgin Mary, donated more linen and money and later—when Acre was taken and they were able to take a whole street which had been promised to them previously, they built a large hospital with nurses and dormitories for the sick. The members of the Order, which was confirmed by the Pope and given the rules of the Knights of St. John, were mostly lay brothers; only a few were clerics. They were to live in poverty, chastity and obedience, to nurse the sick and wounded, to convert the infidels and serve God. Land or houses and rents were the sole property of the Order.

Their original rules were strict. Their shirts were to be of linen and their blankets of sheepskin; they were to maintain silence at table, sleep only in their underclothes in dormitories, and so forth. Above all, they were to live gently and in concord, without lying, swearing, bragging, slandering, quarreling or fighting; they were to set a good example on the road, to kiss no woman—not even their mothers or sisters—and, probably as an indication of conformity, to avoid outlaws and emigrants. If only that had been all!

The Grand Master—who carried a staff and rod, to show that he upheld the weak and chastised the disobedient—and the Knights wore white cloaks; the Brethren wore black crosses on their cloaks, caps, cowls and coat-of-arms. Its rule of unconditional obedience gave to the Order the great power of an independent military organization and its links of kinship with princely houses and mayoral families helped it to exert a widespread influence.

Konrad of Masovia, a Polish feudal lord, is said to have brought the Order to Prussia in 1226, to convert the heathens. As early as 1232, a host of crusaders came to the Brethren's aid. They built the castle and town of Kulm; later, they built Torun. The crusaders slew or converted the heathens, and went back whence they had come. Then, the Pope or the Order hired new crusaders, mostly for a year, who returned to savage Prussia in the service of God, to kill people with different moral views or religious customs. Many plain emigrants also determinedly stuck crosses on their sleeves and went along to Prussia, in armed bands with women and children, to take away other people's fields, shacks, women and cattle and to kill the owners.

Ahead of every new swarm of such "Christians," the Brethren of the Order blew their trumpets and unfurled the flag of war—whereupon all the world marched through the forests and bogs of Prussia, trampling everything, building fortified camps, baptizing a few natives and taking the bulk along as hostages, slaves or whores, bribing, playing favorites, blackmailing, butchering cattle and men, burning, raping and singing masses *ad majorem gloriam dei*. When the year was out, they broke camp and returned to their respective homes. And the Brethren gathered what remained lying about, from posts to nails.

In the fourteenth century the Grand Master moved his seat from Venice to Marienburg (St. Mary's Castle) in Prussia. His household became princely in style; the Knight began to rule Prussia, seized Pomerellen and Livonia, brought German landowners and peasants into the country, struck up friendships and took up commercial relations with the Hansa towns of Torun, Danzig and Elbing, equipped ships on the model of the Hansa, carried on trade and agriculture, built orchards, turned into merchants and slaveholding large landowners and forgot all about poverty, chastity and obedience.

But there was tourneying as in previous centuries; young nobles came from afar, dressed as Crusaders, to be knighted; money was lavished on horses, weapons and clothes. Knighthood had long been unhorsed by infantry and artillery; in Prussia, they redecorated the corpse. They were no longer governed by their pious vows but solely by a "Nordic knightly honor," which was not even Nordic but plagiarized from chivalrous Arab customs. Empty valor, hollow gallantry, erotic devotion and the boastful cross on the sleeve—these things were left. And the Comthurs sat in their castles like counts, shamelessly carousing.

The Lithuanians were no longer heathens; neither were the Prussians. They had learned the whole business along with baptism. They prayed like everybody else. They had God on their lips, blood on their hands, money in their pockets. Who needed the Knights any more? Whom would they convert? The crusades against the Slavs were at an end; now, the Slavs, Lithuanians and Poles, were warring upon the Order, and the towns and estates of Prussia, tired of the Order's arrogance and of the false Christian knights without Christianity, allied themselves with Poland and Lithuania.

The battle of Tannenberg resulted in Poland's victory and the Order's defeat. By the Second Treaty of Torun, in 1466, the major part of Prussia was made Polish, and the Grand Master of the Teutonic Order became a vassal of the Polish King. But whenever Poland was threatened by other enemies, such as Russians or Tartars or Turks—as soon as Poland was at war—the Order would try to throw off the dependence on Poland, would form leagues with the Emperor and German princes, hire new auxiliaries and mercenaries in Germany and open war on Poland, on the Hansa and on Varmia.

The high-flying plans of the three friends—King Jan Albert of Poland, his adviser, Callimachus, and Bishop Watzelrode of Varmia—would have accomplished much. By transplanting the Order to Wallachia, Prussia and Pomerellen, the Order would have formed a mighty bulwark against Turks and Tartars; and Poland, in possession of Moldavia and in co-operation with Hungary, could have driven the Turks out of Europe. These were plans after the King's, the Bishop's and the Italian's hearts.

Everything went wrong for all of them. Callimachus died; King Jan Albert, without allies, made war on the Moldavians in 1497, was ignominiously defeated and died, too; and the Teutonic Knights took their revenge from Watzelrode in Rome, where they spiked his plan to become Archbishop of Marienburg and tenant of the diocese of Kulm.

After Jan Albert's death, Watzelrode got his brother and successor, King Alexander of Poland, to arm against the Order (in the same month in which the Bishop and the Grand Master were borrowing each other's hunting packs as good friends and neighbors). King Alexander also died soon, however—about the time when Copernicus had moved into his uncle's Castle Heilsberg. The new King of Poland—Alexander's and Jan Albert's brother Sigismund I, a fiery youth—called on the Grand Master to take the oath of allegiance. War almost came over that, with the Emperor stirring up the Grand Master and Watzelrode stirring up the Polish King—it was the time when Marshal of the Order, Wilhelm von Eisenberg, wrote his sanguinary libel against Watzelrode and his nephew and secretary, Copernicus. Not much later, uncle and nephew traveled to Cracow for young King Sigismund's wedding and the coronation of the Queen. It was to be Watzelrode's last journey.

On the way, at Castle Stuhm, Watzelrode, accompanied by the two canons Georg von Delau and Nicolaus Copernicus, gave an audience to the "honorable Lord Mayor and Council of Danzig." They came to ask the Bishop to support their cause before the King of Poland. There is a description of the scene in a Danzig manuscript:

"Anno 1512, on the Monday after Prisce, the honorable and notable and sapient gentlemen, Mayor Mathis Zimmermann and Councillor Lucas Reding, came to Stuhme toward noon and presently had themselves announced to His Grace, the Bishop of Varmia, and His Grace requested that they would come to His Grace by the hour.

"As the gentlemen came to the Castle, however, there stood by the stairs the honorable, dignified and highly learned gentlemen, Jerge von der Dele and Nicolaus Copernicus, canons at Frauenburg, and in receiving the gentlemen went with them into a chamber; there they sat with them for a time, then the burggrave came and on the Bishop's behalf asked the gentlemen to be his guests, which the gentlemen accepted, and the Mayor said to Sir Jerge von der Dele that they had come in the view, and in the hope, that His Grace might grant graciously them an audience, at which the said Sir Jerge von der Dele replied that this might well be arranged.

"Shortly afterward, His Grace, the Bishop, came and kept the said canons with him."

The Bishop went to Cracow. On the return trip he began to feel unwell. The fish no longer pleased him. He arrived at Torun running a fever, and died three days later. No physician stood beside the dying Bishop's bed at Torun. The highly learned Doctor of Canon Law, his nephew and personal physician, was absent.

ROMA ÆTERNA
LUCRETIA BORGIA

19

A CASE OF NEPOTISM, OR: DIRECTIONS TO SERVANTS

"The last advice I give you relates to your behaviour when you are going to be hanged. . . .
Swift's Thoughts on Hanging (Directions to Servants)

Ubi terrarum sumus?
CICERO, Oration for Posthumus

WHERE in this world do we live?

The great, quiet man who first touched the universe with a calculating finger and bade the earth revolve and circle, bows to the cold, busy man of affairs whom he serves. The canon stands by the stairs. Later the burggrave arrives. A burgomaster asks the Bishop for an audience. In the end, His Grace makes his appearance. A painful picture—and so like the way of the world.

The mighty Copernicus: a kind of third secretary to a hyperborean bishop, half poor relative and protégé and half high-grade domestic, allowed to consort with the family, an employed idler and superfluous revolutionary, a man who fails to hit the mark, who disappoints, a fellow who will not even get to be a bishop—a man who has yet to prove his public worth.

And what does he have to deliver? How does he pay his extensive debts of gratitude?

The Greek epistles of Theophylactus Simocatta, "offered to the Most Reverend Bishop Lucas of Varmia by Nicolaus Copernicus" and translated into Latin, were published by Johann Haller in Cracow, in 1509. They are eighty-five fictitious letters of famous or fictitious persons, with contents alternately moral, pastoral, erotic—penned about the year 630 A.D. by a late Byzantine author whose main work, a history of Emperor

Mauritius entitled "Oecumenical History," was widely read in the Middle Ages.

The introductory poem was written by a certain Rabe, alias Laurentius Corvinus, a town clerk of Breslau. He praised Torun "for having brought forth good men, among whom Bishop Lucas stands out by piety, seriousness and dignity, with Varmia, a large part of Prussia, happy under his sovereign rule. Standing faithfully by his side, as loyal Achates once did by that of Aenaeas, is the learned man who translated this work from the Greek into the Latin language. He explores the rapid course of the moon and *the changing movements of the fraternal star* and the whole firmament with the planets, the wonderful creation of the universal Father; starting from *amazing principles,* he knows how to explore the *hidden causes* of things." Et cetera.

The author of these earliest versified suggestions of the Copernican theory had been a teacher and friend of Copernicus at Cracow, and furthermore a friend of Conrad Celtes, the itinerant preacher of humanism, with whom Rabe had for many years carried on a literary correspondence intended for posterity. He was also a poet, had written textbooks and a cosmography and had been town clerk of Torun—perhaps on the recommendation of his friend Copernicus.

Copernicus' dedication to his uncle reads as follows:

"Most Reverend Lord and Father of this Country.

"It seems to me that Theophylactus, the scholastic, has quite excellently compiled moral, pastoral and amorous epistles. Surely he was guided by the consideration that variety delights us above all. The inclinations of men are very dissimilar and they are pleased by very dissimilar things. Some like weighty thoughts, others those which lure by levity; some love the serious, while others are attracted by the play of fancy. Because the multitude takes pleasure in so very different things, Theophylactus let light subjects alternate with heavy ones, frivolity with seriousness, so that the reader can choose what he likes best from the rich mass of flowers, just as in a garden, as it were. All that he offers, however, is of such great utility that his poems appear to be not so much epistles as rules and precepts for a useful arrangement of human life. The proof of this is their comprehensive brevity. Theophylactus has taken his subject matter from various authors and most edifyingly presented it in a compressed form.

"Hardly any one will deny an inner value to the moral and pastoral poems. A different judgment might perhaps be passed on the love letters, which from their title might seem wanton and frivolous. But as the physician customarily softens bitter medicine by the addition of sweet ingredients, to make it more agreeable to the patient, so the more frivolous poems have been added here; besides, they are kept so pure that they might as well bear the name of moral epistles. Under such circumstances I deemed it inequitable for the epistles of Theophylactus to be read only in the Greek language. To make them more generally accessible, I have tried to translate them into Latin, to the best of my ability.

"To you, Most Reverend Sir, I now dedicate this small gift which is in no relation, to be sure, to the favors I received from you. Whatever I use and create by my intellectual powers I rightly deem your property; for it is indubitably true what Ovid once wrote to Caesar Germanicus: 'It is your glance that makes my spirit fall and rise.'"

The first biographers of Copernicus knew nothing of this work. It was not until some centuries had passed that the booklet was pulled "out of the dust of the libraries," by a Saxon book lover named Goetze.

The following are samples of the epistles.

The second Epistle, a pastoral one:

"Dorkon to Moschon. The leader of my herd, my splendid ram, has fallen; my sheep lack guidance in grazing. We have suffered a heavy blow and I believe that Pan is angered by our failure to offer him the first of our beehives. I will therefore hasten to the city and tell the citizens of the wrath of the god; I shall say to them, 'On the honeycake's account Pan took away the leader of my flock.'"

The thirty-ninth Epistle, an erotic one:

"Thetis to Anaxarchus. You cannot love Thetis and Galatea at the same time. For Passion does not turn to two sides, the gods of love do not divide themselves, and you cannot bear a doubled love. No more than the earth can be warmed by two suns, can the soul stand two flames of love."

The eighty-fifth Epistle, a moral one:

"Plato to Dionysius. If you would learn to master your pains, walk among the graves. There you will find surcease for your sufferings. And you will realize at the same time that beyond the grave the greatest bliss of mankind counts for naught."

What induced Copernicus to translate just these poems in prose?

Chance plays the same presumptuous role in the literary business as in life. The humanists knew only a part of the ancient literature known to us (though they possessed some things which have since been lost). That which existed only in manuscript was accessible only with difficulty or not at all. A rich man might possess ten or twenty manuscripts, a large library might boast a few hundreds. The first printed books were also relatively rare, especially in outlying districts, and still very expensive. In the absence of an international book trade, they were dependent on the libraries of friends, convents or universities, or on chance.

The humanists did not by any means start by translating the best classical authors. Sometimes they translated the least important texts because they were easiest; or the decision was made by a professor's choice of the most simple text for his pupils—the more so, since there was also a dearth of dictionaries and good grammars. Or again, a manuscript just happened to be offered for sale. And those who did not translate for a living preferred shorter texts.

This publication of Copernicus—the first original print of a Greek author in Poland—was not just an achievement in original philology but also in the field of the politics of ideas. Any occupation with Greek language and literature was viewed as heresy by all theologians and ignoramuses. Had the Church transformed the pagan gods into tailbearing he- and she-devils, only to have them emerge from buried palimpsests and rise up against its own dogmas? The scholastics and theologians even fought the publication of new Latin classics. Enough of the heathens! Reason had conquered only in the narrowest circle. But who knew of its victory? Who would let it count?

The humanists laughed at the hairsplitting nonsense of the scholastics, but the scholastics' helpers merrily burned books and writers of books at their stakes. The victory was won; but at the start it was only a secret victory in the chambers of the scientists, at some courts and in a few large cities; the nations, the Church, the convents and the universities knew nothing of the victory and would not let it count at any price. The contemporary world is virtually never aware of the triumphs of the Zeitgeist—or, if it learns of them, it understands nothing. Once the results of spiritual victories grow popular, they are likely to have lost their meaning.

Gregor the Great said, "One and the same mouth cannot praise Jupiter and Christ." But Latin was the language of the Church; who would condemn it as the tongue of heresy? So the theologians condemned Greek. Erasmus of Rotterdam quoted this sort of obscurantist: "Greek literature is the font of all heresy," and, "Beware of the Greeks, lest you become a heretic!"—and he recalled the New Testament which, after all, was also part of Greek literature. The Dominican Simon Grunau in his chronicle voiced the opinion of Copernicus' contemporaries: "Some had seen neither a Jew nor a Greek in their day and yet could read Hebrew and Greek from the volumes. . . . they were possessed."

It was not until eleven years after the publication of this print by Copernicus, that Libanius announced the first lectures on Greek grammar and literature at the University of Cracow; and in his preface to the poems of the Sibylla of Erithrea he complained that the zealots first prohibited his lectures and then called his students heretics, Lutherans, schismatics or maniacs: "They cry 'anathema' and call for the excommunication of all who learn Greek and Hebrew."

And it was a bishop to whom Copernicus dedicated this first original print of a Greek author in Poland, and of some very pagan epistles to boot—which greatly honors the courage of the author *and* of the Bishop.

And Copernicus let this book appear in the same year, 1509, in which in Germany the inquisitors of Cologne and their infamous stool pigeon, Pfefferkorn, wanted to burn all Hebrew manuscripts and books in Germany—and Reuchlin, Germany's first teacher of Hebrew and Greek, began his battle against the mad obscurantists.

With this publication, Copernicus thus openly and bravely joined the battle line of the humanists against the virtually omnipotent obscurantists.

On a later occasion he translated a Greek prose piece, the apocryphal letter of Lysis, the Pythagorean, to Hipparchus (printed in the Aldine edition of the epistolographers), in which Copernicus found the Pythagorean maxim cited by him: that the master's teachings should be communicated only to the *cognoscenti*. Copernicus had cited this letter in his "Revolutions"; its Latin translation was contained in the original manuscript at the end of Book I, which in the initial version was to be the first of eight books, instead of the later six. In a few introductory remarks Copernicus had cited several Greek philosophers already teaching that the earth did move: Philolaus, Aristarchos of Samos and Plato.

Later, Copernicus deleted the Lysis letter and the few introductory lines, so that in the printed book Aristarchos of Samos, otherwise not mentioned, lost his place among the predecessors altogether. By the way, Copernicus largely adopted the earlier Latin translation of the Lysis letter in Cardinal Bessarion's book (printed 1503 by Aldus) which he had bought at Padua and inscribed with numerous marginal notes. In particular he marked the letter of Lysis; then, Plato's eulogy for Demosthenes and a passage to the effect that many were facile with words but only Homer, Plato and Demosthenes were eloquent, and finally Plato's praise of mathematics. And one more passage: about celibacy.

Marginal notes are found in most of Copernicus' books, sometimes in Greek—once, for instance, the receipt of a hair-dyeing tincture.

20

LIFE WITH A BISHOP

"Fatti non foste a viver come bruti . . ."
DANTE, La divina commedia

"Life's but a walking shadow; a poor player,
That struts and frets his hour upon the stage,
And then is heard no more: it is a tale
Told by an idiot, full of sound and fury,
Signifying nothing."
SHAKESPEARE, Macbeth

CASTLE HEILSBERG was one of the most beautiful castles in Prussia. It was situated amidst fertile hills, near the river valleys. A small river, the Alle, winds past the foot of the castle hill. The castle had a pond; there were oaks and beeches on the hills and bears and wolves, bison and wild boar in the forests. "The dam between the Simser, a tributary brook of the Alle, and the castle pond makes a delightful promenade lined with the most beautiful trees; the dark walls and the fresh green of the surroundings are both doubly transfigured in the clear aqueous mirror."

The Heilsberg palace regulations of 1480 describe the episcopal court with its multitude of high and low officials, with the personal servants, and with the servants' servants. There were a vicar-general, overseers and burgraves, penitentiaries of the Prutenian language, chief chamberlains, cupbearers, chief fishermen, chief foresters, court bell-ringers, a chief castellan, an assistant castellan, young noblemen serving as equerries and young clerics serving as chaplains, vicars, notaries and servants for the lower ecclesiastical offices and for the household and the stables.

Mealtime etiquette was rigid. At the stroke of the noonday bell all of the Bishop's table companions had to wait before the doors of their rooms for the Bishop to emerge from the palace gate. His dogs were let out first; their barking gave the first signal. As soon as the Bishop appeared in his stole, with a mitre on his head, the courtiers fell into line and escorted him to the knight's hall. There, servants handed him a wash basin and a towel. After the handwashing a prayer was said and the Bishop sat down on his elevated chair.

The Marshal showed the Vicar-General to his place by the Bishop's side; others seated at this table were the Chief Judge, the first chaplain, the attending canons, abbots, knights of orders, captains, burgomasters of major towns and the Bishop's guests of honor. At the second table, called the convent table, the Marshal presided over the chaplains, the less honored guests and the higher household officials. At the notary's table sat the chief forester, the chief fisherman, burgraves, village mayors, jurors, head cooks and the interpreter. At the first servants' table sat the grainmaster—commonly a farmhand—and the episcopal coachman, the stable hands, the servants of the court servants and the lookout from the tower. At the fifth table, the Bishop fed three or four poor men. At the second servants' table sat the waiters and carvers. At the third and fourth servants' table sat the lowest servants. A ninth table was *pro joculatoribus, proprie vor dy herolt, vor dy kokeler, in medio coenaculi*—so that the court jesters, gypsies, beartamers, tight-rope walkers and jugglers could entertain the whole room with their arts and pranks.

Copernicus was on leave from the Cathedral Chapter especially for the purpose of functioning as a physician. Probably he supervised his uncle's diet. He bought medical books for his uncle's library; some of them, with his medical notes or prescriptions, are still preserved at Upsala, where they were taken during the Swedish Wars.

Copernicus himself said that 1506 was the year in which he began to develop his astronomical system and to write it down. His biographer Gassendi wrote that Copernicus started in 1507 to conceive and record his system. Laurentius Corvinus, the teacher and friend of Copernicus, hints in his poetic Introduction of 1509 at Copernicus' "miraculous principles."

Copernicus mentions only two astronomical observations made during these years: those of the lunar eclipses of 1509 and 1511. Perhaps the worldly-wise uncle took a lively interest in the researches, calculations and revolutionary ideas of the wise nephew. Perhaps the uncle loved his nephew.

Soon after the uncle's death, Copernicus left Castle Heilsberg and finally, at forty, came to Frauenburg, to live near the cathedral, in accord with the ecclesiastical rule.

In the six years which he spent at his uncle's court, Copernicus, on occasion, was also engaged in business for his uncle and for the Cathedral Chapter. In 1511, for instance, he came as *visitator* to Allenstein with his colleague Fabian von Lossainen, to collect 285 marks. One "Ego Balthasar Stockfisch," in an account book which has been preserved for posterity, describes the session of the chapter, at which Canon Enoch presided and Custos Cletze and Canons Lossainen, Snellenberg and Nicolaus Copernicus were witnesses that Mr. Balthasar Stockfisch had properly received the 285 marks from Messrs. Lossainen and Copernicus, paid them into the cathedral exchequer and accounted for them.

21

LIFE, PART TWO

"Man lebt nur Einmal in der Welt."
GOETHE, Clavigo

"Il n'y a pour l'homme que trois évènements, naître, vivre, et mourir: il ne se sent pas naître, il souffre à mourir, et il oublie de vivre."
LA BRUYÈRE, Caractères

IN THE spring of 1512, Copernicus moved from Castle Heilsberg into his tower next to Frauenburg cathedral, to "maintain residence" there.

Thus, in his fortieth year, he came to this Prussian hole of Frauenburg where he was to spend the next thirty years. What if someone had foretold his life in celibacy with elderly bachelors, among philistines and local politicians, with servants, pastors' cooks, horses and rural rents. What if someone had warned him of the boredom of a provincial canon's life, of the darkening times and the dividing churches, of the thirty years' desolation of political turbulence, of the senile squabble with Bishop Dantiscus over a housekeeper, of the miserable, premature death of his brother Andreas, the poor canon who perished of leprosy (or syphilis). What if someone had predicted the canon's silly dispute with the Polish King over Watzelrode's succession; or Copernicus' governorship of Allenstein, with war and siege and pillage and peasant troubles; his written complaint against the Teutonic Order; the death of the Bishops; the death of many a friend; the dissolution of the Teutonic Order and the birth of Prussia; the memorandum about the improvement of Prussian coinage, to which nobody would listen; the stupid jokes and pranks at his expense; the amateurishness of his medical practice; the entire protracted farce of a long life in the wrong place—what if someone had foretold his future life to Copernicus!

But if we were given the power to do so, what course of life should we have devised for Copernicus? Should we have made him Bishop of Varmia, or Archbishop of Cracow, or a Cardinal, or perhaps the Holy Father sitting in Rome and reforming the calendar? We have seen humanists in the Papal chair before—for example the creature of Emperor Charles V, the learned Dutchman Hadrian VI who wanted to reform everything and merely succeeded in making himself the butt of the jokes of the Roman bureaucracy.

Should Copernicus rather have been the head of the University of Cracow, a teacher of Doctor Faustus and Mr. von Twardowski, or the head of universities like Paris or Bologna? The trouble is that in a world of accidents, the form, once taken, grows immutable—becomes, in fact, as though foreseen for eternities. Talents are nothing. Character weighs more. But only time and opportunity make both the man and his work.

There we see a man great enough for ten whole centuries sent into a stupid province, occupied with trifles, frittering his life away in keeping here the accounts of a few bonded peasants or collecting and delivering a few marks, treating there a poor man's mange (with or without success), going to the same church time and again, saying the same prayers, conversing with the same dozen colleagues; now he has to make out a complaint against a powerful neighbor; now he drafts an essay about the soundness of money; at another time there is a lunar eclipse, at last; then he has to protect a ridiculously small town; a king lists him among his candidates for a bishopric—it is only a derisive gesture, the other one becomes bishop; robbers and soldiers pillage. All this time Copernicus has to be active; constantly he has to spend his time, his strength, his knowledge—and so a great life is frittered away.

Is it really frittered away? Does not a river draw its strength from a hundred sources? Does not the wise man know how to use everything?

The little country is vexed by rising prices—as all of Europe in the sixteenth century, suffered under the invariably high cost of living. There is a desire to unify the coinage, to reform it. Copernicus takes a hand in making the Estates realize what it is that plagues the whole world. Casually, he emerges as one of the great economists of the sixteenth century; he is the first to put into scientific form the law of bad money, which drives good money out of circulation. The phenomenon was noted even by Aristophanes, but no one before Copernicus knew how to formulate the law: "A greater mistake, however, is to introduce new, bad money beside the old, good money, for the bad not only devalues the old, better currency but drives it away."

The Prussians would not listen to the canon, but Poland heeded him: at the diets of Pjotrkow in 1526 and 1528, uniform coinage, according to Copernicus' suggestions, was introduced in Poland and Lithuania and thus Poland had good money.

Rather than fritter his life and himself away, Copernicus studied the great fields of human endeavor and understood them. He tried to further his country and his time in many fields. Thus he did not remain a theoretician only but became a master in many types of practice—an architect, an engineer, an administrator, an economist, a physician, a diplomat. He came to be, in the North, one of those universally educated men of many sides and many faculties who were more frequent in Italy—*an uomo universale,* a universal genius. And he became such a man deliberately, intentionally.

He wrote in his "Revolutions":

"The scientist who would examine the various phenomena individually, without regard to the order and close dependency among them, might be compared with a man who would borrow fragments, such as hands, feet, and other parts of the body which, though truly painted by a master's hand, represent different bodies, and who would attempt now to put these heteroclitic fragments together, which do not fit one to the other, and the composition of which would rather yield the picture of a monster than that of a human body."

The man who understood so many of the practical activities of the world, changed the course of the world with a theory.

"It has always seemed to me," said Simon Newcombe in the Report of the Smithsonian Institution of 1896, "that the real significance of the heliocentric system lies in the greatness of this conception rather than in the fact of the discovery itself. There is no figure in astronomical history which may more appropriately claim the admiration of mankind through all time than that of Copernicus. Scarcely any great work was ever so exclusively the work of one man as was the heliocentric system the work of the retiring sage of Frauenburg."

At the time of Copernicus, Frauenburg numbered about thirteen or fourteen hundred souls. The little town is located on the Frische Haff, a lagoon twelve miles in length, a sweet-water formation of the Baltic, fed by many rivers. Copernicus called the Frische Haff the Vistula (in the "Revolutions," V, 3), but the Vistula splits up ten miles before its mouth. "As is well known," said Prowe, "the left main arm enters the Baltic at Danzig under the name Vistula, while the right arm has to be content with the name of Nogat and together with another arm of the river enters the Frische Haff."

From the Baude, another stream, a canal leads into the town and provides Frauenburg and the cathedral buildings with drinking water. Legend calls Copernicus the builder of this canal—which is, however, mentioned in documents as early as 1427.

The cathedral stands on a hill, eighty feet high, offering a wide view over the Haff. Only a very narrow strip of dunes, a mile distant, separates the Haff from the Baltic.

The *curiae,* the real dwellings of the canons with gardens and utility buildings, formed a row of houses along the interior of the fortified wall of Cathedral Hill. The curiae were not all alike, and the younger canons got the lesser ones. After every death, therefore, a change of the curiae took place.

Copernicus seems to have spent his thirty years at Frauenburg (with interruptions) in the tower which is traditionally called *curia Copernicana* and which he occupied at the time of his death. For his astronomical observations he needed an elevated observatory with an unobstructed view. His tower room was slightly above the church roof. From it, one can see far into the plains and, to the West and North, the distant Haff and the white dunes of the Nehrung.

Of the personal observations listed in the "Revolutions," Copernicus made more than half of them, at Frauenburg—according to his own testimony and to that of Rheticus.

22

THE BROTHER'S DEATH

"Are we not brothers?"
SHAKESPEARE, Cymbeline

LIFE in the cathedral by the Baltic was not monastic. The sixteen canons on their hill—seldom in full number—were noblemen with horses, servants, allods and cooks. One of them became Bishop of Varmia; another, Bishop of Kulm; a third traveled to Rome to the Holy Father for the chapter or the Bishop, and a fourth to Cracow, to the King of Poland. There they sat and negotiated with the Grand Master of the Teutonic Order, with the burgomasters of Danzig or Torun. They studied at Polish, German and Italian universities. They were savants and humanists. One was Ambassador to the Emperor in Spain. Another was secretary of the King of Poland.

They were great businessmen. They owned one-third of Varmia. They levied taxes and administered estates. They held court, and took part in Europe's confused battles for power and fluctuating battles over the faith. They were great lords of the manor and urban administrators. They engaged in trade with the Hansa, with Poland and Prussia. They gambled, studied, prayed, preached and had no more worries in life. They prayed, preached, observed their ecclesiastical ceremonials more or less industriously, took part in many wars, especially in every war between Poland and the Order, defended their castles and strongholds, surrendered occasionally, participated in the peace negotiations and in a hundred intrigues. They fought the Order for the privilege of censuring a castle chaplain, and the King of Poland for the privilege of electing the Bishop of Varmia. They mixed God and the Emperor, the Order and the Electors, the Pope and a dozen other potentates in their game. They increased their library and their estates. They built and ate well. They lived and died in that "farthest corner of the earth"—*remotissimum angulum terrae*—as

Copernicus called it in the dedication of his "Revolutions" to Pope Paul III. Almost all of them were descended from the same few friendly patrician families of Danzig and Torun—all bound by kinship and nepotism.

When Copernicus moved to Cathedral Hill after his uncle Watzelrode's death, it was inhabited only by his brother Andreas and Cathedral Custos Cleetz, Cathedral Cantor Delau, Archdeacon Sculteti, Canons Lossainen, Stockfisch, Snellenberg, Crapitz and Zander. Three others were in Rome, one was studying in Siena, and Tiedemann Giese was in Allenstein as the Chapter's deputy.

This Giese, the truest, most devoted friend and a cousin of Copernicus, was seven years his junior and descended from a good Danzig family. He had studied with his tutor at Leipzig, Basel and at Italian universities, had become a canon at Frauenburg and Cathedral Custos when his uncle was Bishop, and in 1538 moved to Castle Löbau as Bishop of Kulm. Eventually—too late for his friend, five years after the death of Copernicus—he became Bishop of Varmia, succeeding that Bishop Dantiscus, against whom he had been a candidate as early as 1538. At that time, however, King Sigismund I, who wanted Dantiscus for Bishop of Varmia, had made him Bishop of Kulm instead, and so poor old Copernicus unfortunately was not spared the silly trouble on the housekeeper's account.

(Bishop Giese died in 1549 and was buried in the cathedral, next to his friend Copernicus.)

Brother Andreas fell ill soon after his return from Italy; or perhaps he had already been ill when he returned. In the records of the Chapter there are divergent entries: incurably sick—leprosy.

Leprosy had been widespread in Prussia in the thirteenth and fourteenth centuries; there were leper houses in almost all towns, usually the Hospitals of St. George, outside the walls. Among the prescriptions which Copernicus entered in his medical books, there is none against leprosy. But perhaps brother Andreas was not suffering from leprosy at all? Perhaps he was suffering from syphilis?

The good canons felt uneasy in the presence of poor Andreas. They were afraid of contagion. They gave him a one-year furlough. He moved to Rome, to consult Italian physicians. He returned to Frauenburg. The disease appeared even more horribly.

In Rome he had waged a law suit for the Chapter. In May, 1512, he wrote that just recently he had been confined to his bed again; he had wished to return to Prussia, but the news of his uncle Watzelrode's sudden death had arrived and was detaining him for some time. In any event, he would retire from all business.

When he returned, with all the marks and sores still visible, the Chapter decided to cease to associate with him.

Then, as usual, the squabble over money began. The colleagues wanted to cut the sick man's income; Andreas protested. The colleagues, to make him tractable, simply blocked his entire income. They referred to a sum of twelve hundred Hungarian gold gulden which Uncle Watzelrode had given to Andreas "for churchbuilding purposes," and Andreas had spent to God knew which edifying ends.

Andreas countered by arriving for the Chapter sessions of December, 1512 and 1513. Now, the frightened canons raised the arrest and granted him larger payments, pending a final decision by the Holy Father. He left Frauenburg and went to Rome. There he evidently took part in the intrigues over the episcopal election, for the King of Poland, in a reproachful letter, asked him why, despite the favors received, he was intriguing against the King and Poland? King Sigismund also wanted to make his secretary, Dantiscus, the deputy of Andreas; instead, Leo X appointed a cleric of Kulm, Korner, to this office in 1516. In that year, accordingly, Andreas was still alive. Korner also became his successor at the cathedral of Frauenburg and in 1519 was in turn succeeded by Alexander Sculteti. So Andreas must have died between 1516 and 1519, perhaps in Rome.

In 1800, Kries wrote:

"It was fortunate that the disease of leprosy did not strike his brother Nicolaus; otherwise it would certainly have been regarded as a consequence of his heretical system and a warning punishment from Heaven."

23

QUEEN BONA

"Poland is not lost yet . . . The deeds reserved for this nation may be valued more highly by the genius of mankind than victorious battles and chivalrously rattling swords accompanied by the horse-trampling of its national past. Poland will live forever on the most glorious pages of its history!"

HEINRICH HEINE

EMPEROR Maximilian wrote as suitor for Sigismund I: "The King of Poland is a handsome person, a little fat; at any rate he will not gain any more weight; his face and body are white, and he has very white hands and is just the size of Chevalier de Berges; his face is better-looking than that of Chevalier de Berges, for he has a very honest face, without guile. As I heard from his own lips, which are beautiful and red, he is forty-six years old . . . his hair is already a little gray . . ."

The King of Poland was already called Sigismund the Old, however, and was fifty-two; the youngest of six brothers, he survived all of them as well as his whole era. He had been merely a little prince in Silesia, with a Moravian sweetheart, Katrina Telnitzer by name, who presented him with a son and a daughter. All his brothers became great lords: his brother John Albert, the pupil of Callimachus, became King of Poland and died after the Bukovina disaster; his brother Alexander, the second pupil of Callimachus, followed John Albert as King of Poland and died. His brother Ladislas became King of Bohemia and Hungary, and died. His brother Casimir became a saint (he died young, and was canonized soon after) and his brother Frederick became a Cardinal and died as early as 1503.

At last, at forty, Sigismund ascended the Polish throne. He loved peace and had to wage many wars against the Russians and Prussians—losing against both. He loved his comfort, and had to go on with the long family war of the Jagellones, against the Hapsburgs for the domination of Hungary and Bohemia; he lost that, too. King for hardly five years, he had to send away his Moravian sweetheart, Katrina Telnitzer, and sick of heart, married a seventeen-year-old Hungarian from Transylvania. Barbara Zapolya was pretty as a picture but he lost her three years later, during her second confinement.

The recent widower journeyed to the Congress of Vienna, where Emperor Maximilian—astonished to find the King of Poland "a distinguished humanist as he was himself"—offered him the young girls of the Hapsburg family: first his granddaughter, the heiress of Burgundy, who however, went to the bed of the French King Francis I; and then a niece of Empress Bianca, the heiress of Milan and Bari. She was Bona Sforza, a beautiful Italian damsel of twenty-five, with two hundred thousand gulden in cash. She was educated as were no women except Italian Renaissance princesses. She became Poland's greatest Queen and a notorious poison-mongerer, Poland's most accursed woman and greatest blessing.

Archbishop Laski, who opposed the Hapsburgs, had suggested two Polish princesses, mother and daughter, to the King; but a Prince Colonna, in Vilna, let the King see Bona's portrait, and Sigismund the Old dispatched his envoys to Naples. One of them married her by proxy, on December 6. At 2 P.M., after church the guests sat down to the banquet and ate until 11 at night—twenty-seven courses; among them Hungarian soup, stuffed peacocks, pheasants, capons, fish, marzipan. The young Viceroy of Naples, King of Spain, and soon also German Emperor, Charles (then the First, of Spain; later, the Fifth of the Empire) sat at table with Vittoria Colonna, Michelangelo's friend. Bona wore a Venetian gown of sky-blue velvet, embroidered with golden bees. On December 26 she left Naples to take ship at Manfredonia; on April 10, 1518, she arrived in Cracow (by land, of course) and King Sigismund the Old greeted her with a banquet that lasted for eight hours.

Then she had the Old one for her husband, and Poland for her realm. Her youth had not been gay. Her life with the Old one could not have been cheerful. And her widowhood was not pleasant. She was cleverer than a hundred magnates, including the Old one. She loved money and power and order, and for thirty years she remained "the foreigner" on Poland's throne.

What a youth! Her father, young Duke Gian Galeazzo of Milan, a famous weakling, was twenty when he married the daughter of the King of Naples, beautiful Isabella of Aragon who was seventeen. The Duke's uncle, Ludovico il Moro, suddenly fell in love with the bride of his nephew and is said to have used witchcraft in an attempt to keep the marriage from being consummated. Later, Ludovico il Moro poisoned his nephew, to become Duke of Milan himself. Bona was three years old at the time. Her hapless mother, seven years a Duchess and twenty-eight years a widow, lost her seven-year-old daughter Ippolita. Her son Francesco was kidnapped by the King of France and made abbot of a monastery on a sandy little island on the coast of Vendé, where he met his death at twenty-one, a state prisoner, in a "hunting accident." The poor mother, who signed her letters, "Ysabella de Aragonia Sforcia, unica in disgracia," saw both her husband's Duchy of Milan and Naples, the kingdom of her father and brother seized by bold conquerors, Spaniards and Frenchmen; she saw her uncle Federico, the last King of Naples, taken away to France. Once, in fact, French troops under the Duke of Adria were about to storm the city and port of Bari, her widow's residence. It was due to the protest of gallant Captain Yves d'Allègre and his friends, Chevalier Bayard *(sans peur et sans reproche)* and La Palisse, that Duchess Isabella and her town, her daughter and her port were not stormed and violated. Yves d'Allègre successfully maintained that one could not make war on so highly famed and sorely tried a lady as Isabella of Milan. He was the same knight who a year earlier had ridden into Rome with only three friends, to demand that Pope Alexander VI free the Countess of Forli, Caterina Sforza (an aunt of Bona's, sung by Tasso) from one of the cells of Castel San Angelo—for, he stated in the name of France, *on n'emprisonne pas les dames.*

Later, Isabella of Milan tried to marry off Bona to Il Moro's son, the youthful Duke Massimiliano of Milan, and thus put the murdered man's daughter into the bed of the murderer's son; however, after the battle of Marignano the Sforzas lost Milan and the pretty plan fell through.

Finally Bona was twenty-five and still single, and had to take the widower from Poland. She took him, and half of Poland into the bargain. There she came, radiant and blonde, with laughing eyes and breasts and excellent Latin. She rose like a comet on Poland's dark northern sky, with a glittering train of three hundred Italians, lutists and prelates, poisoners and humanists, professors and eunuchs, singers and architects—and lovers, perhaps?—and brought along the sudden brilliance of Italian culture, the celestial fire of the Milanese love of life and the Neapolitan love of art, the lightning of Aragonese intrigues and the whole, shrewd capability of the Sforzas. She turned the Polish royal household into a Sarmatian Renaissance court brimful of joy and fire.

She came to Poland, saw her Sigismund and conquered. With her, she brought all sorts of contested inheritance claims—for Cyprus, Milan, and Naples, including the future inheritance of her mother (who died six years later, at fifty-three, in Naples, where she lies buried in San Domenico Maggiore by the side of her brother Ferrante, the King of Naples). The claims added to Poland's diplomatic interests, and since they were Bona's claims, they also became Bona's diplomatic interests. She soon found that she was more intelligent than her Old one and a dozen Polish ministers and archbishops, and began to direct the whole state. She had Dantiscus sent to the Emperor in Barcelona, as ambassador. Poland intrigued in Spain and in England, in Vienna and in Brussels. The Emperor did not even hand over Bari; allegedly, he feared its surrender to the French, the Pope or the Sultan.

The King was in his mid-fifties and as yet without an heir. The soothsayers and astrologers predicted the imminent end of the Jagellone dynasty.

Bona gave birth to a son. Sigismund the Old kept getting older. Bona took the state and her son in hand. She saw to it that her son was confirmed as the heir to Lithuania, was elected King of Poland two years later, and crowned eight years later. Thus Poland had two Kings, with Sigismund II August becoming Grand Duke of Lithuania during the Old one's lifetime.

With her dowry and Italian income, Queen Bona redeemed the properties which the King had pledged for small sums—to the rage of the great lords, who had profited from the properties. Soon Bona was one of the richest landowners in Poland. She wanted to strengthen the crown, to consolidate the monarchy, to cow the magnates.

King Sigismund was almost assassinated over it. Once, his nephew Ludwig of Hungary and Bohemia warned him of a plot to poison him; at another time on a mild summer evening Sigismund was standing by the window of his castle at Cracow, possibly musing about the virtue of Italian girls, when someone fired a shot at him from the street.

Soon, people throughout the realm began to point fingers at Bona and to ascribe the death of her enemies to her poison recipes.

The two Dukes of Masovia died, one after the other, both at the age of twenty-four—of consumption, perhaps? A Venetian pharmacist of Plock had to flee to Polish Prussia; a former mistress of the young ducal brothers was accused; Bona was accused of having sought to get Masovia for her son. Two accomplices of the wench who was certainly the Duke's mistress, and allegedly their murderess, were executed along with another woman; for a long time the second Masovian Duke's body was not interred; the Masovians called for a criminal investigation; two years later, the King granted it and found—that his spouse, Bona, was absolutely innocent.

She governed. The magnates no longer frequented any chancellery but the Queen's. Genial Bishop Krzycki, who wrote Latin poems under the name Cricius, composed odes in Bona's honor. She distributed the jobs, and did not forget her Italians. It was a woman's government—"for the Queen has so fascinated His Majesty that nothing may be done without her will."

A falcon soared high above ten-year-old Sigismund August when he sat on the throne, in the market place of Cracow, at his coronation. All *intelligentes homines* said that this could not mean a glorious reign.

King Sigismund the Old sat in Poland like his own monument. Nobody went to see him. He was not even asked for pardons or presents. Abroad he was already talked of as dead. The Muscovite envoys brought along special instructions every time, in case of the old King's demise. Alive, he received condolences from the Sultan.

At last the Old one grew senile. "Nobody tells me anything," he complained. He often wept; he was moved to tears without reason. When word of some blunder did get to him, and he understood the matter, he sometimes remembered and said, "I am still the King"—*ego sum rex Poloniae*—and stubbornly insisted on the wrong thing in the wrong place. Passive resistance had been his forte even in better days; it is the energy of the weak. Once, when the King refused something to one of his wife's friends, she did not let him see her for many days. He sat in his room, mourned and wept.

When he died at last, in the course of one of his frequent fits of gout, old and sated of days, on Easter Sunday, 1548, at eighty-two years of age, both Poland and the world once more remembered King Sigismund for a day, and people asked one another, "So the Old one was still alive?" and shook their heads.

In Vienna, Dantiscus, Poland's ambassador to the Hapsburgs, praised the Old one's ingenuousness. King Ferdinand listened to him and said, "He belongs to a past world." In Austrian Minister Herberstein's memoirs the Old one was described twice, thirty-two years apart, as "a blessed, peaceable King." A Catholic, he was tolerant toward Mohammedans, Jews, Orthodox Greeks and Armenians, and burned Protestants.

He took no interest in either Latin or the nascent Polish literature. He—or his wife—liked to build. The Italian architects in Poland made money, and Poland got beautiful Renaissance palaces.

The second half of his long reign saw the beginning of the golden age of Polish literature. It had the King to thank for a long peace.

No one would thank the Queen. She was charged with every conceivable evil, and in some cases justly. The chronicler, Gorski, called her "that beast"—*ita inquietum hoc animal fuit.* She put money into the Royal treasury; she introduced sound economic methods; she paid the King's debts and redeemed his pledged estates. She knew more about economics than her friends—or her enemies. Because she wanted to strengthen the Royal power, she put her creatures in many positions and, according to the Roman custom, took money for many favors. And Tomicki, the humanist, statesman and archbishop, promptly wrote: "As for venality, we also hear that nowadays every thing can be bought at court for goodly sums."

The aristocratic Deputies complained that Bona was bringing up the young King in the wrong way. But only a little earlier the fathers of these Deputies had deliberately kept the King of Poland from learning how to read and write Polish, in the hope that an illiterate would be easier to handle. Bona's son, Sigismund August, spoke, read and wrote Polish, Latin, German and Italian.

The aristocratic Deputies complained of the Roman Law which was sneaked into their old-fashioned judicial practice, of the violation of their privileges, of maladministration. They demanded that the King take his properties away from his wife who had redeemed them with her own money.

Bona scorned the Deputies. But she hated the Hapsburgs. The Austrians had driven Bona's daughter Isabella, the widow of the Hungarian pretender, Zapolya, out of Hungary in rain and storm; in the end, Isabella had come to Poland with her little son. Besides, Bona hated Emperor Charles V for refusing to give up her Milanese heritage. To the Viceroy of Naples she was said to be "as hostile as a spider."

She hated the Germans as she did the Austrians.

She had a passion for oranges. Once, when the Austrians had halted a load of her oranges at a custom station, she swore to tolerate no Germans about her any longer and to exact revenge.

Lokschani, the Roman King's Minister at Cracow, reported: "These days, when they told Queen Bona that Laski was coming back from Turkey (this Pole was Austrian agent at the Sultan's court and had intrigued against Bona's daughter, Isabella) the queen indulged in a fit of wrathful weeping; moreover, she swore that she would not rest her head until she had avenged herself on those who employed such practices against her flesh and blood. It would be polite revenge but no one would fail to comprehend it."

So she "politely" avenged herself. For a long time because of her hatred of Austria and fear of competition she had prevented a union between her son and Elizabeth, the daughter of King Ferdinand of Austria; now she yielded. The sixteen-year-old Viennese girl came to Cracow. Sigismund August, the bridegroom, was twenty-three by then and a pervert. He blindly obeyed his mother. She had given him only girls as playmates; he liked to dress himself up as a girl, and the girls as boys.

"It was a mistake of nature," Bona said once, "to let my daughter Isabella come into the world as a girl, and Sigismund August as a boy." She had him educated by Italian tutors, lutists and dance teachers.

Bona did not let the young couple, Sigismund August and Elizabeth, go to bed together or eat together. Finally she sent the young King to Lithuania and kept the young Queen in the Cracow castle and tolerated no special kitchen for the Viennese. This was when people began to talk. Later, Elizabeth was sent after her husband, was promptly stricken with a grave illness and given up by the doctors; Sigismund August actually grew tender. When she recovered, he became cold again and returned to Cracow, where King Ferdinand's Minister Herberstein—after many threats on the part of the son-in-law—finally on June 3rd "counted out the dowry" to him—one hundred thousand Hungarian gulden in gold.

On June 14th, Herberstein left Cracow. On June 15th his master's daughter, poor young Elizabeth, died. Herberstein, truly sorrowful, wailed, "So with her demise more than three hundred thousand gulden Rhenish or Polish remained in Poland." In his memoirs he wrote that "Elizabeth surely was not deceased of a common, natural death." A diplomat even in his memoirs, he omitted Bona's name. One of the courtiers said that young Sigismund August's mourning could only be noticed by his clothes.

He was already enthralled by beautiful Barbara Radziwill, the twenty-three-year-old widow of the Palatine of Troki. A priest married them in secret. He unbosomed himself to the Old one at the Diet of Petrikow; his mother already knew, from the Palatine of Sandomierz. Sigismund the Old forbade the marriage; Sigismund August vowed he would not wed until Easter of next year. The Old one died of the gout. Bona wrote to her daughter that grief over the ill-bred son has sent him to the grave; she herself was more grieved by "this infamous and unfortunate marriage" than by her husband's death.

Instead of a wake, the young King held his public wedding. He led Barbara into the royal castle of Vilna; he was unshakable in her defense before the Diet, where the Deputies partly raged, partly knelt before him, where the archbishops knew God's will and the great landowners knew their own, where all the rich predicted a revolution and all the pious, with chuckles, predicted the dissolution of the marriage.

Bona was justifiably afraid that her jointure and other properties would be "seized" in the turmoil. She hastened to Masovia, and thus involuntarily made room in the castle of Cracow for Barbara—who was received only by the suburbanites and canons of Cracow, and by three abbots. But the King did not spare money and staged a gay life in the castle. Barbara was crowned in the cathedral on December 12, 1550. On May 8, 1551, she died—officially of cancer; but even Bona's son, the young King, muttered that Bona's poison had been the cause.

He and his mother had little faith in God but absolute faith in the devil. Sigismund was convinced that his mother had bewitched his wife. Shortly before her death, poor Barbara had let her mother-in-law talk her into a reconciliation; at once, the King wrote to his brother-in-law Radziwill in Lithuania: "Now we shall have to beware at mealtimes." After his wife's death, in Petrikow, he put to the torture a hag in Bona's service, a professional soothsayer and witch; on the rack, the old woman was said to have made interesting confessions. Sigismund August avoided his mother; he grew lonely and suspicious.

To King Ferdinand Bona had written (at the time when she and her son were maltreating the King's daughter, the little girl from Vienna): "I am merely doing to the daughter of Austria what Austria did to mine." But King Ferdinand was not content with the suspicious death of his daughter Elizabeth. He now married his second daughter, Catherine, to the man who had abused and disgraced Elizabeth.

Since Bona had loudly boasted of tolerating her son's marriage to the first Viennese for the sole reason of holding a hostage in her daughter's interest, good father Ferdinand had the notion of suggesting that Bona send her grandson to be brought up at the court of Emperor Charles V, or of Philip II of Spain, so that the House of Hapsburg, too, should hold a hostage. Bona's daughter lifted her eyes to the sky and declined with thanks; her little son was too young for courts such as the German Emperor's or the Spanish King's, and she could not so soon take such long leave of her sole joy. Bona had a gypsy put to the torture, and he obediently confessed to being paid by the Hapsburgs to kill Bona's grandson.

The second Viennese girl did not sleep longer in the Polish King's bed than her poor sister. When she failed to bear a son, he wrote to her father and brothers that Katinka was physically repugnant to him; besides, she was epileptic and he was avoiding her bed so as to spare her. He even avoided her presence. "I can't stand the sight of her any more," he told everybody and hoped that she would die. Who knows what the poor girl was hoping? She wrote to her brother, King Maximilian of Austria, asking that he should treat a Moor, who was jester at her husband's court, with special politeness; otherwise the Moor might harm her after his return—the fool might harm the Queen!

King Sigismund August, too, wrote the King Maximilian. "Can I not get a divorce? Then I might recommend a Hapsburg as my successor on the Polish throne." (He secretly believed his astrologers, who whispered to him that not until his fourth marriage would an heir be born to him.)

Eventually he returned Katinka to Austria. In the settlement he was so stingy that the King of Austria had to maintain his sister. The Polish Diet protested against the deportation of the Queen; he replied to the Senate: "I ask not to be forced to do what is against my will and my nature." In October, the second Viennese left Poland—alive, deeply hurt but iron-willed. She told her unwilling husband that although he "would not hold her as his spouse," she would "hold and acknowledge him for her wedded spouse" as long as she lived. She would never consent to a divorce, but would gladly return, if God should "again enlighten the King."

"This event did not take place," says the author of one Polish history.

Sigismund August could not keep more concubines after his third wife's departure than he had kept before. He called them his "falcons" who would kill him yet. He longed for a child like a young, barren woman. He paid physicians and astrologers to explore the secret of gestation. He took women to prove his fecundity—Zajaczkowska, for example, and Barbara Giese who was called the fair Gizanka, and others; all of them promptly had children. The King would have married a beggar-woman, the people said, if only she had presented him with an heir.

The people—merry in practice and rigorous in theory, as all peoples—railed at the Royal concubines. There also was a sister of the King, who was a virgin and took offense. The fair Gizanka lived in the castle of Warsaw (where Sigismund had moved his Polish residence); Zajaczkowska was housed by Sigismund August in a convent near Petrikow. The Papal Nuncio warned him to marry one of these concubines and make her Queen of Poland. Sigismund August replied: "Monsignor, non si farà cosa che non convenge." (One does nothing ill-fitting, Monsignor.)

The Holy Father finally exhorted the King of Poland to drop his unbounded marriage plans. Finally (in 1572) the King received news of the death of Katinka, the foreign Viennese. Sigismund August was persuaded to don mourning, but absolutely refused to bring the body to Poland. She was repugnant to him both dead and alive. The Deputies on the next Diet screamed threats that they would drag the Royal concubines out of the Royal castles with their own hands; the Bishops promised to preach from their pulpits against the King's bedfellows. The King went to his favorite castle of Knizin, with the fair Gizanka; he was not feeling well, he sealed his beloved jewels and died . . .

His mother had left Poland sixteen years earlier. She was weary of Poland and finally wished to depart. Her son, the Diet, the Ministers—none wanted to let her go. The Emperor first had to intervene, and several other European potentates. The King issued an edict threatening any nobleman aiding his mother's departure with loss of honor, any commoner with loss of life. It was not until she yielded the privileges to her rich estates in Poland and Lithuania that they let her go. Bona was ailing. She was yearning for Italy, for its sun, its sky, for the columns in its squares and for the laughter of the people in its streets, for the blue sea, the lemon trees, the baked swallows' nests and her Duchy of Bari.

With rolling carriages and endless baggage she moved through the cold and snow of the Polish winter. At every bend of the road the *schlachzizes* were lying in wait to rob her. They screamed embitteredly that on her horses and carriages and mules she was carrying half of Poland abroad—the poison-monger, the foreigner. She would have been attacked and robbed in fact if a noble Polish *schlachziz* had not protected her. Finally she reached her Duchy of Bari, and wrote a will leaving all her possessions to the King of Spain, Philip II. She kept a great court at Bari, received poets, artists and humanists, and carried on intrigues with Emperor and Pope against her son and Poland. She died in November, 1558, at sixty-five years of age, and was buried in the parochial church of San Nicolo di Bari. There, she is depicted in white marble, kneeling on a black marble sarcophagus, with two Polish saints, St. Casimir and St. Stanislas, standing behind her.

She had left her principalities of Bari and Rosani to the wealthiest man on earth, somber Philip II. To her son, Sigismund August, she left the injunction to pay great legacies to his sisters.

Sigismund August openly declared that his mother's testament was a forgery. Considering testator and heirs, Bona's vengefulness makes the testament probable—and Philip's ruthlessness, the forgery. Philip II did not give up the principalities, and only hesitantly yielded the cash fortune. The latter promptly caused a fight between Sigismund August and his sisters.

The Papal Nuncio, Julius Ruggieri, in 1568 described the aging King a few years before his death: of medium height, gaunt, with black hair and a stringy beard, dark-complexioned and feeble. He could not stand exertion. He suffered from podagra. In his youth he loved bright clothes, even fancy dress during the carnival; later, he went dressed in long black garments and had his room papered with black fabrics.

Never one to talk much, he became monosyllabic in his declining years, and taciturn. He had no confidant. He loved horses, and kept many thousands of Neapolitan, Turkish, Spanish, Mantuan and Polish breeds on his estate near Castle Knizin.

He loved jewels, like his mother. He would go into his treasury and enjoy the sight of the jewels, and of the gold. Few knew the extent of his treasures.

Once, he spent half a million scudis on a few jewels. He did not touch them even when he was in the greatest need of money; he preferred to borrow and complain of his poverty.

He spoke Polish and Italian with ease, and could make himself understood in German and Latin. His education was mediocre. Ruggieri said: "He has a certain knowledge of remote countries, their kings and their power; he is sufficiently familiar with his neighbors, and perfectly familiar with the ways of his subjects, to whom he knows how to adapt himself but whom he also knows how to direct at will."

He was a skillful diplomat. He saw and utilized the weaknesses of men. He was a master of delay, for which reason he was called *Cunctator* or "King Tomorrow."

His subjects did not love him. They said of him that he was "false." He was a great whorer.

But he was peaceful. The period of his reign was the greatest age of Poland. For many years he kept his country at peace. He attached Livonia to his realm. He founded Polish sea power. He strove to submit the magnates to the executive, without wading in blood like his contemporary, Ivan the Terrible of Russia. He furthered a stronger union of Poland and Lithuania.

He also loved the company of humanists and books. He collected a great library but was no Maecenas; perhaps because he collected too many "falcons" and jewels.

This son of the last Sforza was the last of the Jagellones.

BOOK FOUR

THE ASTRONOMER

24

"FOR MATHEMATICIANS ONLY!"

"The simplest truths are precisely those latest found by mankind."
LUDWIG FEUERBACH

"IN THIS book," Copernicus wrote in his *De Revolutionibus,* "we shall, with the help of God, make all this clearer than the sun; at least for those who are not quite without mathematical knowledge—however difficult, nay, all but incomprehensible it may appear to many, and however it may conflict with the ideas of most. . . . On mathematics you write *for mathematicians only.*"

A few ancient Greeks taught already that the earth and other planets were moving around the sun. Their thesis was as interesting and inconsequential as many bold sentences of the Sophists. Copernicus was the first who recognized this hypothesis as the truth and tried to prove it mathematically, based on the celestial observations of the ancients, of Arabs and Jews, of Peurbach and Regiomontanus and Walther and of his own.

He was an observing and calculating astronomer; above all, however, he was a thinking astronomer—above all, a philosopher. Independent even of beloved masters and venerable textbooks, of the thunderous dogmas of the Church and the bearded prejudices of the sciences, he freed himself and mankind of the sanctioned geocentric concept of the world. Truth *could* not be involved. Nature could not be complicated.

Therefore, he sought a simpler explanation of the movements of the planets. Copernicus compared the results of his observations with those of the ancients, to determine the changes in the sky.

As a starting point, he chose the star named Spica Virginis—whose longitude, however, he determined by taking its distances out of the stellar catalogue of Ptolemy, which differs by almost forty minutes from the calculation of today. With such a basis of calculation—forty minutes wrong at the outset—one may imagine the difficulties bound to arise if Copernicus wanted to bring his theory into accord with the sky, or with as much of it as he could see with the naked eye.

Copernicus, "with the intuition of a genius, hit things, which later generations ascertained with telescopes and photography, so correctly that hardly a difference exists . . . For instance, he all but correctly determined the obliquity of the ecliptic, recognizing its gradual decrease and sensing that it would reach a goal and then turn back." (Maedler, History of Astronomy.)

The implements of astronomy were scant at the time. The fixed stars were not where they should have been according to the planetary table of Ptolemy, and Copernicus, who had to work with this unreliable catalogue, frequently pointed out the errors to Rheticus and advised him to undertake the task (later accomplished by Tycho de Brahe in his *Restitutio 1000 inerrantium*) of redetermining the celestial places of the fixed stars—especially the places of the stars of the zodiac, which were of particular importance to the calculation of the planetary courses.

In pointing out the mistakes of the ancients again and again, Copernicus wanted, first, to come nearer the truth, and second: every new deviation from the truth, of which Ptolemy could be convicted, shook the credibility of the entire old astronomy and made it easier to listen to a new theory. By means of his calculations and observations, and of the observations of others, Copernicus wanted to prove that the earth was actually moving and that his theory was not a mathematical prop but the formula of reality.

Rheticus, in his *narratio prima,* said: "For almost forty years the learned doctor, my teacher, observed lunar eclipses and the course of the sun, in Italy and here in Varmia."

For thirty years, said Copernicus (*de rev. orb. coel.* III, 6), he frequently observed the obliquity of the ecliptic. By the way, he believed that Frauenburg and Cracow were located on the same meridian, and therefore related all his observations in Frauenburg to the meridian of Cracow—while the difference amounts in fact to more than 17½ minutes.

Copernicus' instruments were primitive. In the "Revolutions" he enumerated the instruments which had been in use among the Greeks, and later. In addition to a simple gnomonic apparatus (a gnomon is a sundial) Copernicus seems to have used the *triquetrum,* which he manufactured himself to obtain the altitudes of the sun, the moon, the planets and the most important fixed stars and their distances from the vernal equinoctial point. After the death of Copernicus this *triquetrum* was preserved; later,

Canon Hanow of Frauenburg had it delivered to Tycho de Brahe as a present by Tycho's assistant, who had traveled to Frauenburg for his master in order to check the location of the observation-point of Copernicus. The assistant determined the polar elevation of Frauenburg at 54 degrees 22½ minutes; Copernicus, in *De rev.* III, 2, had stated it at 54 degrees 19½ minutes; today we arrive at a third figure. Tycho was pleased with the relic; when he died, it came into the possession of Emperor Rudolf who had bought all of Tycho's instruments and collections; after the battle of the Weisse Berg everything was destroyed or dragged off.

Copernicus mentions his use of this *triquetrum* or *parallacticum* several times in the "Revolutions." Gassendi assumed for certain that Copernicus made use also of a Jacob's-staff.

And it is probable that Copernicus did not possess many more astronomical instruments—in contrast to the Alexandrine and Arab astronomers, who had colossal instruments at their disposal. His residence was too small for large apparatus. True, he was wealthy enough to have those improved instruments made for him, in Nuremberg, which had made them for Regiomontanus.

Johannes Kepler, too, was later content, like Copernicus, with the crudest instruments built by himself. But Kepler was too poor to buy instruments.

Thus three sticks of wood constituted the "magic tools of the great Copernicus—tools with which he extracted secrets from the Muse, Urania, which were unknown to Antiquity and on which rests the entire modern astronomy."

Besides, he had to suffer from the Baltic fogs and all the other impediments of the northern atmosphere, and of the high polar altitude of Frauenburg, which, for an astronomer, was not an ideal place to work. He often speaks with open envy of the wonderful skies above Alexandria, of the pure, soft air over the Mediterranean. "Fortune," he says, "did not give me, as it gave Claudius Ptolemy, that beautiful opportunity of experience. For him, the skies were more cheerful, where the Nile does not breathe fogs as does our Vistula. Nature has denied that comfort to us, and that calm air. Therefore, due to the great density of the air, we see Mercury less frequently."

Still, Copernicus attempted to carry out observations of Mercury. He sighed: "Much toil and effort was imposed on me by this planet, with its irregularities which I had to calculate."

His disciple Rheticus, making a virtue out of necessity, said by way of praise: "He disliked bothering with the determination of minute distances, as sought by others who with painstaking exactitude believe they have found the place of the stars to two, three or four minutes, while actually erring by entire degrees."

Rheticus said: "I remember how, in juvenile curiosity, I once wished to enter the innermost world of the stars, as it were. Thus I once came to dispute with the best and greatest of men, with Copernicus. Although pleased by my honest passion he used to put a gentle arm around me and to implore me finally to stay my hand and refrain from overstepping the bounds. 'I myself'—said he, Copernicus—'should be no less delighted than Pythagoras after the discovery of his maxim, if in the results of my observations I could approach as closely to the truth as ten minutes.' "

When young Rheticus retorted in astonishment that, after all, one had to do his best to explore truth with greater and ever greater precision, Copernicus pointed to the difficulties in the path of our recognition of truth, naming three in particular. "First, the ancients were not disinterested in many observations, but had arranged them to fit their special theories about the movement of the planets; therefore, one had to apply unusual attention and care to the sharp distinction of these corrupted observations from those which the observer had made quite uninfluenced by his theory, without adding or omitting anything. Second, the ancients had determined the places of the fixed stars only to an exactitude of 10 minutes. Third, we moderns had not had for our immediate predecessors such men as Ptolemy succeeded then—such luminaries of science as Hipparchus, perhaps, Timochares, Menelaus and the rest, on whose observations and directives we proceed and in whom we can trust. He, Copernicus, would rather rest on statements of which he could guarantee the truth than display erudition and acumen by means of a dubious recitation of allegedly precise determinations." (Rheticus, *Ephemerides novae.*)

• • • •

(Ernst Zinner terms this story by Rheticus rich in contradictions, and even fantastic at many points. For if Copernicus had expressed regret over the lack of adequate contemporaneous planetary observations, would he not have admonished his pupil at first to devote his time to observations of the planets? And if Copernicus valued the observations of the ancients more than those of the moderns, why did he doubt the exactitude of the observations of the ancients?

And how did he come, on the basis of such uncertain observations, to compute the diminution of the sun's distance from the center of the

BONA SFORZA
REGINA POLONIÆ
ST

earth's orbit? And if he considered Walther's observations of Mercury inadequate, why did he use them for far-reaching deductions?

Zinner also compares the observations of the Greeks with those of Walther, and concludes that Walther's observations were more exact. Nor were Copernicus' observations by any means so bad that he needed to be ashamed of them at any point!

Zinner concludes that in 1551 Rheticus did not tell what he had really heard in 1541. In the end he asks: how much confidence had the old master in the twenty-five-year-old Rheticus?)

25

A HUMORIST CONDEMNS THE PTOLEMAIC SYSTEM

"Copernicus tied the duration of his fame, so to speak, to the duration of the world itself."

LICHTENBERG

THE Egyptians and Chinese were the first to collect astronomical data; the Babylonians and Greeks took over some results and constructed systems. Long before the Greeks the Chaldeans had computed the periods of certain planetary revolutions, divided the zodiac into signs, classified the stars according to their constellations and constructed several types of astronomical apparatus. The priests of Babylon were official prophets and astrologers. (Their almanacs in which they indicated the positions of the planets are known to have existed as early as 425 B.C.) They glorified the sun, the "Star of the King," for according to them the power of the sun kept the planets suspended in space, caused them to move, and was responsible for the changes in the weather and the return of the seasons.

King Amenhotep IV (Ikhnaton), too, who ruled from 1375 to 1357 B.C. and was a rebel and a poet, and sought to make Aton (the sun god) the sole god, celebrated the sun in his Sun Hymn:

When thou risest in the eastern horizon
Thou fillest every land with thy beauty.
Thou art beautiful. Thou art great.
Thou glitterest high over all countries.
Thy rays embrace the lands
And everything thou hast created.
When thou settest in the western sky
The earth is dark as though it were dead.

. . . .

Thou makest the seasons in order that all thy works may prosper,
Thou madest the distant sky in order to rise in it
And gaze upon everything that thou hast made, thou all alone,
Rising in thy shape as the living Sun,
Glittering, shining, going afar and returning . . .

From Egypt to Hellas came the twenty-four-hour day, the water-clock, the calendar year and the names of the months. But the Greeks ignored the best teachings, to wit, the Babylonian doctrine of the sun's royal position among the planets and the Egyptian idea that Venus and Mercury revolved around the sun.

Even the most cursory examination of the astronomy of the Greeks reveals three curious facts:

First, that it does not take long to make the gigantic step from natural poetry or sheer absurdity to the discovery of the truth;

Second, that it has always been dangerous to publish the truth, even if only about the stars in the heavens;

And third, that truth is inextricably mixed with falsehood, and reason with absurdity!

One of the first cosmogonies in the world was developed by Philolaus, a Pythagorean. According to him, the fire of Hestia rests in the center of the world. This "hearth of the universe" is surrounded by ten spheres which support the heavenly bodies: Earth, Counter-Earth (which was perhaps invented for the express purpose of obtaining a total of ten bodies, for ten was a sacred number among the Pythagoreans), Moon, Sun, the five planets and the starry sky. The daily revolution of the earth around Hestia's fire explains the daily motion of the starry sky; the music of the spheres is produced by their gentle gliding. The sun does not give light, but like a mirror it throws the reflection of Hestia's hearth fire upon the earth and other planets, which are by nature dark bodies. All of creation is numbers, music and harmony, in accordance with the Pythagorean ideals.

Anaxagoras, a contemporary of Pericles, taught that the earth was flat and was held in suspension by the air.

He is said to have predicted that a meteor would fall in 466 B.C. In that year a shining ball of fire like a comet appeared at night and thereupon a meteor dropped from the sky. Anaxagoras thought that there was a connection between these two events and declared publicly that the meteor came from the sun which was also a red-hot lump of iron. He was immediately accused of godlessness. What? Apollo, the god of the sun, the ray-fingered, resplendent in his sun chariot, only a red-hot lump of iron?

Pericles had to intervene in order to save the philosopher's life. No sooner saved, Anaxagoras made another discovery—that the moon was a dark solid body with plains, mountains and ravines, illumined by the light of the sun. The godless man was the first to explain how the moon is darkened by the shadow of the earth, and how the shadow of the moon produces an eclipse of the sun. Finally, he even discovered that the sun was bigger than the Peloponnesus! And that the stars were stones hurled off by the earth and made to glow by the rotation of the sky! And that Mind had set the world in motion!

After Pericles, in the fourth century B.C. some men began to say that the earth was a globe.

Then, in the third century came Aristarchus of Samos. He tried to clarify the relations among the sun, moon and earth. In a famous passage of his *Computation of the Sandgrains,* Archimedes tells us this: "As you know, most astronomers call the universe the sphere whose center coincides with the center of the earth and whose radius connects the centers of the sun and the earth. Such is the conception usually found in their writings. But Aristarchus published various hypotheses accompanied by drawings, from which it follows that the universe is much larger than the one just mentioned. These are his hypotheses: the fixed stars and the sun are motionless; the earth revolves in a circle around the sun . . ." etc.

In brief, according to Archimedes and Plutarch, Aristarchus thought that the earth probably moved around the sun and turned daily on its own axis.

We know that the Babylonian Seleukos of Seleukia considered these two motions of the earth as demonstrated facts, although we do not know how he proved them. He also tried to explain the tides of the Atlantic Ocean by the currents of the air, which according to him were caused by the motion of the moon and the simultaneous revolution and motion of the earth.

Ingenious as Aristarchus' hypotheses were, they remained fruitless. Ernst Zinner, a German astronomer under Hitler, finds a partial explanation of this fact, no doubt on the basis of his own experience, in "the Greek philosophers' and scientists' fear of the stupidity of their own fellow-citizens."

Aristarchus, too, was accused of impiety, because he taught that the earth, the "center of the universe," moves. Plutarch tells us about it. Most contemporaries of great men—as Lichtenberg puts it—"want at least to persecute those whom they cannot refute."

Plato and Xenophon state explicitly that their teacher, Socrates, admitted astronomy among the sciences only as the handmaiden of land-surveying and time-computation. This wise man considered that investigations of the orbits of the planets, the periods of their revolutions and their distances from the earth were immoral, if not subversive. And yet he had to drink the cup of hemlock!

Ptolemy (*Claudius Ptolemaeus*), the encyclopedic genius, who worked in Alexandria from 127 to 141 and died after 161 A.D., systematized all the learning of his time in various scientific fields and transmitted it to posterity in textbooks which remained authoritative for more than a thousand years. Several of his writings, as for example, those about Euclid and Mechanics, were lost, except for some quotations from them by other writers. We still have his works on music, geography, chronology and optics, his sketch of dials for sun-clocks and his astronomical writings.

The motions of the planets are discussed in his "Manual of Astronomy," the famous *Almagest,* as the Arabs called it—the only detailed work on astronomy that has come down to us from antiquity. It is regarded as one of the most sagacious volumes ever written, full of real knowledge and excellent accurate observations, and as a first-class geometrical work. It constituted the sum of the astronomical knowledge of the ancients and was dominant in the West among Christians, Moslems and Jews.

These are Ptolemy's most important astronomical hypotheses: (1) The sky has the form of a sphere and revolves like a sphere. (2) The earth has the form of a sphere. (3) The earth is in the center of the universe. (4) The earth is like a point with regard to the firmament. (5) The earth is motionless.

He gives us a catalogue of stars which contains 48 constellations with 1,022 stars of which positions (latitudes and longitudes) and sizes are indicated; the positions refer to 137 A.D.; they are given for stars of the first through the sixth magnitudes. He also describes the Milky Way and gives instructions for the building of a celestial globe.

Copernicus adopted Ptolemy's catalogue of stars unchanged in his *De Revolutionibus*. Ptolemy thought that he had listed all the visible stars, but actually he had included only the majority of stars visible in Alexandria down to the fourth magnitude, and a few of the fifth and sixth magnitudes. His catalogue differs from that of Hipparchus, which contained more than 1,000 stars, perhaps as many as 1,600.

In his mathematical exposition of the planetary motions Ptolemy followed Hipparchus (160-125 B.C.) who had used eccentrics and epicycles. He represented the seemingly irregular motion of a planet by a motion along an epicycle and a motion along an eccentric. The center of an epicycle revolves around the center of the universe, while the planet revolves around the center of the epicycle. An eccentric is a circle whose center does not coincide with the center of the earth, the alleged center of the universe. The speed of the planets on the epicycle was equal to that of the center of the epicycle.

Ptolemy terms his own Manual of Astronomy "a great deed, verily the ultimate goal of a mathematics founded on a philosophical basis."

"He haughtily rejects the reproach that his hypotheses are too artificial. The simplicity of the celestial events must not be appraised according to our human ideas of the simple, particularly as there is by no means any agreement as to the notion of what is 'simple' on earth. From these human points of view, none of the heavenly events would appear simple, not even the invariability of the daily revolution; for this very behavior which remains identical in all eternity is . . . entirely impossible among us, humans. . . ." (Almagest).

In his essay on *Nicolaus Copernicus,* Georg Christoph Lichtenberg, the humorist of Göttingen, describes the Ptolemaic system as "the most delicate, most artificial and at the same time the strangest mixture of sagacity, subtlety and delusion that the human mind had ever accepted."

26

THE LONG WAY: FROM PTOLEMY TO COPERNICUS

The stars? Hm . . . A glittering rash on the face of the sky!
HEGEL to Heine, as he looked at the night sky

The history of science is the real history of mankind.
DU BOIS-REYMOND

SCIENTIFIC truth is becoming ever more shortlived.

In 1929 Harlow Shapley wrote that: "The big American instruments have added more to our knowledge of the stars in the last twenty years than we had learned in all the time that went before."

All the time that went before . . . Our earth and the other planets are hardly three billion to eight billion years old—according to the "tidal evolution hypothesis," advanced by the Englishmen Jeans and Jeffreys and by Chamberlin and Moulton, professors at the University of Chicago.

At some point three billion to eight billion years ago, our sun, which until then had been traveling in its course quite alone, came dangerously close—only a few million miles, in fact—to another, much bigger star. As a result, a part of the gaseous clouds of which the sun is composed (more accurately: one-seventh of one per cent of its entire volume) flew into space and did not rejoin the original mass. Instead, these split-off lumps began to circle around the sun in elliptical orbits. They formed the planets including the Earth, as well as the asteroids and comets and a few meteors, nebulas and gaseous clouds. The gaseous surfaces of the smaller planets such as the Earth soon liquefied and turned partly into solid crusts and partly into oceans: the oceans are liquefied gas, the mountains, frozen gas.

Eight billion years of astronomical history revealed by the American instruments developed in the last twenty years! How different are the figures used by *the astronomers from* those of the sociologists!

The oldest known eclipse of the sun occurred more than four thousand years ago, according to *Shu Ching*. Two drunken Chinese astronomers were beheaded for having failed to predict it; the shock of this unexpected event terrified the imperial family and the people.

For some time the ancient Greeks investigated the heavens with their usual intelligence and without too many prejudices. They measured the size of the earth and determined the diameter of the sun and the moon and the distance from the earth to these bodies.

The motions of the planets were described with great accuracy by *Ptolemy* and *Hipparchus,* but they had little to say about the motive forces of the universe. And the development of Greek astronomy ended with Ptolemy and Hipparchus. As has so often happened in the history of astronomy, astrology took the place of science. (Even the astrologers sometimes grew dull, as Ptolemy complains.)

Certain Greek and Roman authors had made the sun the king of the universe: Poseidonios, Cicero, Pliny the Older, Plutarch and Theon of Smyrna. *Plutarch* even wrote: ". . . how can one say: The earth is in the center—in whose center? The universe is infinite; but the infinite, which has no beginning and no end cannot have a center either. For the center, too, would be a limit. But infinity is the transcendence of all limits . . ."

Arab astronomers continued the studies of the Greeks. They were motivated particularly by religious and practical reasons. Islam demanded that the faithful observe the periods of prayer and eclipses exactly and that they face Mecca while they prayed. The Arabs had to study the stars in order to determine place and time and to make charts and almanacs. They also invented many astronomical appliances and trigonometry, the science of computation with angles instead of arcs. The first astronomical treatises of the Arabs may have reached the Christian Occident as early as the tenth century, through *Jewish translators* in Spain.

Gherardo da Cremona (1114-1187) translated the *Almagest,* as well as two Arabic studies of the planets and the *Toledo Tables* into Latin. His work inaugurated a new era and superseded the writings of Macrobius and Capella, Ptolemy's compilators, who at least mention the so-called "limited" Egyptian heliocentric System. John Scotus Erigena, the Irish Pantheist at the court of Charlemagne, refers to this concept in the following terms: "Jupiter, Mars, Venus and Mercury, which always describe their circles around the sun . . ."

Arab and Jewish Aristotelians of the twelfth century (like Averrhoes,

Maimonides, Abubaker and Alpetragius) at first attacked the Ptolemaic theory. Geber wrote: "A motion like the epicyclic or concentric one is impossible . . ." Heinrich von Langenstein, the famous university professor who worked in Paris and later in Vienna, was also inspired by the attacks of Arab scholars on the Ptolemaic theory to compose his own work against the concentrics and epicycles.

That king of Castile called *Alfonso* by his mother, the Wise by his people and the Tenth by history, polemized against the mad capers of the Ptolemaic planets with a witticism: If He had consulted me beforehand I would surely have given the Creator a better plan. (The arrangement of the human body, too, seemed rather clumsy to this king.)

This Alfonso the Wise is said to have summoned to Salamanca some fifty Arab and Jewish astronomers from Cordova, Toledo and Paris to improve the *Toledo Tables*. But according to Ernst Zinner their planetary tables have not been preserved, and the so-called *Alfonsine Tables* were really composed in 1300-1322 in Paris.

The invention of new instruments for the observation and measurement of the stars and time intervals created the technical prerequisites for modern astronomy. The ancients with their sundials and water-clocks could determine only the hours, to wit the planetary hours of variable length (one-twelfth of the day or night, counted from sunrise to sunset, or from sunset to sunrise, and as a result of the changing length of the day and night of variable length). Only the mechanical clock permitted man to determine time exactly to the second, and to establish hours of invariable length. (Minute hands were probably not introduced before 1500.)

Nicholas of Cusa, whose ideas about the motion of the earth were sometimes strictly orthodox, wrote the famous phrase: "We know already that our earth moves, even though this motion is not visible, but becomes clear only when we compare it with the fixed stars."

This Cusanus, or Nicholas of Cusa (Cusa is a village near Trier, on the Moselle), "a very learned German" (1401-1464), charged the ancients with plain ignorance because they thought that the earth stood still.

The son of a boatman named Krebs, trained at the famous school at Deventer, became a Doctor of Law at Padua, and finally a cardinal.

In his philosophical works, he published his theories of motion, especially the motion of the planets. Only God, he says, who constitutes the center of the universe, is motionless; every other body has its own characteristic motion, hence also the earth. And on the last parchment page of an astronomical manuscript he had bought in Nuremberg, he noted that in the center of the world the earth turned on its axis going in twenty-four hours from east to west, and in addition turned around an axis perpendicular to the first. The starry sky and the sun, too, each followed two motions . . .

Nicholas of Cusa may have communicated his ideas about the motion of the earth to Peurbach. Peurbach was the teacher of Regiomontanus, Regiomontanus the teacher of Novara, and Novara that of Copernicus . . .

But Copernicus, who investigated the opinions of all the older authors on the motions of the planets and the earth, as he relates in his Preface to Pope Paul III, did not refer to any author later than Capella.

The Viennese astronomers Peurbach and Regiomontanus, who both died young, filled the fifteenth century with their fame, their errors, their forebodings of the truth, and their new scientific methods.

Brudzewski, "the teacher of Copernicus," made the first commentary on Peurbach's theory in his lecture at Cracow in 1483; like Erasmus Reinhold after him, he particularly stressed the oval orbits of Mercury and the moon.

In his theory Peurbach does *not* mention Cusa's ideas on the motion of the earth. Neither did Regiomontanus believe in the motion of the earth, unless we assume as proof of his belief, the piece of the alleged letter in the hands of the Nuremberger, Georg Hartmann.

Nevertheless, thanks to the humanists, the Occident finally rediscovered its great heritage. Translations from the Arabic and original Greek texts took the place once held by the writings of the late-Roman scholars.

The Ptolemaic theory with its excentrics and epicycles was well known, as was Eudoxos' theory with its concentrics. Known also were the objections of the Arab Aristotelians, and those of Langenstein and Julmann, to wit, that the Ptolemaic theory assumed improbable variations in the size of the planets. The so-called Egyptian doctrine of the revolutions of Venus and Mercury around the sun was familiar because Capella, Chalcidius and Macrobius had mentioned it. Aristarchus' doctrine was widespread through the Latin translation of Archimedes' works; Nicholas of Cusa, Peurbach, Regiomontanus and Paul of Middelburg had all heard of it. The glorification of the sun by the Babylonians and Egyptians, Greeks and Romans was also known.

Indeed, all this was known. But not all of it had equal influence.

Greek and Roman discoveries had reached as far as China and India without having any particular effect. The Arabs discussed the Greek theories endlessly and uselessly. And Christian Europe, expert in copying, read them and copied them, without being influenced by them.

Copernicus waged a titanic struggle. True, he fought against windmills;

but they had been erected by some of the greatest men that ever existed.

No duty is more completely neglected by men than their duty to become wiser.

The few passages in ancient writers which mention incidentally that the earth turns on its own axis and moves in a circle around the Great Fire are not distinguished in any way from many other classical passages whose absurdity is generally admitted. Who had not read them? But who had taken any notice of them? They proved nothing; nothing was founded upon them. Almost all the thinkers of antiquity, and all Christendom contradicted these passages.

Religion was naturally inclined to hold the earth, the seat of mankind, as the center of the world. And language obeyed (as it still does today) appearances.

"Thus a mere phrase finally became the Word of God," says Lichtenberg. "That first idea of the motion of the earth was thereby excommunicated, as it were; to advocate it was not only awkward, it could become dangerous. Now just think: this idea condemned by the greatest sages of antiquity, an idea which was disreputable, awkward, dangerous and seemingly contemptible . . . this idea comes to Copernicus' notice from casual descriptions; it arouses his attention, he tests it—and defends it. This was done by a fifteenth-century canon, living among canons (which means something), not in the gentle climate of Greece and Italy, but among the Sarmats in a region which at that time was on the frontiers of the civilized world. He follows up this idea with indefatigable patience, not for a couple of years, but throughout half of his seventy-year long life; compares it with the sky, finally corroborates it, and thus becomes the founder of a New Testament of astronomy. And he achieves all this —something that must never be forgotten—almost a hundred years before the invention of the telescope, with wretched wooden instruments, on which the divisions were often shown only by lines marked in ink. If he is not a great man, who in the world can claim such a title? This was the work of the spirit of order that dwelt in him, the spirit that itself originates in heaven and manifested its own nature in his work, and discovered order all the more easily because it remained free through inner strength. Kepler says this in a few words with great emphasis (Praefatio in *Tabulae Rudolphinae*): *'Copernicus, vir maximo ingenio et, quod in hoc exercitio magni momenti est, animo liber'*; the spirit of sectarianism and parochialism did not weigh upon him."

Ernst Zinner, however, gives more importance to Copernicus' predecessors. (The Birth and Spread of the Copernican theory, Erlangen, 1943.) He points especially to the ideas of Nicholas of Cusa and the modern methods of observation introduced by Regiomontanus: the circumstances of the observation were noted, the time was accurately established, the instruments were chosen accordingly, a net of coordinate stars was created with the help of which the positions of the planets could be determined. Regiomontanus' yearbook permitted him to select the most favorable moment for observation. His table of sines and tangents facilitated the calculations based on his trigonometry. Everything, Zinner says, was prepared.

It is true that sometimes everything is prepared for the prophet—but he does not come.

This time he did come! The man who had enough knowledge, boldness and luck to inaugurate the greatest of all world revolutions was Nicolaus Copernicus. He was seventy when after a life of leisure he announced his revolutionary ideas to the world, and he had to be persuaded, almost forced, to do this by a few audacious friends, like the old bishop Tiedemann Giese and the young Wittenberg professor Rheticus. Then his genius had to wait another two centuries for its vindication and triumph!

27

THE COPERNICAN THEORY

Mathemata mathematicis scribuntur (Mathematics is written for mathematicians).
COPERNICUS

He who desires to have understanding must be free in mind.
ALCINOUS (motto of Rheticus' Narratio Prima)

THE fame of Copernicus is posthumous. He owes it to the theory expounded in his Book of Revolutions.

We do not know how he developed this theory, nor when he formulated it for the first time. None of the existing documents give us any information on this question. On the occasion of the publication of Werner's work, Wapowski asked Copernicus about his plans. Under some pretext Copernicus refused to answer.

In the *Commentariolus* and in the Book of Revolutions Copernicus cites the motives which led him to make his revolutionary investigations: the existing theories of the cosmos seemed to him either too complicated or irrational.

In his Preface to Pope Paul III, Copernicus insists gracefully but firmly that his world-shaking theses are true. Without cringing, a canon here speaks freely to the pope, the head of the church organization of which he is a lowly member. And he gives the Pope an elementary philosophical lesson in cosmology which, again to quote Lichtenberg, "was at that time currently regarded as a branch not of philosophy, but of His Holiness."

For a long time Copernicus meditated upon the outworn theories. And he grieved in his heart that man should have made so many felicitous discoveries and yet have only impoverished and disorderly notions of the cosmos. Was not the world the work of the Perfect Architect and was not supreme order one of its essential qualities?

Out of this grief Copernicus began to read.

At first he was struck by a passage in Cicero, according to which Nicetas of Syracuse believed that the heavens, the sun, the moon and all the stars stood still and that only the earth turned very quickly around its own axis; this created the impression that the heavens moved in a grandiose circular motion and that the earth stood still.

In Plutarch he found the statement that Heraclides of Pontus and the Pythagorean Elephantus held similar views; and also the passage about the Pythagorean Philolaus who saw the earth turning around the Fire, in a slanting circle, and the sun and the moon running around similar circles.

Then Copernicus began to wonder whether the earth did not move after all. True, everyone called this idea absurd. But had not many people declared with impunity that various arbitrary circles and motions were traced by the heavenly bodies?

And so Copernicus began to turn the earth around its own axis, as well as to lead it around the sun. When in the course of his long life every new observation confirmed these hypotheses, he was certain that he held the truth in his hands, and everything fitted together so divinely well that not one of the thirty-four circles in which he thought he had encompassed the universe could be displaced without confusing all the others and the whole structure.

Thus true astronomy began.

While working with Novara he seems to have acquired the desire to make astronomical observations. He observed the star Aldebaran. Then Novara observed the sun, while Copernicus watched the moon and the conjunctions of the planets.

When did his revolutionary dissatisfaction with the dominant world system begin?

Presumably in Cracow, in that famous year 1492, when the fantastic son of a Genoese brothel owner, the descendant of Spanish Marranos, first set his foot on a new continent.

While the Genoese who dreamed about mountains of gold was making his little voyage which turned out so badly for the Indians, and just as he set foot on American soil and claimed the title of first Viceroy of America in the name of the Catholic Kings, Ferdinand and Isabella of Spain, and in agreement with his Catholic Holiness, the Pope,—a young student from Torun walked silently along the streets of Cracow, pursuing only truth and cosmic order, and, at first only in his silent thoughts, pulled down the pillars of the old world. But this revolution in the brain of an unknown student in the end gave mankind the most gigantic figurative kick it had ever received. Copernicus hurled all humanity with its dramatic history into the unfathomable abyss of solar systems and Milky Ways. Through a few bold axioms, and Arabic numbers and trigonometry (those children of the desert), he inaugurated that colossal joke of man, modern astronomy, with its grotesque laws of numbers, such as the fact that the light of the stars is billions of years old when it reaches us—the oldest spooks reasonable people have ever been asked to believe in.

What a piece of luck for *Copernicus* that throughout his long life he had the leisure to test his revolutionary ideas against the wheeling firmament, the time to measure the course of the stars, to compute the time necessary for the planetary motions, to adapt his theories to his observations, and to win some attention for his principal work, despite his revolutionary ideas, through ever more exact observations.

And, what is more, the canon of Frauenburg had the great good fortune to have a few excellent friends, especially that devoted and reasonable man who, as a friend of Copernicus, became also one of mankind's best friends—the good Tiedemann Giese.

This lifelong friend was learned enough to be able to follow Copernicus' studies. He ordered an ingenious sundial to be made for Copernicus in England. He bought him an instrument with which to observe equinoxes. And Giese loved his friend rationally, that is to say, not only the bad habits and odd manners, the mortal things that usually seem so charming to us mortals, but above all what was great in his friend: his immortal ideas and his inexorable opposition to the cherished follies of mankind and the pious prejudices of the past thousand years.

In his Commentariolus Copernicus sketched for a few of his scientific friends the degree to which astronomy could be reformed.

He summed up his ideas in seven propositions (which follow here in Edward Rosen's translation. Three Copernican Treatises. The Commentariolus of Copernicus. The Letter against Werner. The Narratio Prima of Rheticus. New York, Columbia University Press, 1939):

ASSUMPTIONS

(1) There is no one center of all the celestial circles or spheres.
(2) The center of the earth is not the center of the universe, but only of gravity and of the lunar sphere.
(3) All the spheres revolve about the sun as their mid-point, and therefore the sun is the center of the universe.
(4) The ratio of the earth's distance from the sun to the height of the firmament is so much smaller than the ratio of the earth's radius

to its distance from the sun that the distance from the earth to the sun is imperceptible in comparison with the height of the firmament.

(5) Whatever motion appears in the firmament arises not from any motion of the firmament, but from the earth's motion. The earth together with its circumjacent elements performs a complete rotation on its fixed poles in a daily motion, while the firmament and highest heaven abide unchanged.

(6) What appear to us as motions of the sun arises not from its motion but from the motion of the earth and our sphere, with which we revolve about the sun like any other planet. The earth has, then, more than one motion.

(7) The apparent retrograde and direct motion of the planets arises not from their motion but from the earth's. The motion of the earth alone, therefore, suffices to explain so many apparent inequalities in the heavens.

Copernicus describes the order of the spheres, the apparent motions of the sun, the motions of the moon, those of the three upper planets, Saturn, Jupiter and Mars, those of Venus, and finally those of Mercury. He concludes his *Commentariolus* with this triumphant passage:

"Then Mercury runs on seven circles in all; Venus on five; the earth on three, and around it the moon on four; finally Mars, Jupiter and Saturn on five each. Altogether, therefore, thirty-four circles suffice to explain the entire structure of the universe and the entire ballet of the planets."

What was new in these seven assumptions? First, the idea of the motion of the earth, its daily rotation on its own axis and its yearly rotation around the sun which rests near the midpoint of the universe. Second was the idea, soon rejected by posterity, that there is a third motion of the earth. For Copernicus this third motion explained its slanting position with regard to its orbit.

The Commentariolus does not cite any of Copernicus' own observations. Thus it is probably based on the Alfonsine Tables.

When did Copernicus write his Preliminary Report or Commentariolus?

It was not printed during his lifetime. (Its exact title is: *Nicolai Copernici de hypothesibus motuum coelestium a se constitutis commentariolus.*) Copernicus sent out a number of manuscript copies of this work, but only two are known to have survived. Maximilian Curtze thinks that the Commentariolus was written between 1533 and 1539.

Birkenmajer was the first to point out that the heliocentric system expounded in the Commentariolus differs in certain essential points from that expounded by the mature Copernicus in his Book of Revolutions. Therefore, Birkenmajer thinks, the Commentariolus was worked out before 1509 and completed not later than 1512.

Zinner thinks this report was completed in 1514 at the latest, the year that Copernicus was invited to Rome to participate in the revision of the calendar. At that time he began his investigations of the length of the year, and in connection with it of the motions of the planets. In his dedication to Paul III Copernicus relates that upon the request of Paul von Middelburg, he began to observe more exactly the course of the sun and the moon. Zinner sees in the Commentariolus all the symptoms of a hasty work, and assumes the time of its writing to be the period between 1510 and 1514.

Like every author who sends his manuscript to colleagues or critics, Copernicus hoped for enthusiastic applause. He was completely disappointed in this hope. The only reply to his work was icy silence. Exactly one mention of it by contemporaries has been discovered and even in that one the name of the author and the title of his work are not given. In a book catalogue drawn up by Mathias Miechow of Cracow, dated May 1, 1514, we find the following item: "A manuscript of a theory of the planets, in which it is asserted that the earth moves while the sun is motionless." This item may refer to the Commentariolus.

Ernst Zinner enumerates three objections to this study that even "a well-intentioned man would have to recognize as justified." First, Copernicus was mistaken in assuming that only thirty-four circular motions were needed for his System. He forgot to include the precession of the equinoxes, the motions of the aphelia, and the revolution of the line of nodes performed in nineteen years, all of which required four more spheres. Thus thirty-eight circles were necessary. Secondly, the data of the Commentariolus could not be checked. Third, Copernicus built his cosmology not on his own, but on other people's observations, obviously on the Alfonsine Tables, of which the defects were generally known even then, and, as it appears from Copernicus' marginal remarks on his own copy of these Tables, had been noted by him, too. Thus the data on which he based his trajectories were really inadequate for a correct exposition of the movement of the heavenly bodies.

Ernst Zinner asks why the astronomers should have changed their theories only to obtain a representation of astronomical facts inferior to that which they already had. And most of them, he thinks, would have only laughed at the peculiar idea of making the earth move. Fortunately, Zinner points out, Copernicus was able to devote several more decades to his theory and get some consideration for it by making observations. According to this authority, if Copernicus had died at the age of forty, as did Regiomontanus, his Commentariolus would have been forgotten, and so we would have no knowledge of his attempt to explain the universe. Only the fame of the author of *De Revolutionibus* led to the rediscovery of his earlier work.

Gemma Frisius mentioned the Commentariolus in a letter to Dantiscus in 1541.

And in *De Nova Stella anni 1572* Tycho de Brahe speaks of the "little treatise by Copernicus on the hypotheses he worked out."

But the astronomers did not pay any attention to the references of Gemma Frisius and Brahe, or if they did, they connected them with the Narratio Prima of Rheticus.

In his *Introduction to Three Copernican Treatises* Edward Rosen discusses the question whether Copernicus considered the motion of the earth a hypothesis and whether he believed in its reality. Maximilian Curtze pointed out that in the title of the Commentariolus (Nicolaus Copernicus, Sketch of His Hypotheses on the Heavenly Motions) Copernicus had spoken of the hypotheses of his astronomical system as a hypothesis. Thereupon, Leopold Prowe explained that the title did not come from Copernicus, that he could not have spoken of his "hypotheses" because he was convinced of the absolute truth of his theory.

According to Rosen, such an inference is based on a misunderstanding. Although Copernicus is firmly convinced that the earth really moves, he terms his theory a hypothesis. Rosen refers to the correspondence between Copernicus and Osiander, the chief clergyman of Nuremberg. After Rheticus' departure from Nuremberg Osiander supervised the printing of Copernicus' principal work and in a letter dated April 20, 1541, urged him to present his astronomical system not as the true picture of the universe, but as an auxiliary mathematical hypothesis—true or false—which gave a satisfactory explanation of the phenomena.

Kepler who tells us about this exchange of letters and quotes a passage from them, justifies Copernicus' attitude. The great canon was anything but an opportunist, like the leader of the Lutheran church. Kepler writes: "Strengthened by a stoical firmness of mind, Copernicus believed that he should publish his convictions openly, even though science might be hurt as a result."

In the eyes of Copernicus the motion of the earth was a physical reality, the naked truth. Copernicus was a realist. He sought the truth and believed he had found it. If he added to his revolutionary work letters and prefaces by popes, cardinals and bishops (or letters and prefaces addressed to them), he did this out of respect for the preposterous claims of religion to be the teacher of science, out of respect for the power of the church, which could simply burn revolutionaries, and out of respect for scientific truth, in comparison with which popes, cardinals and bishops were of secondary importance.

With justifiable pride Copernicus replied to Luther and Melanchthon, to the inquisitors and Grand Inquisitors, and to all the Protestant and Catholic zealots, who answered the axioms of mathematics by quotations from the Bible. He anticipated their attacks and called them babblers and falsifiers, whose ignorance he despised: "If perhaps there are babblers who, although completely ignorant of mathematics, nevertheless take it upon themselves to pass judgment on mathematical questions and, improperly distorting some passage of Scripture to their purpose, dare to find fault with my system and censure it, I disregard them even to the extent of despising their judgment as uninformed." (Liber Revolutionum 7.16-20.)

Even a father of the church became absurd when he meddled with things astronomical, Copernicus declared, to the Pope, of all people: "For it is not unknown that Lactantius, otherwise an illustrious writer, but no mathematician, speaks quite childishly about the earth's form, when he mocks those who have stated that the earth has the form of a sphere." (Liber Revolutionum 7.21-23.)

But Rosen quotes various passages from *De Revolutionibus* in which Copernicus uses without distinction, the terms: principle, assumption and hypothesis, for fundamental axioms: "Furthermore astronomy, that divine rather than human science, which inquires into the loftiest things, is not free from difficulties. Especially with regard to its principles (principia) and assumptions (assumptiones), which the Greek call 'hypotheses' (hypotheses) . . ."

These axioms, in order to be recognized as true, must satisfy two conditions: 1) apparentias salvare (save the appearances): "the results deduced from them must agree with the observed phenomena within satisfactory limits of error." (Rosen): 2) aequalitatem tueri: "They must be consistent with certain preconceptions, called 'axioms of physics,' such as that every celestial motion is circular, every celestial motion is uniform, and so forth."

His greatest innovation, the motion of the earth (an axiom which satisfied both conditions) Copernicus himself called a hypothesis (Book of Revolutions, 34, 14-19): "For this reason some thinkers believed that the sphere of the fixed stars also moves, and hence they adopted a surmounting ninth sphere. This ninth sphere having proved insufficient, the moderns now add a tenth, and even so do not attain the goal. For we shall use the earth's motion as a principle and hypothesis in demonstrating the other motions."

Rosen also quotes statements to the same effect, from the Book of Revolutions and the Letter against Werner. Thus Prowe was wrong. Copernicus called his ideas hypotheses, and at the same time believed in their physical reality.

Let us conclude with a passage from Johann Gottfried Herder's enthusiastic essay: "Some thoughts on the life of Nicolaus Copernicus": "What the lonely Copernicus kept within him so completely and for so long, was what we can read in his face: he is objective, calm; he looks upon himself without presumption or pretentions, full of strength and youthful self-reliance. All this is revealed in the countenance of the noble Sarmat. One can see that this man gazes at the world with the deepest and most selfless vision. He is capable of committing acts of rashness (and his Hypothesis was the rashest act that a mortal, especially a clergyman, could commit in his day), but this does not worry him. He holds his hypothesis for himself and for those who want it; the earth is no more the centre of his existence than it is the centre of his cosmos."

28

THE BOOK OF REVOLUTIONS

To explain the entire structure of the world.
COPERNICUS

Give me a sufficiently big lever and a place to set it, and I will move the earth.
ARCHIMEDES, upon discovering the laws of the lever

IN 1514, when Copernicus refused the Pope's invitation to reform the calendar because he had not yet completed his computations of the motions of the sun and the moon, the great astronomer knew better than anyone that the fate of his whole theory was at stake. He must create a new foundation for his system in better observations, at least as exact as those of Ptolemy.

And so, in 1515, he began his observations of the sun; he wanted to determine the elements of the solar orbit (according to the Ptolemaic system) or of the earth's orbit (according to the Copernican system). From the spring of 1515 to the spring of 1516, he observed the sun's altitude in order to determine the declination of the ecliptic and the altitude of the equator and the pole, so that he could compute the length of the solar orbit.

The observations of which he made use in his principal work are lost. Rheticus reports that he noted down all the observations he knew of, his own and others', on loose sheets of paper.

In addition to the orbit of the earth, whence he deduced the length of the year, he was very much interested in the motion of the moon. He wanted to prove that the distance of the moon from the earth varied much less than Ptolemy had believed. With the help of a pinewood wicket marked with ink and fixed to a post in such a way that it could be turned like the leaf of a folding door, Copernicus observed the altitude of the moon and the star Spika from 1515 to 1525. Later, when

Tycho de Brahe received this wicket as a gift and examined it, he was amazed that Copernicus should have been able to make such exact observations with so simple an instrument. From 1509 to 1525, in an effort to determine the orbit of the moon, he regularly observed the eclipses of that body. He also had an astrolabe made following Ptolemy's specifications and used it from 1512 on to determine the positions of the planets and the stars. For his principal work, Copernicus determined only the longitudes of their planets, not their latitudes.

Together with the Ptolemaic observations, and three observations of Mercury he had taken over from the Nuremberg astronomer, Walther, his four observations of Saturn, four of Jupiter, four of Mars, and one of Venus, constituted the foundation of the Book of Revolutions. Only after having completed his observations for this work did he improve his methods. After 1537 he used his astrolabe to determine both the longitudes and latitudes of the planets, and probably to test the elements of his orbits.

In the whole work sixty-one observations can be found, of which nine are of the sun, twenty of the moon, thirty of four planets, and two of the Spika. It goes without saying that he must have made many more observations than these.

He observed the course of the moon from 1497 to 1541; that of the sun from 1515 to 1516; the precession from 1515 to 1525; Mars and Saturn apparently from 1500 to 1538; Jupiter from 1520 to 1529, and Venus from 1529 to 1537. Despite all his efforts, he did not succeed in observing Mercury, presumably because of the Baltic Sea fogs.

Other great astronomers made a greater number of observations.

In addition to his experimental basis, Copernicus created his own mathematical basis, his trigonometry. Since he alludes to this in his Commentariolus, he must have begun to use it in about 1510. He published this trigonometry in chapters XII to XIV of Book I of his Revolutions. Zinner thinks that Copernicus wrote these mathematical chapters (on chords, arcs, angles, plane and spherical triangles) at one stretch, probably in 1529. Incidentally, Copernicus never used the term sine. As Rheticus informed Praetorius, Copernicus abhorred this word.

His original manuscript, which everywhere shows traces of laborious and repeated revisions nowhere reveals as many changes and additions as in the chapter on spherical trigonometry.

In the winter of 1541-1542, during the last months of his stay at Wittenberg, Rheticus had these mathematical chapters XIII and XIV printed separately, added a table of sines to them, wrote an introduction and dedicated the printed work (Nicolaus Copernicus. De Lateribus et Angulis Triangulorum, tum planorum rectilineorum, tum Sphaericorum libellus) to the Nuremberg mathematician, Georg Hartmann, vicar of St. Sebald's Church and constructor of globes.

In his preface, Rheticus wrote: "Regiomontanus' treatise (de triangulis omnimodis) has recently been published but the famous and learned Dr. Nicolaus Copernicus had composed his excellent manual of trigonometry long before he knew of Regiomontanus' treatise; he did this when he once again revised Ptolemy and scientifically elaborated his own theory of the motions of the heavenly bodies."

For centuries the question was debated whether Copernicus had found some of his trigonometric solutions independently of Regiomontanus. Priority belongs to the latter. Copernicus saw Regiomontanus' trigonometry (which had been composed in Italy before Copernicus was born, preserved in manuscript by Walther, bought by Pirckheimer, and printed after the latter's death by Johannes Schoner as late as 1533, at Johannes Petrejus' press in Nuremberg) only in 1539. In that year Rheticus, after having met Petrejus through Schoner in Nuremberg, brought Petrejus' edition of Regiomontanus' trigonometry along with other recent books to Frauenburg, and presented them to his master and host.

Rheticus is supposed to have collaborated on the mathematical part of the Book of Revolutions in Poland; at least so says Lucius Valentine Otho, Rheticus' disciple. As a young man, Otho collaborated with Rheticus in the writing of his main mathematical work, on which the latter spent twenty-five years. Later Otho completed it and published it twenty years after Rheticus' death, under the title of *Opus palatinum de triangulis;* but Otho's assertion concerning his master's collaboration with Copernicus may be correct only to a very small degree.

Rheticus, himself a great mathematician, was full of admiration for Copernicus' mathematical genius: "The erudition which Copernicus possesses in all fields, but especially in astronomy, is so great," he said, "that he can be compared to the first masters of antiquity. Verily, verily, we can congratulate our century that such a master is living among us! And nothing more fortunate could happen to me than to share the intercourse and teaching of such a man! And if I can contribute anything of general use to the world of learning, it is entirely the merit of such a teacher!"

Copernicus explains why he wrote his mathematical chapters in his introduction to them. In Euclid's Elements, he says, much can be found, but not "what is here the principal subject: to wit, how one obtains the sides from the angles and the angles from the sides." It is also necessary, he goes on, to develop the scattered remarks of Ptolemy, given only as illustrations, concerning the sides and angles of plane and spherical triangles.

On the basis of his own observations and his own trigonometry, Copernicus could now verify his theory. He did this from 1514 on. In the sketch for his main work, which was rediscovered during the nineteenth century and which contains many changes and revisions in Copernicus' own hand, he summarized his computations and observations and reverified them. At the beginning of 1541 he was still engaged in revising and perfecting his Book of Revolutions, as Rheticus reported to Wittenberg (see L. A. Birkenmajer, in his Stromata Copernicana, Cracow, 1924).

Rheticus must have copied this sketch himself and given his copy to the Nuremberg printer; in certain details, however, it deviated from the sketch in Copernicus' own hand.

Originally Copernicus had planned to divide his work into eight Books. Later, after several cuts, he organized it in seven sections and finally limited it to six. The first four books were written first, with the axioms and hypotheses, with the mathematical chapters and the investigations of the courses of the sun and the moon. These latter were completed in 1525 at the earliest, for they use observations made from 1515 to 1525. The two last books, which treat of the motions of the planets, also include observations made as late as 1529, so that they could not have been completed before 1530.

According to Zinner, the sketch of the main work as far as chapter XIX of Book V, that is up to the end of the theory of Mars, was written at one stretch. But the later chapters not infrequently show traces of hasty handwriting which we know was characteristic of Copernicus' last years. This part of his investigations must have been copied from loose sheets or a rough draft at a later date than the rest. The investigations themselves may have been completed by 1533.

Thus he probably worked on *De Revolutionibus* from 1515 to 1533; the sketch prepared on the basis of the investigations was most likely written sometime after 1528. Copernicus wrote this sketch himself and continued revising it until 1541.

In his Commentariolus Copernicus had explained the astronomical phenomena by the motions of the earth, but the figures he cited could not be checked. However, in order to dethrone the Ptolemaic system, Copernicus had to supply verifiable figures and new planetary tables for a different computation of the astronomical movements. In order to facilitate a comparison between the two systems, Copernicus in his Book of Revolutions imitated the design and structure of the Almagest. Like Ptolemy, he placed his hypotheses and mathematical chapters in his first Book. In this book his hypotheses are developed in greater detail than in the Commentariolus.

Rheticus admits in the Narratio Prima that Copernicus intentionally imitated the outward structure of the Almagest. He says: "My teacher has written a work of six books in which, in imitation of Ptolemy, he has embraced the whole of astronomy, stating and proving individual propositions mathematically and by the geometrical method."

How curious is this classical or mediaeval attempt to encompass a whole science in one work, this desire to embrace at once the whole and its essence. It reminds us of the legend of the pagan who promised the Jewish teachers in his city to become converted to Judaism if one of the sages could tell him the essence of their religion while he himself stood on one foot, whereupon one sage impatiently boxed his ears, while another, the gentle Hillel, said to him: "In these three words you have the whole essence of Judaism: Weohavto lereaho komoho!" (Love your neighbor as yourself).—Thus the poor heathen became a Jew, and woe to his descendants!

"The first Book," Rheticus says of the Liber Revolutionum, "contains the general description of the universe and the foundation by which he undertakes to save the appearances and the observations of all ages. He adds as much of the doctrine of sines and plane and spherical triangles as he deemed necessary to the work."

Copernicus begins with a paean to astronomy, the queen of the sciences. He mentions the efforts of Ptolemy and the fact that most of the observations of ancient scientists were not in accord with his tables. It is particularly difficult, Copernicus says, to determine the length of the year.

Then he states his hypotheses; the first three deal with the form of the sphere. This is the perfect form and therefore probably the form of all the heavenly bodies, of the moon and the sun, and it is even highly probable that the whole world is round. The universe must behave like the drop of water, which when left to itself strives to achieve this form and having once attained it, remains in it.

It is an old prejudice in the dubious science known as aesthetics that one form is superior to another.

Copernicus enumerates the proofs of the roundness of the earth. These are really Ptolemy's best proofs: departing ships sink gradually below the horizon, etc. From the roundness of the earth he proceeds to its motions.

Chapter IV deals with the motions in the firmament, all of them circular motions, of course; only circular motion can lead to repetition. And, more generally, everything in nature is arranged in the best order. That is why there is no inconstancy in the nature of the mover and no unevenness in the moved body. The irregularities are only apparent, resulting from the position of the earth.

In Chapter V Copernicus inquires whether the earth moves and where it is. It is believed, he says, that the earth rests in the center of the universe and it is even deemed ridiculous to believe the opposite. But if the matter is considered carefully one realizes soon that it is far from settled. Just reflect upon what we base our judgment as to whether something is moving or not. "For every apparent change of position is due, either to a motion of the object observed, or to the motion of the observer, or to unequal changes in the positions of both. . . . If, then a certain motion be assigned to the Earth, it will appear as a similar but oppositely directed motion affecting all things exterior to the Earth, as we were passing them by." (De Revol. I, 5.)

We see the heavens in a motion which carries everything along with it, except the earth and what is around it, and "if you will allow that the heavens have no part in this motion, but that the earth turns from west to east, then, so far as pertains to the apparent raising and setting of the sun, moon, and stars, you will find, if you think carefully, that these things occur in this way." (De Revol. I, 5.)

Various ancients believed that the earth moves. Heraclides, Ekphantos and Hicetas, Copernicus points out, explained the daily revolution of the hours by the rotation of the earth; and he, too, explains it this way.

And the earth is not in the center of the world; this is proved by the varying distances of the planets from it; thus the centre of the earth cannot be the centre of the planetary orbits. Even in ancient times Philolaus, a Pythagorean, had taught that the earth had a multiple motion and that it was one of the planets. Or, as Copernicus puts it, (De Revol. I, 5): "If someone states that the Earth does not occupy the centre of the Universe, but nevertheless does not admit that its displacement is so great as to be comparable with the sphere of fixed stars, though appreciable and obvious in comparison with the spheres of the Sun and of the other planets; if then he supposes that the motion of those planets will therefore appear non-uniform, being referred to a centre other than the centre of the Earth, he will perchance be able to offer a not unfitting explanation of this non-uniform apparent motion." That not only the diameter of our terrestrial globe, but also the distance of the earth from the centre of the universe is an imperceptible point, a mere nothing, in comparison with the distances of the fixed stars, is clearly revealed by the fact that the horizon always exactly halves the zodiac, wherever the earth may be. "If the initial point of Cancer lies in the eastern horizon, that of Capricorn lies exactly in the western, and inversely, when the latter is in the eastern horizon, the former lies in the western. Thus the horizon is a plane which always appears to pass through the centre, at whatever time it is placed through the earth, which does not stand in that centre."

Lichtenberg makes the following remarks on this passage: "I need not . . . prove in detail that this is one of the greatest and boldest ideas ever ventured by man, but one which could be expected of the man who in the first lines of his book evoked a drop of water in discussing the roundness of the sun and even of the universe."

Thus, in Chapter IV, Copernicus proves that the heavens are infinitely great in relation to the earth. And because of this grotesque disproportion it is unbelievable that the infinitely great heavens should revolve around the infinitely small earth.

"Nihil aliud habet illa demonstratio," Copernicus concluded his Chapter VI, "quam indefinitam coeli ad terram magnitudinem. Ad quousque se extendat haec immensitas minime constat." (What follows from this demonstration is that the heavens are infinite in relation to the earth. The extent of this immensity we do not know at all.) "It does not follow," he goes on, "that the earth is in the centre, indeed it would be rather astonishing if the immense sphere of the stars revolved around this little point in twenty-four hours, rather than this little point around itself."

Chapters VII and VIII contain Copernicus' polemics against Aristotle's and Ptolemy's reasons for believing that the earth is in the centre of the universe.

"The ancients," Copernicus says, "therefore found other proofs that the earth was motionless. They said that if the earth rotated around its own axis nothing could fall or rise in a straight line. All the clouds, Ptolemy thought, would move from the east to the west, and the earth itself would necessarily be dispersed by this rapid rotation."

Copernicus answers this argument as follows: "I consider gravity as nothing but a natural striving with which the Creator has endowed the parts in order that they may combine into one *whole* while they collect into a sphere. The same is probably true of the sun, the moon and the other planets, and yet they are not fixed.

"As for falling and rising bodies, it is clear that their motion is composed of the straight and circular motions. As parts of the earth they do not lose the motion common to the whole, but preserve it in every other motion. Only this common motion, for the very reason that it is common, appears as immobility. The clouds do not move from the east to the west like the stars, because the lower atmosphere in which they are suspended is part of the earth and consequently rotates with it, either because the air is mixed with watery or earthy parts endowed with this motion or because the earth communicates this motion to it. As for the dispersion of the earth because of the rapidity of its rotation, the eventuality which Ptolemy fears, one should rather fear it with regard to his sphere of the stars because of the immense rapidity with which this sphere would have to rotate."

Moreover, only circular motions can exist in the universe; straight-line motions are a disease of nature.

Chapter IX deals with gravity and the motions of the earth, and shows that the earth cannot be the centre of the circular motions of the planets. The centre of the world is rather the sun.

In Chapter X Copernicus explains the new arrangement of the heavenly bodies. All the difficulties inherent in the Ptolemaic system are removed if one accepts the doctrine of Martianus Capella according to which Mercury and Venus revolved around the sun, with Mercury running in a smaller circle than Venus. If it is further admitted that Saturn, Jupiter and Mars also revolve around the sun as their centre, it can be easily understood why these planets seem further away from us when they rise with the sun than when they rise while the sun is setting. When he thinks, Copernicus says, of the great space that exists between the convex side of the Venus orbit and the concave side of the orbit of Mars, *he is not ashamed* "to place the orbit of the earth with her companion in this space, and to set the motionless sun, centre of the planets, at the centre of the whole, although the apparent positions of the fixed stars are not changed by the motion of the earth in its orbit."

(Incidentally, the Jesuit Riccioli censures this passage most sharply; it begins with the words: *perinde non pudet nos fateri*—therefore we are not ashamed to say; Riccioli notes that previously Copernicus said only that the revolution of the earth around the sun was perhaps not an unsuitable means of explaining the phenomena, but that in this passage he puts all shame aside and actually introduces his idea as something real in the system of the world.)

About the position of the sun and the orbits of the planets within the motionless firmament, Copernicus says: "But in the centre of everything rules the sun; for who in this most beautiful temple could place this luminary at another or better place whence it can illumine the whole all at once? Therefore some not unfittingly named it the luminary of the world, others its soul, and still others its guide. Trismegistus names it the visible god, Sophocles' Electra 'the all-seeing one.' In fact, the sun sitting on his royal throne guides the family of stars surrounding him. And the earth is by no means deprived of the services of the moon; on the contrary, as Aristotle says in his book on living creatures: the moon has the greatest kinship with the earth. Nevertheless, the earth conceives by the sun and through him becomes pregnant with annual fruits. In this arrangement we thus find an admirable harmony of the world and a constant harmonious connection between the motion and the size of the orbits such as could not be found otherwise."

Against the objection that the annual revolution of the earth would have to manifest itself through the stars, Copernicus points to the infinite distances of the stars, which are much further away from us than Saturn, as is proved by their twinkling, whereby they are distinguished from the planets. The distance of the earth from the sun is imperceptible in comparison with its distance from the stars.

Chapter XI deals with the three motions of the earth: its rotation around its axis, its course in the zodiac, and the ominous third motion, whereby the axis of the earth retains a slanting position. Then follow the trigonometrical chapters.

Lichtenberg comments: "Copernicus now proceeds with the sure and resolute step of a genius, always going in a straight line toward the truth, unmindful of the powerful voices that call to him from all sides: *You err*. And thus the great mystery which remained impenetrable to the diligent searching of thousands was revealed to him.

"Every one of his steps is in the path of the inventor; where the ancients guessed that it might be so, he says: it *must* be so. The suppositions of the ancients therefore do not diminish in any way Copernicus' inventive genius; on the contrary only through his work can they claim the honor of having at least spoken of a new world that he discovered.

"How symmetrical and orderly is the edifice of the world according to his plan! . . . How simple everything is here, how easily all the difficulties are removed!

"Copernicus ascribed three different motions to the earth: a daily one around its axis, an annual one around the sun, and finally a third one, by virtue of which the earth makes one annual revolution around the poles of the ecliptic in a direction opposite to the order of the heavenly signs, a second annual motion through which he explains the change of the seasons.

"The first of these motions was known by Nicetas of Syracuse; the second by Aristarchus of Samos, and, as Copernicus thought, by Philolaus; but the third is entirely his own. Although modern astronomy does not recognize this third motion, since it explains the same phenomenon more simply than Copernicus did, it cannot be denied that the great perspicacity of the man appears most sharply in his manner of treating this problem.

"Its solution perhaps cost him more effort than any other part of his immortal work. He is also the first to have raised the problem."

How does Copernicus imagine the motions of the planets? He gave no precise indications of them, and his terms varied. According to Zinner, he thought that the stars were fixed to the firmament and that the earth and the other planets moved with their orbs (orbes) whose centre was at the edge of another orb and was drawn around the sun with it. In the course of his investigations Copernicus was led to affirm the existence of various composite motions, for instance, the so-called librations by which the poles of the earth perform two alternate pendulum-like motions. He shows that rectilinear motions can be represented by two opposite circular motions, but he remarks in a note which he later deleted that if the circles are different the result is not a rectilinear, but an *elliptical* motion.

Book II of *De Revolutionibus* is devoted to spherical astronomy and the description of the armillary sphere. It contains a catalogue of stars, which reproduces Ptolemy's catalogue with a few errors corrected.

Book III contains the important investigation of the length of the year and the orbit of the earth. Its second part is devoted to the explanation of the Tables computed in such a way that it is immaterial whether the earth or the sun is considered in motion. It still remains in doubt whether the centre of the universe is situated outside or within the sun. Copernicus writes here: "We shall have to say more about this question in the exposition of the five planets, which we intend to carry out to the best of our abilities."

Book IV deals with the motion of the moon and its eclipses. Copernicus' theory of the moon is particularly important for his whole doctrine; through it he could prove that his theory of the planets eliminated the drawbacks of the Ptolemaic system, according to which the moon at its apogee or perigee, during the first or last quarter, would occasionally have to show a diameter twice as large as during the full moon; Langenstein and Julmann had already pointed this out, and Regiomontanus and Peurbach criticized it in their Epitome.

Copernicus' theory of the moon was much simpler than Ptolemy's. After investigating its course he investigated the motions of the planets. Here, too, his task was to replace the Ptolemaic circles and to demonstrate the advantages to be derived from ascribing motion to the earth.

In Books V and VI he describes the planetary motions. As Zinner remarks, Ptolemy in his theory of them created a miracle; like a magician he conjured up a woof of floating orbits for each planet, so ingenious and beautiful that the reader loses his sense of reality and only upon second reading notices that this exquisite construction has been built up without benefit of observations.

Copernicus did not start from observations, either, but limited himself to finding out to what extent the motion of the earth modified the Ptolemaic data.

Copernicus *concludes* his books with the exposition of the motions in terms of latitudes. He worked on this from 1515 to the end of 1532, a period of more than seventeen years. Including the preliminary studies for the Commentariolus, he spent more than twenty years on this work. Compared to the Commentariolus, the main work shows great steps forward: instead of the inexact data about the motions of the earth and the moon, exact values for these motions are indicated, and in order to make future computations possible, the initial angles for four determined periods are cited: noon of the First Hecatomb of the First Olympiad, noon of the First Thot of the first year after Alexander's death, midnight of January 1 of the first year of Caesar and midnight of January 1 of 1 A.D. The zero meridian is that of Cracow and Frauenburg. The distances and, later, also the apparent diameters of the sun and the moon, were measured anew, and thus a foundation was created for the new cosmic system. In his planetary theory, too, Copernicus achieved great progress by referring not to the Alfonsine Tables, but directly to the Ptolemaic observations, thus giving his computations a sounder basis.

The main work does not conclude with a summary of the results obtained, although a work as difficult as this really needs a summary. When Copernicus treated the question of the earth's motion, he promised to discuss whether the sun was situated in the centre of the universe or outside it, and he referred to this matter when dealing with the motion of Mars. According to his indications, the sun is three sun diameters distant from the centre of the earth's orbit, to which he referred the motions of the planets. All the centres of the planetary orbits are placed outside the body of the sun, the centre of the orbit of Saturn is even outside the orbit of Venus, and the centre of the orbit of Jupiter is very close to the orbit of Mercury. As a result the sun could not be regarded as the centre of the world (then the world of the planets).

This, Ernst Zinner thinks, might be considered by Copernicus a serious argument against his own system. True, he recognized the peculiarities of circular motion and used them for the exposition of planetary motions better than his predecessors; moreover, by introducing the motion of the

earth he greatly simplified planetary theory and gave a very simple ex
planation of the apparent pauses and retrograde motions of the planets
But could his system stand the test of criticism?

And Zinner proceeds to ask: "Did not Copernicus try in vain to adap
the Nuremberg Mercury observations to his theory and was he not i
the end compelled to content himself with an expedient? And hov
about the rotation of the centre of the earth's orbit on the little circl
near the sun? Were his observations so exact that they confirmed th
modification of the distances of the centres of the other planetary orbit
caused by this rotation?

"Had not his theory moved away a great deal from the convincin
simplicity which it seemed to have in his eyes, when he joyfully wrot
his preliminary report and referred to the thirty-four circles which h
thought sufficient to represent the celestial phenomena? What had hap
pened to that idea? Eight motions were imposed upon the earth alone, an
new motions had to be introduced for the other planets in order to ac
count for the phenomena. Were these motions real and necessary, or onl
the consequence of inadequate observations?

"And had not Copernicus become disloyal to his fundamental assump
tion? Had he not compared the rectilinear motion of a heavenly body t
a disease, and yet ascribed such a motion to Mercury? Had he not remove
the earth from the centre of the universe on the ground that it was no
situated in the centre of the planetary orbits? But is the sun in the centr
of these orbits?

"Such and like thoughts may well have tormented him. What was
needed? To make new observations and perfect his system."

And so Copernicus again observed the heavens. He began his new
observations in 1530. He wanted to perfect his methods. The best way
to prove his theory would be through observations, with the help of year
books of planetary motions based on his planetary tables.

Zinner thinks that Copernicus computed such yearbooks for the years
after 1533; for Bernhard Wapowski, the Cracow canon to whom the
pamphlet against the Nuremberg astronomer Werner was addressed, came
to see Copernicus in Ermland in the fall of 1535, found him engaged in
the computation of a yearbook and asked him for a copy of it for a publication. From Wapowski's letter of October 15, 1535, to Sigismund von
Herberstein it appears that Copernicus had not yet completed the entries
concerning the aspects. According to Wapowski the data in this yearbook
were based on the tables of Copernicus who assured Wapowski that for
many years he had held the view that the planets could be correctly
represented only if motion were ascribed to the earth and that the earth

FRAUENBURG

really moved, even though one could not see it do so. Wapowski wanted Herberstein to see to it that this copy was made known to the German astronomers who were computing yearbooks; thus they would become aware of the errors in their planetary tables and correct them.

Copernicus' yearbooks were to be printed in Vienna for the general use of European astronomers, for no one could predict the weather nor other periodic phenomena without knowing the correct motions and positions of the planets. Publication was desired by Wapowski, Copernicus and others only so that the new data might be more widely used. Wapowski was to transmit this letter with the copy of the yearbook to the Polish ambassador in Vienna, who in turn was to transmit them to Herberstein.

Apparently the yearbook was not published. Wapowski died on November 21, 1535. The announcement of the existence of the yearbook seems not to have borne fruit. In fact, Copernicus was always an unsuccessful author during his lifetime, even though he was a famous scientist.

The great man diligently continued his observations. He observed Mars and Venus and the eclipses. Moreover, he improved his draft of *De Revolutionibus.*

According to Zinner, this draft reveals "all the marks of rapid work. Haste is manifested in the written characters, in the constant changes of the forms of individual figures and letters; on the same page two different forms of 2 and 3, of *d* and *g,* and even three different forms of the number 5 can be found; likewise, the titles of the chapters change constantly; for instance, the title 'How to find the initial angle' is formulated differently for each planet."

Zinner also notes defects of structure and above all errors in computation, the latter resulting from Copernicus' slight practice in calculation; there are also errors in copying, mistakes in the quotations from older authors, and omissions of an angle or a sentence.

For instance, Copernicus attributed the observation of a sun-spot to Averrhoes; and poor Maestlin in vain went through Averrhoes looking for the reference. The sun-spot was observed by Aven Rodan, as Pico della Mirandola reports. Copernicus may have read Averrhoes instead of Aven Rodan in Pico della Mirandola.

From 1533 on, Copernicus tried to complete the draft of *De Revolutionibus.* He reduced the number of his Books from eight to six and crossed out the apocryphal letter of Lysis to Hipparchus and his mention of Aristarchus as one of the believers in the motion of the earth. Furthermore, he crossed out the computation of the inclination of the ecliptic made by his teacher Novara. He amended his observations of

Saturn and included the results of his new observations of Venus, etc. He also supplemented the mathematical part. His very numerous notes and corrections are the evidence of his hard work.

Unfortunately, he did not succeed in perfecting his draft as much as he desired. Zinner also mentions a few instances of erroneous corrections, as when the great astronomer replaced "Machometus" by "Albategnius," and errors in certain observations.

Copernicus could not correct most of these defects; it appears that he never again thoroughly revised his work, particularly because of his ever stronger doubts concerning the data of Ptolemy and other ancient authors. In his pamphlet against Werner he still condemned the latter's doubts in the sharpest terms. In his draft he still took the exactitude of Ptolemy's observations for granted, rejecting only his deductions and his general theory. He even used Ptolemy's deductions of planetary motions and apogees.

Only later did Copernicus grow distrustful of these. He remarked that the ancients adapted their observations to their planetary theories, for which reason it required particular care to separate the objective observations from the biased and distorted ones. This was later quoted by Rheticus.

This discovery must have been one of the severest disappointments in Copernicus' life. For his theory and his planetary tables were based on the observations of the ancients. His own observations sufficed only for the representation of the motions of the earth and of Mars. Thus the foundations of his cosmos began to totter.

Now he had to begin from the beginning again, and make new observations of the planets, in order to improve the tables for modern use. This is why he did more and more observing from 1537 on.

He might have completed his investigations, if the zealots had not finally declared war upon him, the war of Bishop Dantiscus against the alleged vices of Canon Copernicus.

PHILOLOGICAL APPENDIX TO 28

Before you say a word turn it over in your mouth nine times.

GERMAN PROVERB

In that passage of his Introduction to Three Copernican Treatises, entitled *The Doctrine of the Spheres* (Columbia University Press, 1939)

Edward Rosen deals with the question: what did Copernicus actually mean by the terms *orbis, planeta, sidus, sidus errans, stella errans* and *corpus?*

Eudoxus, the ancient astronomer (fourth century B.C.), invented the imaginary spheres for the apparent planetary orbits: each planet was situated like a spot or point on the surface of the invisible sphere. The planets were not supposed to have motions of their own, but only to share in the motion of the sphere. Because of the complexity of their motions the planets were given several spheres each. Kepler did away with all this by showing that the planetary orbits were elliptical.

Copernicus filled his whole Book of Revolutions with these spheres (*orbes*). There had been an old discussion as to whether these spheres were imaginary or real, whether they were an auxiliary mathematical construction and a geometrical hypothesis or whether they had a physical existence in space. Were they a part of the cosmic theatrical machinery, a real piece of the machine which hurled our planets around in space?

Pierre Duhem, in *Le Système du Monde* (Paris, 1913-17), tells of this stupendous controversy. Rosen quotes the following interesting passage from Tycho de Brahe: "But there really are not any spheres in the heavens . . . and those which have been devised by the authors to save the appearances exist only in the imagination, for the purpose of permitting the mind to conceive the motion which the heavenly bodies trace in their course and, by the aid of geometry, to determine the motion numerically through the use of arithmetic . . . Of course, almost the whole of antiquity and also very many recent philosophers consider as certain and unquestionable the view that the heavens are made of a hard and impenetrable substance, that it is divided into various spheres, and that the heavenly bodies, attached to some of these spheres, revolve on account of the motion of these spheres. But this opinion does not correspond to the truth of the matter . . ."

Copernicus uses the term *orbes* (spheres) as though he thought that the planets were fixed, sometimes to a three-dimensional sphere, but more frequently to a two-dimensional great circle of the sphere. For an astronomical theory, unlike an astrophysical or cosmological theory, it was immaterial whether the planets were fixed to a sphere or to its great circle.

This inexactitude in Copernicus' terminology, together with his shifting from sphere to circle and back again, has caused many difficulties. "Although Copernicus wrenched astronomy loose from its geocentric past," says Edward Rosen, "his sentences abound in language, that presupposes the earth to be in the center of the universe. The revolution in ideas did not at once precipitate a complete transformation of the terminology."

Rosen concludes that Copernicus uses the term *orbis* for "circle" when he discusses details of his planetary theory; but when he speaks more generally about the structure of the universe or the principles of astronomy, he uses the term *orbis* for "sphere."

The title of his main work, as it appears in the first edition at Nuremberg, and in later editions, *De Revolutionibus Orbium Caelestium,* means "Concerning the Revolutions of the Heavenly Spheres," not "Planets."

To denote planets Copernicus, in the Book of Revolutions *(liber revolutionum)* uses the terms planeta, sidus, corpus, sidus vagans, sidus errans, stella, stella soluta, stella errans, errans, globus.

BOOK FIVE

L'UOMO UNIVERSALE

29

THE REFORM OF THE CALENDAR

Nature conceals God—but not from every one!

GOETHE, Maxims and Reflections

AT THE age of twenty-seven Copernicus took walks in Rome and delighted in observing the eclipses of the moon. Fourteen years later, when the Curia invited him to return and help reform the Christian calendar he sulkily refused. A few years earlier the pope had summoned the great Müller to Rome for the same purpose. Müller had gone there and died.

At the end of the thirteenth century Roger Bacon, the monk who was so thirsty for knowledge, had felt the urge to reform the calendar. If something were not done soon, he used to lament, people would eat meat on all the fast days, instead of fasting for the glory of God.

In the fourteenth, fifteenth and sixteenth centuries the popes attempted to reform the church, and the calendar, but without success.

As early as 1513 the learned Paul von Middelburg, a canon in Holland, who became court astronomer to the Duke of Urbino and finally Bishop of Fossembrone, wrote an extensive work entitled "Paulina, etc.," in which he took up this question. He asked Julius II and later Leo X to comment upon his work at the Lateran Council.

On July 21, 1514, Leo X wrote long letters to the Emperor and many of the kings asking them to send their theologians and astronomers to Rome or to get their expert opinions and those of their university faculties. He also sent invitations directly to certain well-known theologians, professors and astronomers, to the good Dr. Poll, the Emperor's physician in ordinary, to a Carthusian monk, the author of *Margarita Philosophica,* to a now forgotten fashionable philosopher named Gregor Reisch, and finally to the Ermland canon and astronomer, Nicolaus Copernicus. The upright bishop Paul von Middelburg urged him to go. Bernhard Sculteti, Copernicus' colleague from Ermland, who was a member of the Rome calendar committee and a chamberlain of Leo X's, wrote Copernicus a courteous invitation.

Many learned men did come to Rome; expert opinions were sent there, too, for instance, from the universities of Tübingen and Cracow. The calendar committee under the chairmanship of the worthy bishop of Fossembrone, drew up thirteen theses, which were submitted to the universities, with a request that they deliberate upon them and then send their comments to Rome in order that the calendar committee might consider them. The second expert opinions were duly sent, but they arrived too late. No reform took place.

In 1516, Paul von Middelburg reported on this matter in his "Second Compendium of the Calendar Reform." In it he gave a roll call of all those who agreed with him, among them Dr. Poll and Reich and Stoeffler (Melanchthon's teacher), and Copernicus.

We do not know what Copernicus answered to Paul von Middelburg's entreaties.

Only in 1543 did he explain, in his preface to his Book of Revolutions, why nearly thirty years earlier he had thought it necessary to reject such a flattering invitation.

The calendar could be reformed, he said, only if the courses of the sun and moon were determined with the greatest possible exactitude. In 1514 he did not feel that he possessed such exact knowledge, and that was why he had been unable to give any advice on the matter. And he could not send his preliminary works to Rome for these were not yet completed. But, of course, since then he had devoted all his efforts to this problem which was indeed of vital importance for the church.

And the Lateran Council, Copernicus went on to say, did not reform the calendar because they realized that the length of the year and the months and the courses of the sun and the moon had not yet been determined with sufficient accuracy. And now, he, Copernicus, had made the necessary exact observations, in accordance with the exhortations of the most excellent Bishop of Fossembrone, Paul von Middelburg, who at that time was in charge of the reform of the calendar.

Only twenty-nine years after the Lateran Council did Copernicus publish the results of his computations of the length of the tropical year, in his Book of Revolutions. These results and the "Prussian Tables" drawn up by Erasmus Reinhold on the basis of Copernicus' observations and computations, were later used in the Gregorian reform of the calendar. (Gregory's rule for interpolations corresponds to Copernicus' rule.)

The calendar we use today is the reformed Julian calendar, introduced in 1582 under Pope Gregory XIII. Because of the faulty arrangement of the old Roman calendar, the priests of ancient Rome had once celebrated the spring festivals in the summer; then the bald-headed Julius Caesar who had already turned half Rome upside down, commissioned Sosigenes to reform the calendar also; thus was our time-computation introduced, with years of 365 days and leap years of 366 days. Rome also gave our months their names, lengths and order of succession; and because of the vanity of another Caesar, Augustus, whom Horace so generously praised, we still suffer today from an irritating irregularity in the alternation of thirty-one-day and thirty-day months; for Augustus refused to permit the month named after him to be shorter than the one named after Julius.

But the Julian year is 365¼ days long—longer by eleven minutes than the astronomical year; that is why from 325 A.D. when the Council of Nicaea fixed the date of the Easter holiday, until the time of Pope Gregory, the year was displaced by ten days.

By a papal brief which was like a piece of astronomical sleight-of-hand, Pope Gregory made these superfluous ten days vanish.

On October 4, 1582, all good Christians went to bed as usual, alone or with their wives; the following morning they got up and it was October 15, 1582.

Since 1900, the difference between the Julian and Gregorian calendars has been thirteen days.

In 1752, Great Britain, by an Act of Parliament, adopted the Gregorian calendar for herself and her American colonies.

A few famous fools: Savonarola, Robespierre and Mussolini, by introducing a new calendar tried to convince the world that they had initiated a new era. In Florence, this attempt ended in the execution of the dictator; in Paris in the coronation of a new dictator (on January 1, 1806, to be exact); in Rome it ended even before the liquidation of the overthrown dictator.

30

THE PAMPHLET AGAINST THE NUREMBERGER

A reprimand, it is true, is rarely useful.
COPERNICUS

The improvement of the world follows a very slow course.
PLATEN

ON FEBRUARY 11, 1524, the men of that day believed the world would come to an end, after a gigantic flood had covered all the earth. This was because of the so-called great conjunction of the planets; a famous mathematician had computed the date under the sign of the Fishes, and the Fishes had a frightful reputation with the astrologers.

Stoeffler of Tuebingen, the teacher of "the teacher of Germany," Melanchthon, had prophesied this junction of the planets as well as the deluge and the end of the world in his astrological almanac and thus put all Europe in a state of terror and fearful expectation.

In many places shrewd people got busy building arks. Some drunkards remarked cunningly that old Father Noah was a drinker of wine, and drew the wine of hope from this coincidence. Gluttons hauled great baskets of foodstuffs up to the mountain tops so that they could enjoy their meals there for a few additional days. Rich blockheads who could afford to, consulted theologians, astrologers, philosophers and astronomers; the university faculties flourished. One philosopher was able to buy a vineyard on the Moselle out of the fees he earned by predicting the end of the world. The Grand Chancellor of an all-powerful young man named Charles (the Fifth in his family of that name) implored him to accompany his humble servant to a mountain peak at least for the first world-end season; perhaps, he argued, the Emperor and Chancellor would get away with a mere cold in the head. Charles, who at that time was still lightheaded, refused; young people are always afraid of ridicule; only in old age did he realize that absolutely nothing can make the mighty ridiculous.

Naturally numerous writings appeared for and against Stoeffler. The learned bishop of Fossembrone himself wrote a whole pamphlet against the false prophet Stoeffler (although the latter had been on Paul's side at the time of the Lateran Council). Paul prophesied that there would not be too much water, and that the world would not end. There would not even be any small partial floods. The only flood was in Stoeffler's head.

Thus almost every astronomer expressed his opinion on the end of the world, just as they had all had their say on the question of the reform of the calendar.

But what about Copernicus? He seems to have kept completely silent concerning the end of the world.

And one hundred years later, the insolent Gassendi related with malicious pleasure that the month of February, 1524, as though to mock the astrologers and particularly Stoeffler, was the brightest and sunniest February in many decades.

Instead of writing about the end of the world, Copernicus in that very year of 1524 wrote a pamphlet against a Nuremberger who had expressed doubts as to the exactitude of the observations made by the ancients. This was Johannes Werner, who for the space of thirty years was a vicar in his native city, a friend of Pirckheimer, Walther and Schoner. An accountant from Vienna was his patron and published his collected geographical and astronomical-mathematical writings in two volumes. (This accountant was called Lukas Atlantsee; let no name of a patron be passed in silence!)

In a work entitled *De Motu Octavae Sphaerae* (On the Motion of the Eighth Sphere), vicar Werner tried to support the doctrine of trepidation advanced by the Arab astronomers. Werner published this work and others in the second volume of his collection in 1522, and died at Easter of the same year.

Canon Bernhard Wapowski (Vapovius), Copernicus' fellow-student at Cracow and one of his astronomical correspondents, who was a secretary of the King, a chamberlain of the Pope and the author of a history of Poland, sent Copernicus this much-praised treatise by Werner on the motion of the eighth sphere, in other words, on the precession, and asked for his opinion of it.

Copernicus answered in an open letter to Wapowski written from Frauenburg and dated June 3, 1524. At that time such epistles were circulated in handwriting among learned friends, taking the place of the scientific periodicals of today. The original letter is lost, but copies of it have been found in the libraries of Upsala, Berlin, Oxford, Paris and Schweinfurt.

Copernicus praises only the zeal of the Nuremberg vicar, and he does this in a most ambiguous fashion by recalling Aristotle's saying that gratitude is owed not only to all the scientists who have done their work well, but also to those who tried to follow the right path but missed it.

Copernicus continues in the following words: "A reprimand, it is true, is rarely useful; it is a sign of presumption when, instead of doing something oneself, one chooses to admonish others. Therefore I, too, fear that I will be reproached because I know how to reprimand others, but am unable to produce better work than they. . . . On the other hand I consider that there is a great difference between attacking someone in an injurious manner, and leading back a mistaken person to the right path, even though with sharp words. . . . And in order to avoid the appearance of desiring lightheartedly to reprove someone, I will try to show in detail wherein Werner has erred and that his theory of the motion of the firmament cannot be accepted despite the fact that it may contribute in some measure to the discovery of the truth."

Copernicus reproaches the vicar with making errors of computation, errors of principle and errors of method. In computing the interval of time between the observations of Timocharis and Ptolemy Werner made an error of eleven years. (Werner computed the date of an ancient observation of Regulus to be February 2, 150 A.D., Copernicus found this date to be February 22, 139 A.D.; according to Manitius, the date was February 23, 139 A.D., and according to Siegmund Günther, a professor at Ansbach, September 25, 138 A.D.). Furthermore, Werner had spoken of a uniform motion of the firmament in the four hundred years between Timocharis and Ptolemy. But Werner's own figures proved that the motion had become gradually accelerated. Finally Werner had questioned the precision of Timocharis' observations, in obvious contradiction to the data given in the Almagest.

Copernicus violently attacked the Nuremberg vicar for accusing the great and respected astronomers of antiquity, especially Ptolemy, for having made unreliable observations and cited unreliable data. Werner, says Copernicus, accuses the ancients of very serious errors yet Ptolemy was the most careful of observers. This constitutes a betrayal of the sacred cause. Copernicus mentions this twice: "We must closely follow their procedure and bow to their observations which have been handed down to us like a testament. And if anyone imagines that these observations cannot be fully trusted, at least in this respect the entrance to our science is closed to him; lying before the gate he will, like a sick man, dream dreams of the motion of the eighth sphere, since he believes that by slandering the ancients he is bolstering up his own fantasies. It is irrefutably certain that the ancients made their observations with the greatest care and with painstaking zeal and that these observations have given us many magnificent and admirable discoveries. Therefore I can by no means be convinced that in indicating the positions of the stars they made errors of ¼ or 1/5 or 1/6 of a degree, as this author thinks." And: "this is why it is less credible that they/the ancient astronomers/ or Ptolemy erred so much, when they were able to observe exactly many other things and more difficult things to the hair."

What tragic zeal and foolish orthodoxy this reveals. Compare this homily to the admission made by Copernicus to Rheticus in his later years that the ancient astronomers all too often adapted their data to their theories!

How violent must have been Copernicus' disillusion after such credulous enthusiasm!

And how curious that, after all, the Nuremberg vicar was right, and not the greatest astronomer of our era. It can be seen from this that it is not fitting for a little man to be right; it does not get him anywhere, he cannot do anything with it.

Copernicus did not pull his punches; he called Werner unintelligent, inept, and in one passage, *ineptior,* that is, more unintelligent than usual, and he even said that Werner suffered from childish hallucinations (*ubi nimis pueriliter hallucinatur*). And when vicar Werner deduced that the observations of the ancients were erroneous, it struck Copernicus almost as though someone had said that the road from Athens to Thebes was not as long as that from Thebes to Athens. "And so he puts the burden of his own errors of computation upon the ancient astronomers, that is, upon Timocharis, while he simply lets Ptolemy pass. . . . But if he wants completely to discredit the discoveries of the early astronomers, how can he ask that we give any credit to his own observations?"

At the conclusion of this "panning," Copernicus said that it might be justly asked what his own views were on the motion of the firmament. He refused to expound it here in this pamphlet. "As I intend to do it elsewhere, I consider it superfluous and inappropriate to dwell any longer on this subject, especially since I have fulfilled your request [Wapowski's] that I give you my opinion concerning this work."

Copernicus gives his views on the complicated problem which preoccupied the vicar at the beginning of his Book III of *De Revolutionibus.*

The third motion he ascribes to the earth, the "libration," is in agreement with the basic thesis of the trepidation theory. But the Ansbach professor, Siegmund Günther, thinks that Copernicus gave this fluctuation of the ecliptic a deeper significance and that in his polemics against Werner's hypothesis he understood the doctrine of trepidation in its full geometrical purity and cleansed it of all dross.

Be that as it may, we cannot help being charmed by Copernicus' noble scholar's pride; he treats the Nuremberg vicar as an ox because the latter very properly questioned the data of those ancient demigods whom Copernicus was even then, and with complete justification, preparing to push off their thousand-year-old pedestals.

We are pleased to see the learned Copernicus in the role of a thunder-hurling Zeus. Does he not seem to be shouting out to the poor Nuremberg vicar who could find only a Viennese bookkeeper as a patron: *Quod licet Jovi, non licet bovi?* Only the poor ox was already dead!

Copernicus wrote other scientific pamphlets on special occasions, for instance, a table of the sunrises and sunsets and the length of the day. He must have composed this table at the request of his colleagues at Frauenburg. In 1540, Nicolaus Human included it in the oldest Ermland breviary. Franz Hipler reports on it in his essay entitled: A Table for the Determination of the Beginning of the Vesper Period in Ermland by Nicolaus Copernicus.

Copernicus is said to have designed sundials at various places, in Frauenburg, Allenstein, Torun and Leslau; but according to learned investigations made on the spot only the dial of a sundial on the southern side of the northern building of Allenstein Castle could have been designed by him.

Zenocarus von Schauenburg, in his biography of Charles V, says that Copernicus took part in a great debate concerning the comet of 1533 with Peter Apian, Gemma Frisius, Cardano and Hieronymus Scala. However, this seems improbable. Between 1500 and 1538 fifteen comets were observed in Europe. And there is not a single work on comets by Copernicus. The interpretation of comets was at that time one of the most profitable of the astronomers' activities.

But Copernicus did not make a business of astronomy.

31

"'TIS WAR, ALAS, 'TIS WAR!"

"Habet mundus iste noctes suas et non paucas."
ST. BERNARD

"The Christian religion was supposed to be a revolution; having failed it later became moral."
GOETHE, Maxims and Reflections

"We are done with partial heresies."
LOISY on Luther

AT THE age of forty-three the mighty Copernicus became an administrator of two Lilliputian districts in Ermland, Mehlsack and Allenstein. For four long years he, with his *puer* and *famulus,* lived with the burgrave and castle chaplain, the stable-boys and other menial servants, at the Allenstein Castle; there, on fifteen pages of a day-book which has fortunately been preserved he made an entry in his own hand each time when in presence of two witnesses, he had to transfer a piece of land to a little peasant liable to serfdom at a rent for which the poor creature, made in God's image, had the right to work himself to death.

The fortified castle of Allenstein was situated on the Alle among green hills, twelve miles from the Cathedral of Frauenburg; in order to appoint a common farm laborer, the great man had to leave his castle and sometimes traverse his entire district; it took two days to travel ten miles.

At that time Copernicus wrote the following letter to his Chapter:

"To the most venerable and noble Prelates and Canons and the whole Chapter of Ermland diocese, my most especially revered Lords and Superiors! Through the Lord our Bishop I learned yesterday what you wrote about the reception of which I am in charge; everything has been prepared, be it for a fish-day or a meat-day. Philippe Greusing's letters induced me to hasten my departure from Allenstein; the Burgrave of Heilsberg whom I took with me there received more detailed information so that Philippe Greusing will not be able to complain that he was refused his due. Our most venerable Bishop has also commissioned me—in case the letters have not yet gone out—to instruct you, Right Reverend gentlemen, to add to the answer of Your Graces to the Lord Grandmaster: 'that sacred justice must not be prevented,' so that any distorted or sophistic interpretation of it will be excluded. His Episcopal Grace has learned that the Muscovite has concluded a perpetual peace with the King; His Grace hopes to learn at any hour under what conditions. Thus all the hopes of our neighbors collapse. I recommend myself to your favor, most venerable lords. Mehlsack XXII. October 1518. I will set out from here as soon as possible.—N. Coppernic."

So these were the cares of this illustrious man: meat-day . . . fish-day . . . another perpetual peace . . . news from Moscow . . . Right Reverends and Graces. . . .

The weird transition from peace to war was effected by the classical methods. First there was a trade war between Ermland and Ordensland, that is to say, the people on one side of the frontier refused to eat the herrings salted on the other; then, in the midst of peace, those "anonymous" mercenaries whom everyone recognized as of the Order, made their appearance in Ermland, which was "for the time of two years attacked, destroyed, devastated and ruined, with cruel murder, firebrand, church plunder, exactions and hostile invasions. . . ." The Master of the Order alleged that all this was being done by "some people whom no one knew"; the Bishop of Ermland replied with righteous indignations that "after all he (the master) also knew that such robber gangs did not float in the air and pick their horses from the ground." The Grand Master of the Order answered with counter-complaints. He went to his cousin in Berlin and asked for troops or money, concluded an alliance with Muscovy, negotiated with the Emperor. The King of Poland, for his part, sent troops to Ermland. This would have led to a general war if fortunately the Emperor had not died and the Tartars had not invaded Poland.

At that point Copernicus was just returning to Frauenburg after the three years of his first term at Allenstein.

Meanwhile a new Emperor was elected, Poland repelled the Tartars, King Sigismund entered Torun in December, 1519, "with great show and pomp as befits a powerful King," was greeted by the Bishop of Ermland in Latin and was not greeted at all by the Grand Master, who as a Polish vassal had been summoned to meet him, but failed to appear, whereupon the Polish captains sent the Grand Master a challenge and marched into his land.

Thus, the war began, and each party took a town belonging to the other: the Poles, Goldau, the Grand Master, Braunsberg, which was surrendered to him without a battle by the burgomaster, Philipp Teschner, Copernicus' cousin.

For the rest, during a period of fifteen months there were only the usual atrocities—none of the laws of war was observed, no quarter was given, each party slew the civilian population loyal to the other, and solemnly protested that the other did the same thing.

Since the bishop was neutral, Ermland was sacked by both parties. When the Grand Master invited the Bishop to participate in peace negotiations in the city of Braunsberg, which city he had just stolen from the Bishop, the latter, despite the Grand Master's solemn and sacred promises, feared an attack on his person, and so he sent in his stead two canons whose life he was more willing to sacrifice than his own; one of these must have been Copernicus, for we know that at this period the Grand Master made out a safe conduct for the "honored highly-learned Mr. Niklas Koppernick," giving "free, safe and Christian conduct, to him together with his horses and servants. . . ."

The negotiations proved fruitless, but the negotiators remained alive. In the spring of 1520, a captain of the Order overran Frauenburg and burned it down; he wanted "to destroy the nest in such a way that at least during the summer no bird could nestle there." About the same time—in February, April and July, 1520—Copernicus made astronomical observations.

In the autumn he returned to Allenstein as commissioner of Ermland. In this war Copernicus played the role of an unsuccessful negotiator and successful defender of Allenstein Castle, the Grand Master had occupied most of this district, burned down the villages, slain the peasants or driven them off. Most of the canons had fled and were leading a gay life in exile at Danzig or Elbing.

Finally, the Grand Master laid siege to Allenstein Castle. Only one of Copernicus' colleagues, the lazy Heinrich Snellenberg, had taken refuge with him in the castle. In February, 1521, Johannes Sculteti, the old archdeacon, wrote from Elbing to Copernicus, the brave defender of the castle, telling him of the Emperor's peace feelers and urged him "to keep his hands firmly together and not to open them to surrender the castle; he himself, if he had only two coats, would gladly give away *one,* if he could thereby preserve the castle." He offered to send him foodstuffs if necessary; he also mentioned that his colleague, Balthasar Stockfisch, had died in the meanwhile and that he had deposited the seal and documents of the Chapter in the house of a friend of his, a merry widow at Elbing.

In a second letter the old Sculteti again wrote about the deceased Stockfisch; he asked Copernicus whether he should hand over the seal to the canons who had emigrated to Danzig and "who call themselves the Chapter"; he said the latter were infuriated because their good money had been spent on cannon instead of being sent to them to spend in Danzig . . . The good old man also warned Copernicus, who was then actually being besieged in his castle by the Grand Master, of the Grand Master's plans—this personage, he said, had cast his eye on the castle!

The Bishop, he wrote, had also urged him to send a few blunderbusses to Allenstein. "And so I have sent the blunderbusses at the cost of great effort to this place where they will surely be most needed." He would also send powder and lead if Copernicus needed them for the bombards; in short, he was ready to do everything in order "to avoid losing the bulwark of the whole diocese, Allenstein!" He termed the Grand Master "worse than a thief," and added in the same breath that the price of wax was high and that he had sold the flax dearly—and "God is my witness," he exclaims repeatedly, whether referring to the flax or the Grand Master!

Finally, sated with slaughter, the belligerents concluded peace; the Emperor mediated their dispute.

It was now Copernicus' task to create order in devastated Ermland. Peasants believed to be dead reappeared. Land titles long settled were disputed anew; wolves tame from hunger came to the huts to be fed like dogs, and ratlike marauders became wolfish so that it was necessary to fight them.

In June, 1521, Copernicus completed his thankless duties. At Frauenburg Copernicus found his curia outside the cathedral town devastated. So he bought himself a new house situated inside the town walls because of the prevailing unrest (it was probably that northwestern tower in the town wall, later named the Copernicus tower, where legend had placed his observatory). Until his death twenty-two years later he stayed at Frauenburg, except for short trips.

Concerning the peace reparations (which are seldom paid) Copernicus drew up a memorandum, as requested by the Chapter. He did not mince words: The Order had illegally occupied peaceful cities! The Order had burned down barns, houses, villages and towns! The Order had stolen! Had set fires and pillaged! Had murdered hostages! Had driven away teams of horses and cattle and torn down whole houses and set them up again on the Order's own territory!

Copernicus and Giese brought the memorandum to the Prussian meeting of the estates at Graudenz. As is customary when the weak indict the strong, the decision was adjourned to the next session; this next session was never held—because of the plague in Prussia!

* * *

Saint Polycarp, the well-known epistle-writing martyr of Smyrna who perished for his faith in 156 A.D., never missed an opportunity to say, "My God! In what a century have you caused me to live!"

From several remarks of Copernicus we suspect that his reaction to his own century was not very different.

How contradictory is the fate of great men! The same Copernicus who was busy rebuilding the universe was commissioned by his contemporaries to rebuild one tiny little region!

And did he not love his century? The few letters that have come down to us are restrained in tone. He sees clearly into his own times, looks at them thoughtfully, deliberately, objectively. True, one does not commit the most audacious act of his millennium without knowing full well the enormous audacity of his own century, indeed, without potentially feeling ready to commit every magnificent audacity.

And Copernicus lived in two of the most dissolute centuries in the history of Europe.

Before him, Columbus had extended the frontiers of the world. The humanists had won back freedom of thought for the learned. The printer's art, which seemed to make writing and even thinking machine-like, created popular education and semi-education—two potent prerequisites of revolution.

The Renaissance, with its pagan delight in the senses and reason, furthered that most anaemic of all revolutions, the Reformation, which, taken over and falsified by reactionary powers, nevertheless in the end brought a greater degree of religious tolerance to the masses.

During the very years that Copernicus was no more than the administrator of a small county, when even his closest colleagues passed over in icy silence his Commentariolus, his Yearbooks and his whole truly world-shaking theory, the "soft flesh of Wittenberg," the defrocked monk who had married a runaway nun, became the talk of the world only because he had broken his vows. Or, as Friedrich Nietzsche put it, "Luther's merit is greater in nothing than that he had the courage of his sensuality—then called, delicately enough, 'evangelic liberty.'"

Before the Pope had condemned Luther, enlightened Catholics in many countries had been moved by his words and actions, more, several Catholic dignitaries openly displayed their sympathy for him, as well as for other reformers. In Copernicus' province, too, people argued for and against Luther.

The Bishop of Ermland, Fabian von Lossainen, in reply to the strict minds who had come to urge him "to keep the clergymen from separating from the Catholic religion with their flocks" said: "Luther is a learned monk and has his opinions on the Scriptures; if anyone is so bold let him oppose him."

And in 1520, when King Sigismund the Old came from Poland to Prussia, he found Luther's teachings already so widespread, especially among the seafaring people of Danzig, that full of pious fear, he issued an edict against him, and sent a few inhabitants of Danzig to the stake because of their peculiar ideas.

As always, the thinking individuals were in the minority against the believers; whoever was caught in the act of having a thought was done away with quickly.

Copernicus witnessed the great controversy concerning the merits and nature of the Reformation and especially of Luther, its noisiest representative.

Before the thundering Saxon, Martin Luther, began to shout and curse, to the jubilation of Germany and the terror of Rome, the gentle and sensitive Erasmus, the witty skeptic of Rotterdam, had been considered the sage of his century. He called his religion "The Philosophy of Christ." In his Greek Testament (his edition of the New Testament in the Greek text with a new Latin translation and his own notes was published in 1516) he wrote the following annotation to Matthew XI, 30: "Everything according to nature is easily borne, and nothing accords better with the nature of man than the philosophy of Christ, of which almost the sole end is to give back to fallen nature its innocence and integrity . . . The church, divided and tormented by discussions and by heresy, added to it many things, of which some can be omitted without prejudice to the faith . . . The sacraments themselves were instituted for the salvation of men, but we abuse them for lucre, for vain glory or for the oppression of the humble . . . What rules, what superstitions we have about vestments . . . How many are judged as to their Christianity by such trifles, which are indifferent in themselves, which change with the fashion and of which Christ never spoke! . . . How many fasts are instituted! And we are not merely invited to fast, but obliged to, on pain of damnation . . . What shall we say about vows . . . about the authority of the pope, the abuse of absolutions, dispensations, remissions of penalty, lawsuits, in which there is much that a truly good man cannot see without a groan? The priests themselves prefer to study Aristotle than to ply their ministry. The gospel is hardly mentioned from the pulpit. Sermons are monopolized by the commissioners of indulgences; often the doctrine of Christ is put aside and suppressed for their profit . . . Would that men were content to let Christ rule by the laws of the gospel and that they would no longer seek to strengthen their obscurant tyranny by human decrees!"

Thus unsparingly spoke the Sage! But Erasmus feared the "tumult" that Luther sought. Erasmus was the aristocrat, who translated God into Latin, spoke to scholars, and exchanged friendly letters with popes. He might almost have ended up as a cardinal.

Luther, who began as a people's tribune and ended as a servant of princes, spoke German to God and to the people, and shouted even to the Emperor! Of a lusty temperament, he loved wine, women and song! He was unable to tame his appetites or his tongue. He caused the greatest riot of his century and made considerably more noise than Columbus and Copernicus. The break of his vow was at that time a dangerous deed and was understood as such by the masses; the poor man is always eager to overstep the mark. In Luther's words the downtrodden heard the great bell of freedom toll. Luther climbed up the back of the people like a ladder, and having arrived at the top kicked the ladder down.

Without the poor, the Reformation, which was a vulgar continuation of the medieval disputes and their cascades of abuse, would have ended in a quarrel of theologians, not in a revolution.

After Reuchlin and his humanist friends had triumphed over the obscurantists, in their quarrel with Dr. Hoogstraaten, the inquisitor of Cologne, over the burning of all Hebrew books (except the Bible), Luther came. In 1517 he nailed his ninety-five theses on the door of the Wittenberg church, inveighing against the "imposts of the apostolic Chancery for individual sins, anything from a theft of food for immediate consumption to murder."

After having refused at the Augsburg Diet of 1518 to say only one six-letter word (*revoco,* I recant), Luther in 1519 publicly burned the pope's bull that condemned him, and jubilant students stood around and cheered. And Ulrich von Hutten called upon the Reich to secede from Rome and exclaimed in exultation over his own courage: "I've dared it!"

Luther, too, boasted of his courage after he had refused the twenty-one-year-old Emperor Charles V's invitation to recant at Worms, but the ill-fated German revolutionary, Thomas Münzer, told him rudely and clearly: "You would be stabbed by the Knights if you wavered or recanted!" Four hundred unnamed noblemen in a public placard signed with the revolutionary catchword: *Bundschuh* had threatened with death anyone who ventured to attack Luther's "Freedom of a Christian," and Münzer obviously thought that this threat applied first of all to Luther himself!

The world tyrant Charles V let Luther go free but put him under the ban within the Empire and outlawed him. (Only after he knew that Luther was dead and buried, did the cunning Habsburg become sublime.) "Let his bones lie in peace," he declared, "if he has done evil, God will call him to account for it; I am an Emperor of the living, not of the dead."

Luther's Elector hid him in one of his castles, the Wartburg, where Luther, as *Junker Jörg,* grew a beard and hurled his inkpot into the devil's face in order to win peace from temptation and quiet for his translation of the Bible.

Meanwhile his colleagues, Carlstadt, Melanchthon and Zwilling at Wittenberg were reforming the street-walkers and the nuns; the former were forbidden to love, the latter ordered to marry; the same zealots confiscated the funds of the churches, ordered the priests to take wives and drove the monks out of their cells, and the reformers were quite popular as those who improve conditions on the money and love markets always are.

In Zwickau, too, the weavers, led by Thomas Münzer, set out to regenerate society and religion, in Regensburg the Emperor, through his council forbade by decree any innovation in the world for all time to come.

But Luther (under the influence of the Protestant princes) was as little disposed to joke as the Catholic Emperor when inherited rights, that is inherited wrongs and the perpetuation of that inequality of men which is so evil in the sight of God, were at stake.

Luther rushed to Wittenberg, drove out Carlstadt and Zwilling and cursed Münzer and all the weavers who thought they had enough of their misery. He spoke the language of the revolution with the natural grace of a son of the people, and betrayed the people's cause with the uncouth insolence of a parvenu.

The language of the revolution was at that time the common language of Europe; by mistake it sometimes rang even in the mouths of Emperors and Popes. The entire world seemed dissatisfied with religion and government.

In Germany several estates rebelled simultaneously: clergymen, knights and peasants.

The knights who for the most part had not yet adopted firearms, whose strongholds were no longer impregnable to modern artillery, whose horses and armor could no longer cope with the infantry, had declined militarily, as well as economically and culturally, and waged war on the open roads against the free cities and princes; woe to any merchants' caravans which ventured on the roads where these robber knights reigned supreme. They confiscated the goods and cut off the right arms of their prisoners; the hapless merchants and their servants begged them in vain to cut off their left arms instead.

Ulrich von Hutten was the pamphleteer of the knights' cause, Goetz von Berlichingen "of the iron hand," their most popular figure, and the mighty Knight of the Empire, Franz von Sickingen, their leader. Forerunners of the Prussian Junkers, they wanted to centralize, nationalize, reform, rule and expropriate the Empire.

Sickingen promised to cleanse the Empire of monks and priests, to distribute their goods, and to give "evangelic freedom" to Germany. His partisans muttered that he would soon be Elector, King and Emperor. Sickingen wanted to ally himself with Luther, but Luther would have none of his alliance. To the imperial tribunal Sickingen declared that he had his own tribunal made up of soldiers who administered justice with cannon.

Then the disunited princes banded together, and the Empire put Sickingen under the ban. In his fortified castle he was besieged and shot down in the tower. When he lay mortally wounded in the vault of the castle he lost hope. Where are the lords, my friends who promised me so much aid, he asked? Where are the Swiss? Where are the people of Strassburg?

He was dying when the princes broke into the vault. The Elector of Trier asked: What do you reproach me with, Franz, that you have attacked me so furiously, me and my men?

The landgrave of Hesse asked: Franz, what did you have against me?

After Sickingen's death the princes set out to smash the strongholds of many of the other knights. It was a general defeat for the free knighthood. Ulrich von Hutten, too, was hounded and compelled to flee; he went to Switzerland, moved from one place to another and borrowed money from other men of letters. He wrote his last pamphlet against Erasmus when the latter refused to see him at Basel. He perished at the age of thirty-five of syphilis at Ufnau on the lake of Zürich, where Zwingli had urged him to go in order to be cured there by a pastor skilled in the art of medicine.

Nor did the peasants have any luck. For thirty years trouble had been brewing among them; social, political and religious issues had all come sharply to the fore. In 1513 Joss Fritz tried in vain to revive the "Bundschuh" in Breisgau. In 1514 "Poor Konrad" or "Poor Kunz" was crushed. Finally, in 1524, the peasant war broke out. City and peasant agitators made common cause; everyone longed for justice, the end of the corvée and exploitation. The church, they said, was anti-Christian, the princes were tyrants. If all men were children of one Father, as the Scriptures taught, there should be no inequality, neither of wealth nor of class. Enough of abuses and wars!

There were serfs, the bondsmen and the hired farm laborers, three different classes but all of them starving, all equally wretched for different reasons. Dr. Luther knew how to express their sufferings: "The people will not and cannot endure your tyranny any longer; God will not bear it any longer; the world is no longer as it once was, when you could harass and hunt down the poor people like beasts!"

At Stuehlingen, near the Swiss border, where the Black Forest separates the sources of the Danube from the upper Rhine Valley, the bloody rebellion began and spread northwards like a forest fire.

The immediate pretext for it is supposed to have been the curious whim of Countess von Lupfen (if the Villinger Chronicle is to be believed) who on a holiday ordered her subjects to collect snail-shells, wind thread, pick strawberries and wild plums and do other similar tasks . . .

Hans Müller of Bulgenbach set out at the head of the indignant peasants with a black, red and white flag. He wanted to establish an evangelic community in order to free all the peasants in the Empire. And in every village Thomas Münzer preached to the rebels. He was behind the whole movement.

Elsewhere the serfs submitted petitions. Sometimes one of the great lords made a few promises.

In February, 1525, several agitators printed the so-called *twelve articles* embodying the demands of the peasants. What did the poor people want?

Freedom to hunt, to fish and to cut wood and an end to the depredations of the lords' pigeons upon their crops.

The abolition of several new burdens, new kinds of punishments and regulations and the restoration of the common land which had been taken away from them.

The peasants no longer wanted to be serfs! For Christ had saved them, too, with His precious blood. They were willing to continue paying the "great tithe," to wit the tithe of fillies and lambs, of corn and oats; for God so ordained in the Old Testament; but they refused to continue paying the "small tithe" of hay, hops, cabbage and bilberries—in short, the vegetable taxes, to the clergy.

Cabbage was too dear, they lamented; the rent for their miserable huts was too high; and the widows of the serfs complained of having to pay too high inheritance taxes.

Above all, they demanded for each community the right to elect its own pastor in order to be instructed by him in the true faith "for if God's grace work not within us we remain in flesh and blood which availeth nothing."

And the peasants rose in Swabia and Franconia; villages and small towns were forced to join them; any peasant who refused to adhere to the movement had a pale driven in the ground before his house, as a sign that he was a public enemy. Nowhere could the church bells be tolled for mass; the bells tolled only for the storm.

Hans Müller, dressed in a red cloak and a red cap, marched from village to village at the head of his partisans; the war standard was borne behind him on a carriage adorned with foliage and ribbons.

Thomas Münzer, the German revolutionary, cried to the miners in Mansfeld: "Go to it! Go to it! Go to it! Beloved brothers, do not be moved by pity! Let not your sword become cold, lacking blood! Strike blows on Nimrod's anvil, throw down his tower, for the day is yours."

Dr. Carlstadt, a native Franconian, appeared in a peasant's coat and a white felt hat at Rothenburg and aroused the rural population. The Franconian peasants drew up plans for the reformation of the Empire. They wanted to be freed from all clerical and secular levies. They wanted to secularize the clergy's estates. All customs were to be abolished. Only every tenth year was a tax to be paid. The courts were to be popularized; the doctors of Roman law were to be driven out! Only one currency was to be valid! Uniform weights and measures were to be introduced. All classes were to act as brothers toward each other! The movement spread to Saxony, Thuringia, Alsace, the Tyrol, Lorraine and the Rhineland. For a short while it looked as though the whole Empire would belong to the peasants. Thomas Münzer now preached rebellion in Thuringia. He despised Luther's "invented Gospel," his "Christ sweet as honey," his doctrine that Anti-christ would be destroyed by the word alone, without violence. He found it impossible to tell the people the truth as long as the princes ruled, impossible to honor God and serve the princes at the same time. The princes were publicly worshipped; the rule of the princes must be abolished. It was intolerable, he taught, that all the creatures of this world should be chattels, the fish in the water, the birds of the air, the plants in the soil—these creatures, too, must become free if the pure word of God was to rise like the sun. He overthrew all the concepts on which the state rests. He recognized only the pure Gospel. Only the revelation! "But a new Daniel must interpret it and march at the head of the people, like Moses." He became a prophet, presided at the council, administered justice according to the revelation, seized monasteries and had cannon cast, all this from his headquarters at Mühlhausen in Thuringia.

All around in the mountains multitudes of people assembled, it seemed that the great German revolution, the revolution from below, was at last breaking out.

So the poor people burned down the monasteries and castles, did the act of darkness with certain highborn ladies and drew up demands. At Weinsberg they even slew a count, whose wife, a natural daughter of the Emperor, vainly threw herself at their feet, begging for mercy.

The peasants formed a gauntlet, then one of them marched forward whistling; amidst the blare of shawms and the thunder of trumpets the leaders hurled the count onto the spears of the peasants.

Just as they had banded together against the knights, the princes, including some of the leaders in that first struggle, like the young Landgrave Philipp von Hessen, now set out against the peasants. The poorly armed rebels had more right on their side than wisdom in their councils; their leader Thomas Münzer waited for a miracle in a mountain. Here and there the peasants were slain. Then Thomas Münzer was captured, tortured and compelled to sign a long confession. When he was reminded of the numberless people who had been tortured by his orders, he began to laugh aloud, and exclaim: "They did not want it otherwise!" Whereupon he was put to death.

Now the lords once again slept with the wives of their peasants by the *jus primae noctis,* and with their daughters without any *jus* at all; of the fathers and husbands they made salt-meat, as they had always done. The number of slaughtered peasants was estimated at one hundred thousand. The noisy revolution in Germany failed. In Poland, Copernicus began his silent revolution.

And injustice, as always in times of counter-revolution, was more rampant than ever.

In April, 1525 (the year of his marriage with the runaway nun, Katharina von Bora), Luther published his Exhortation to Peace with regard to the Twelve Articles of the Swabian peasants. In an excess of justice he declared the poor and rich to be equally guilty.

The rebellious monk told the peasants that tyranny was no excuse for rebellion. He called their refusal to pay special taxes on vegetables "robbery," and the slaves' demand for freedom utterly unjustified: for it made freedom an outward thing! Moreover, had not Paul, the apostle, said that the slave should not ask for freedom? (I Cor. VII, 20.)

And then the fat and newly wed Luther sat down and wrote his pamphlet: "Against the Thievish Murderous Hordes of Peasants." In it he warned the all-too-softhearted princes not to be pitiful toward the poor people and that the time of anger and of the sword had come. A poor man should be avoided like the devil; a peasant should be slain like a rabid dog! He who perishes in this duty is a martyr of Christ. It was better to slay all the poor than to let the good princes and officials be ruined! For the peasants had taken up the sword without God's authority.

The old rebel Luther argued: "One cannot argue reasonably with a rebel. He must be answered with the fist until blood spurts from his nose!"

Melanchthon, Luther's friend, wrote: "It is fairly written in Ecclesiasticus XXXIII, that as the ass must have fodder, load and whip, so must the servant have bread, work and punishment. These outward, bodily servitudes are needful, but this institution (serfdom) is certainly pleasing to God."

Luther combated the Anabaptists with the same ardor that he had formerly displayed against Zwingli or the poor people. The Anabaptists, too, wanted Christ's words to come true. Next to the Copernican revolution, these naïve experiments constituted the most terrible revolt in Christendom.

Anabaptists was the name assumed by the followers of many sects which followed varied teachings and usages and lived in a variety of ways. All of them rejected the baptism of little children, partly as useless, or as abominable. Some demanded that all goods should be held in common; others considered only mutual support to be the general duty. Some separated themselves from all the other faithful, others held such separation to be a sin (as is reported by Sebastian Frank who was one of them and knew them well).

Many refused to perform armed service and to take oaths. To kill, they believed, was always a crime, to swear always a sin. Others wanted to reform marriage. The rule of the church seemed unbearable to them. Everyone should be allowed to preach, they thought. They called the institutions of the Protestants a new papacy.

They nurtured the apocalyptic expectation of an imminent reversal of all things: "for night is beginning to fall, and the end of time is at hand."

One of their chief preachers was the wandering furrier Melchior Hoffmann. We find him now in Alsace, now in Stockholm, now in Livonia, now in Frisia, now in prison, now a friend of great princes. Finally he went to Strassburg which, he thought, was destined to be a new Jerusalem whence, according to Revelation XIV, a hundred and forty-four thousand virgin apostles would set out with him in order to gather all the elect of God around the Lamb.

Soon an attempt was made to bring about this condition by violence. Throughout the country these pacifists, these separatists, these pious Anabaptists, became enthusiastic world reformers. The conservatives began to slaughter them. At Munich, for instance, "some were mutilated in the limbs, others had their heads cut off, others were hurled into the Isar, still others were burned alive at the stake." The Anabaptist Jacob Hutter, when he and his brothers were driven out of Moravia, cried: "We are in the desert, on a wild heath under the luminous sky."

In the Netherlands the Anabaptists were suppressed more ferociously than anywhere else, otherwise the whole people would have joined them, as one writer said in 1531.

Jan Matthys, a disciple of Hoffmann and a baker at Leyden, was convinced that the overturn of the whole world was imminent and must be brought about by the sword. He sent twelve apostles to the six neighboring provinces; one of them, Jan Bockelson, moved from place to place, baptized adults everywhere and founded small communities of ten or fifteen faithful.

The leader of the Reformation in the rich city of Münster, the preacher Bernhard Rottmann, yielded to the Anabaptists. A respected burgher of Münster, Bernhard Knipperdolling, received many Anabaptists in his house. They preached, baptized and attracted other Anabaptists, the most influential of whom was Jan Matthys. In 1534 there was a great disturbance, the Anabaptists occupied the market place and seven-year-old children prophesied. One wintry day, in a snowstorm, the Anabaptists drove out the other denominations and appropriated all their possessions and money.

They destroyed the sculptures of the cathedral and the market place and solemnly burned all the books and manuscripts (except the Bible) in public. They did not even spare musical instruments and introduced a primitive sort of communism. All of them became one single religious warlike family. The prophet Jan Matthys became the dictator and lawgiver. When he perished during a sortie against the enemy, he was succeeded by Jan Bockelson, a tailor.

The latter was born at Leyden, the son of a village-mayor and a Westphalian serf whom her husband had redeemed. As a journeyman tailor Jan went to England and Flanders, and settled at Leyden by The Hague road gate. Soon afterward he took the widow of a boatman for wife, set up a tavern with her help and went into trade which took him to Lisbon and Lübeck. In the *Kammer van Rhetoryke,* the poetic society of Leyden, he wrote verses and plays in which he performed himself. He was baptized by Jan Matthys in person, read Hoffmann's writings and became learned in the Holy Scriptures. He was well formed, eloquent, young and ardent. Jan Matthys had deserted his wife and married a pretty young girl, because, as he explained to her, such was the will of Heaven.

Because Jan Bockelson wanted to marry this widow of Jan Matthys, he introduced polygamy in Münster. One day he had a revelation that he should become king. So Johann of Leyden became King of Münster and the world. Knipperdolling became governor and the preacher Rottmann, *Worthalter* (Keeper of the Word). Münster was ruled by a monarchic theocracy on a communistic basis. It was supposed to be a community of saints, God's kingdom on earth come at last. The hidden meaning of the Scripture was that through God's word all the things were created good in the beginning; but they did not remain good; God's order required their restoration through the Word. The Anabaptists rejected the baptism of little children as un-Christian: for baptism was salvation from ignorance; it should be given only to those who were learned and pious, it was the sign of their admission into a holy community.

A new prophet, formerly a goldsmith, proclaimed Johann of Leyden king of the whole world. And so Johann of Leyden called himself the just King in the New Temple. On a golden chain around his neck he wore a golden world globe.

When he rode through the city two boys marched beside him, one with the Bible, the other with a bared sword.

When a woman of Münster who had boasted that no man would ever have her finally lived for some time with Johann of Leyden, then had enough of him and wanted to leave him, King Johann of Leyden personally led her to the market place, beheaded her and pushed her corpse away from him with his feet. The King's other wives intoned the song: "To God alone be honor given."

The Bishop of Münster, who was very annoyed by all this, shot at his renegade subjects with cannon, hurled fire into their houses and ordered them to be slaughtered. The survivors, even women, were driven from the city; those who sheltered them were threatened with being treated like Anabaptists themselves; and so the movement died out.

It goes without saying that the Protestants, too, were driven from Münster and the city once again became piously Catholic.

King Johann of Leyden, Knipperdolling and a few others were torn to pieces with red-hot tongs on the Münster market place. Many Anabaptists fled to England and later to the North American colonies, particularly to Providence and Pennsylvania; many of their religious ideas were adopted and developed by the Quakers.

In Münster a citizen was no longer allowed to have more than one wife. And what had belonged to the poor, once again became the general property of the rich, as it had been before and was all over the world. The poor people and the humanists began to protest most violently against Luther's behavior.

"Where Lutheranism reigns," Erasmus wrote to Willibald Pirckheimer, the humanist of Nuremberg, who at first had been for and now was against Luther, "true learning perishes." Lutheranism won chiefly the middle classes and a part of the upper classes.

* * *

We know only what Luther said about Copernicus: "The fool . . ." etc. What did Copernicus say about Luther? Rheticus "forgot" to tell us. And the judgments of posterity on Luther differ as though he had never died.

Heinrich Heine said that from Luther to Kant a constant development of thought took place and no less than two revolutions; that Luther had given his people language and Kant had given them ideas; that Luther had deposed the Pope, that Robespierre had beheaded the King and that Kant had dethroned God; that all this was the same revolt against the same tyrant under different names . . . Heine called Luther, that promoter of the German language and the German book trade, the greatest German, or more accurately, the most German of the Germans, because he combined all the defects and virtues of the Germans. "His ideas," says Heine, "had hands and wings; he spoke and acted. He was not only the tongue, but also the sword of his time. And he was also a cool, hairsplitting scholastic and an inspired prophet, drunk with God. . . . From him came to Germany so-called freedom of mind or freedom of thought. Thinking became a right, and the powers of reason became legitimate."

However, Friedrich Nietzsche termed Luther's Reformation "the coarsest form of moral mendacity . . . Luther was a drag on German righteousness which was no longer consistent in itself . . . The Germans, as is well-known, grew numb with reverence before princes or party leaders . . . The Protestants grovelled before the most miserable little princes—a people of servants. . . ." And: "The Reformation was a reaction of old-fashioned minds against the Italian Renaissance . . . It was the rage of the simple against the complex."

King Frederick II of Prussia who was not at home in any language explained the extraordinary influence of Luther, Germany's greatest linguistic genius, in this way: "Mediocre minds often are the most successful."

Voltaire compares the Protestants with the Mussulmans and says that the dispute which developed into the Reformation, began between two sects, Dominicans and Augustinians, over the booty of the indulgence trade, "and this little squabble of monks in one corner of Saxony produced more than a hundred years of discord, fury, and misfortune for thirty nations. . . ."

Voltaire held the dogmas of the reformers to be as unreasonable as those of their adversaries. And in his Philosophic Dictionary he wrote: "There are some nations whose religion is the result of neither climate nor government. What cause detached North Germany, Denmark, most of Switzerland, Holland, England, Scotland . . . from the Roman communion? Poverty, Indulgences . . . were sold too dear. The prelates and monks absorbed the whole revenue of a province. People adopted a cheaper religion."

In the eyes of Hume the most dreadful result of the Reformation was that it exaggerated the importance of "those wretched composers of metaphysical polemics, the theologians."

Goethe called the Reformation "a sorry spectacle of boundless confusion, error fighting with error, selfishness with selfishness, and the truth only here and there heaving into view." To a friend Goethe wrote: "The character of Luther is the only interesting thing in the Reformation, and the only thing, moreover, that made an impression on the masses. All the rest is a lot of bizarre trash we have not yet, to our cost, cleared away."

Chesterton said that the Reformation was "the revolution of the rich against the poor."

Professor S. N. Patten proves that overnourishment and undernourishment are the causes of all revolutions and the cause of the Reformation, he thinks, was "the growth of frugalistic concepts."

32

GOOD MONEY

Money's neither bad nor good;
It all depends on how it's used.
German Proverb

What seems to me so superfluous when I have it, and so indispensable when I have it not . . . fatal, baleful money!
LESSING, Nathan the Wise

ABOUT money, too, Copernicus reflected deeply.

Naturally money did not interest him until it began to be problematical. Inflation made him, like so many other millions, reflect upon the nature of money. Unlike these millions he reached more sane conclusions than the necessity of running out into the street and killing his neighbor.

More expert in writing than in killing, he composed in Allenstein Castle an essay on money and the improvement of coinage, in the German language, and three years later he handed it without success to the Lords of Prussia assembled in the diet at Graudenz.

As is customary in wars, not only the people became coarser and lost their finer values but their money became worthless. The small provinces of Prussia, some of which were subject to the King of Poland, and some to the Grand Master or the Bishop of Ermland, but all of which formed one economic whole, waged war against one another, or at least trade war. The Grand Master began with the favorite theft of princes: he devalued the money of his subjects. There was no longer any country abroad with which one could carry on trade; only misery throve.

The King of Poland wanted the same currency to be in use in Prussia and in Poland. The Grand Master and the Prussian cities, too, declared that they wanted a uniform currency and negotiated about it for a long time. But because they did not want to agree, they could not agree. For in addition to monetary unity, the Grand Master and the Prussian cities

L'UOMO UNIVERSALE

also wanted monetary freedom, that is to say, the right to coin their own money, and the right to inflate it and make the handsome profits one can make from inflation. For inflation is like a girl with whom everyone is glad to go to bed, but whom no one wants to greet in public.

Copernicus began with a definition of money. ("Muncze wyrdt genennet geczeichennt Goldtt, adir Sylber"—Coin is the name given to stamped gold or silver). He discussed the difference between the nominal and real value of a coin, explained why money was coined, and how its value decreases, to wit, through the deterioration of the alloy or the diminution of the weight of the coin.

"An insufferable error" is made, that is, irreparable damage is done, "when the sovereign or the rulers of a country or community try to make a profit out of coinage, to wit, when they add a new coin to the previous and current coin, a new coin which, while imperfect in the grain or in cut, is yet valued equally with the previous one. For such a ruler cheats not only his subjects but also himself.. When he rejoices over a temporary gain which in fact is only insignificant and very small, he is like a stingy farmer who sows bad seeds in order to save good ones, and then there will be even more bad produce than he sowed. This destroys the value of coins, just as the weeds destroy the grain, when the former win the upper hand."

In the second part he spoke more specifically of the Prussian currency. He showed how it had gradually grown worse and worse during the first half of the fifteenth century until it was worth only half its original value. "From such deep damage the Prussian coin suffers, and thereby the entire country. The goldsmiths alone draw profit from this ruin of the country. For they buy up the old coins, separate the silver from them and then take more silver in other coins from unintelligent people."

In the end Copernicus gave his remedy for this state of affairs: "how such a reform might be made." First of all he demanded "that only one mint be set up, where the coin will be coined not in the name of one single city, but with the stamp of the entire country." Nor should anyone have the right to stamp new coins if the country and all the cities had not decided it in common. And a law should be made that from one pound of fine silver no more than twenty marks must be coined.

And so Copernicus read his memorandum aloud to the lords in the diet assembled. Virtue itself, supreme reason in human form, had spoken through the mouth of this canon. ("Who is making this dissertation?"—"A canon."—"A canon? How so? Where does he come from?"—"From Frauenburg. He is a nephew of Bishop Watzelrode, of blessed memory, of a Torun family."—"A nephew? And what does he know about money? What is his occupation?"—"He gazes at the stars . . .")

Copernicus had spoken. The delegates of Torun, Danzig and Elbing declared that they were the representatives of the great cities of Danzig or Elbing or Torun, and that never would their cities give up the right to coin their own money, the symbol of their sovereignty. The nobility and the gentlemen of the clergy shook their heads and expressed the opinion that if there was to be only one mint, it must naturally be in Prussia, not in Poland. The Poles declared that it would be to the general advantage to create monetary unity, and naturally the mint should be in Poland, which, after all, was one of the greatest kingdoms of Europe. The Grand Master did not express any opinion, for he was not there.

On other scores, too, disorder and dissension prevailed all around. One half of Ermland was still held by Poland, the other by the Teutonic Order; for there had just been a war, and thus a new war was around the corner or the old war was still continued (unofficially); so it was in Ermland as all over the rest of the world. The canons of Ermland were in conflict with the bishop of Ermland over money, and what they were interested in was who would receive the greater part of any funds that might exist, not in monetary theories.

Yet the Bishop was a liberal and tolerant man; only recently he had received the cardinal's hat from the Pope, and the syphilis, God knows from whom. The old Ermland church historians at least knew *why* he got it: "He was too complaisant toward the seditious Lutheran heresy. Very probably God punished this bishop chiefly for that reason so that he was ruined by the French disease and in his wretched torments vainly implored the aid of the physicians . . . For the French had attacked and corroded him to such an extent that he could in nowise be cured. The more his physician and his mother filled him with medicines, the worse he grew, so that they had to amputate one of his legs in which the French had affected him, and then he got the cold fever and died of it." (Krecz mer, "Vom Bischthumb Ermlandt," a Torun manuscript.)

The good Bishop had no sooner died than the Ermland bailiff, Georg Preuck, drove the mother and brother of the poor deceased man out of Heilsberg Castle and handed over the body of their beloved kinsman only at the gate. He also chased the two excellent canons, Tiedemann Giese and Leonard Niederhoff who had come to Heilsberg Castle by order of the Frauenburg Chapter to receive the homage of the citizens and officials. Worse still, he gave orders to collect the state revenues and paid his mercenaries with the funds thus obtained. Then, of course, the Grand Master really had to send an envoy to Rome with the proposal to grant the Ermland diocese to the Teutonic Order, so that the Prussians could restore order in Ermland.

Amidst this dangerous unrest the Chapter elected Canon Copernicus general administrator of the diocese during the vacancy of the bishopric. He performed official duties for half a year, until the fall of 1523. Although the new bishop, Moritz Ferber, had been elected as early as April 14, out of purely legalistic caution he chose to await confirmation by the Holy Father before beginning to rule his diocese.

During his six-month term as General Administrator, Copernicus' chief effort was directed toward regaining the lost estates of the Ermland church. First, the King of Poland, by an edict, made restitution of the Ermland castles and towns to the diocese. The Order went on plundering them until the Peace of Cracow.

Meanwhile, the Grand Master had secularized the possessions of his Order, and had solemnly promised to discontinue minting coins. The same promise was made by the cities of Torun, Danzig and Elbing.

Thus, when the King of Poland, Sigismund the Old, came to Prussia, he issued many new regulations, one of which abolished the old Prussian currency and replaced it by a new currency—groshen, shillings and pennies with the coat-of-arms of the King of Poland and the coat-of-arms of Prussia; it was to be equal in value to the new Polish money and to be valid in all his territories, in Poland, Lithuania and Prussia. But Duke Albrecht of Prussia (as the Grand Master of the Order was now called) and the cities of Torun, Danzig and Elbing began to resort to subterfuges.

Then, in 1527, Copernicus revised his monetary memorandum of 1519 (and 1522).

This time he was even clearer than before. He begins at once: "Among the innumerable evils which bring about the ruin of entire states (monarchies and republics), four are certainly to be regarded as the most important: inner dissension, high mortality, barrenness of the soil and deterioration of the currency. The first three are so evident that hardly anyone will dispute them. But the fourth evil, which results from bad money, is noted only by a few people, and only by those who reflect more seriously than others, because the states exposed to this evil do not perish at once from its first attack, but quite gradually and, as it were, in an imperceptible manner."

If an earlier attempt had been made to improve the currency, a pound of silver would scarcely have contained twenty-four marks; now at least thirty marks would have to be melted down in order to obtain a scanty pound of silver.

"Woe to you, poor land of Prussia, that you must now do penance for such bad administration!

"Unless the situation is remedied, Prussia will soon have coins containing nothing but copper. Then all foreign trade will stop. For what foreign merchant will sell his goods for copper coins? . . . The powers that be calmly witness this decay of the land of Prussia; they are letting our beloved fatherland to which we owe everything, even our lives, perish wretchedly through brainless neglect, more and more each day."

Once again Copernicus castigated the speculators who buy up all the coins in circulation and melt them down. "This results necessarily in increased prices of all means and subsistence. Everything rises and falls with the value of money; the prices of things are not determined by brass and copper, but by gold and silver."

It was a mistake, he said, to think that the poor people could buy their bread or grain cheap with bad coins; only the gentlemen who mint them and a few traders grow rich. "The common weal suffers, the state, and the majority of the inhabitants . . . Aside from logic, we know from experience that those countries flourish which have good money; they decline when their money becomes bad. Thus Prussia, too, once flourished, when the mark was worth two Hungarian gulden . . . but now when our coins are deteriorating from day to day, our fatherland is sinking and is even now close to ruin.

"Moreover, trade and communication, arts and crafts flourish where money is good. With bad money, however, the people grow slack and inert, they neglect cultivating the spirit. We can still remember how inexpensive everything was in Prussia when good money was circulating. But now the value of all means of subsistence has risen. It is quite clear that light money furthers laziness and in no wise relieves misery . . . Nor will improvement of this state of affairs impose any burden on those who are liable to pay interest; if they seem to pay their masters more than otherwise, it must not be forgotten that their receipts for cattle and corn are larger. Revenues and expenses increase in the same proportion."

Did not this man have a great heart? Did he not have a warm feeling for the poor? Did he not rebuke the wicked princes and even more wicked merchants loudly? Even more sharply did he formulate his recommendations in his later memorandum. All coins should bear the coat-of-arms of the King of Poland. Monetary unity! Economic unity! In brief: unity! The currency must be valid throughout the country. The King of Poland should control all mints! "This would contribute not a little to the reconciliation of men's minds and the common furtherance of commercial relations."

The old coins should be called in. Only radical measures, thought Copernicus, could help. So let us be radical! Inevitable drawbacks for some individuals would be balanced by the assets and lasting advantages for the community.

So this Copernicus was also a currency expert, a financial genius, a free-trader, a man of peace, a man with a warm heart and understanding of the needs of the poor—a philosopher who knew what was right not only in the cosmos, but in his own little world.

To be a great man, this greatest of all astronomers had no need of astronomy. I am reminded of a saying of the famous astronomer Pierre Laplace. In 1796, when his book *Exposition du Système du Monde* was published, God's ally of that time, General Bonaparte, asked Laplace why he had not mentioned God once in his entire book. The quiet scientist replied: "Sire, I had no need of this hypothesis."

At other Prussian diets (in 1528 and 1529) Copernicus had new opportunities to present his monetary theories and to learn that he who fights for the general interest is compelled to pin his hopes on those advocates of special interests who are usually the most bitter enemies of the common good. One of these sessions was attended by Copernicus' colleague, Felix Reich, also a financial expert, as the second delegate from Ermland. Reich gathered together a collection of writings on currency, thanks to which Copernicus' memorandum was preserved among others, as well as a letter from Copernicus to Reich on monetary problems, dated April 8, 1528, in which we find the following characteristic statements: "It is not of little value when one can spread light on things that are obscure by nature. It often happens that someone grasps a thing quite correctly, but cannot make clear to others a thing which is clear to himself. I fear that sometimes this happens to me. . . . But however that may be, I acknowledge freely that I can err, because I am only *one* man, have only *one* mind, and do not always learn or observe what may have been thought out by others in a more efficacious manner."

Another attempt was made at Elbing. Copernicus went there, too. The King of Poland brought the vexatious monetary problem before the Polish diet at Piotrkow, and when this did not avail anything, the ancient remedy of sending a matter to a committee was resorted to. Copernicus went to this committee, too; instead of Felix Reich, his colleague and good friend Alexander Sculteti was the second delegate from Ermland.

Sculteti had just returned from Livonia where he had prepared a map which he had sent to Bishop Moritz Ferber, whereupon the bishop had requested him by letter (July 29, 1529) to draw up a similar map of Prussia together with Copernicus.

The negotiations in the committee broke down, as had those in the general body. Already in the above-mentioned letter to Felix Reich, Copernicus had written: "If in the monetary matter things are done in the same way as before, I fear that the situation will grow even worse; for the stamping of coins in the customary fashion will not be discontinued. Why should they cease doing it, if only profit can be expected therefrom, and no damage, whatever the outcome may be . . . I hear that negotiations are to be held at the same time about the special levy. So I think that nothing will be decided with respect to the currency; for after all it is impossible that the people should be oppressed simultaneously by two burdens. We shall grant the levy, but the currency will remain as it is, or more accurately, deteriorate further. We will give the King much money; this is the chaff; but where will the seeds remain? It might have been more beautiful, more worthy, more royal and even much more useful, if the taxes had been remitted and in their stead the currency restored; if this had not been enough, there would always have been time to levy the contribution later."

Copernicus was also concerned with other administrative matters. He was the *nuncius capituli,* that is, the Chapter's envoy, in 1524, 1526 and 1531. In company of a colleague he toured the districts of Mehlsack and Allenstein to inspect the administration, collect the rent from the tenant farmers for the cathedral and oversee everything. Several times his companion was his best friend, Tiedemann Giese.

Copernicus also helped to work out new regulations for artisan apprentices, journeymen and guilds. He even drew up a project for a bread-tax, which was necessary because of the fluctuation of money and grain prices, and the resulting scarcity of food and misery of the poor. (This document is called *Panis coquendi ratio Doctoris Nicolai Copernicus.)*

In the library of Upsala, a curious letter from Copernicus written at that period (1524) has been found. In it the great man complains to his bishop about his recalcitrant debtor, Heinrich Snellenberg, a colleague and compatriot of his. During the "Franconian Knights' War" Snellenberg had received one hundred marks from a Danzig merchant for Copernicus, but had paid Copernicus only ninety.

Copernicus was unable to get the remaining ten marks, try as he might. Finally, Snellenberg, after many dodges, told him to start legal proceedings if he wanted to have his ten marks back.

And so before his bishop Copernicus sued his countryman and colleague, the notoriously lazy Canon Snellenberg.

Did Copernicus get his ten marks in the end? . . .

The great theoreticians of finance are not always the best businessmen.

33

SOME TREMENDOUS TRIFLES

In New York there are ninety different Christian confessions; each of them worships God in its own way, without being disturbed by the others. In the science of nature, indeed in every science, we must progress as far as that; for what does it mean when people speak of liberalism, yet try to prevent others from thinking and expressing themselves in their own way?
GOETHE, Maxims and Reflections

WAS Copernicus an atheist?

In his Book of Revolutions the good canon naturally speaks of God, but he does it in such academic terms that one might suppose God was for him part of the geocentric terminology to which he was accustomed and which he continued to use in the very book in which he played the devil with the geocentric theory. This son of the church always had God on his lips, the term slid off his pen with the greatest of ease. But no one before him had driven God so far away from man.

Copernicus, that most tranquil of revolutionaries, shook the world in the quietest and most concealed way. He won the greatest of all battles without mounting the pawing steed, without flying flags, without the thunder of canon, without blood and tears.

This most stubborn pedant among astronomers and revolutionaries had an exceedingly gentle demeanor, he seemed mild and tolerant, a wide awake servant of the church at the edge of the civilized world. Luther thought he could call him a fool with impunity. And Melanchthon simply called for the police when he heard of his work: any king seemed to him powerful enough to make such a restless head roll.

There were other revolutionaries who spoke of God in the language of saints or children while they set fire to the fuse with which they blew

God up in the air. Newton wrote pious commentaries on the Bible for twenty years. Or listen to the virtuous Kepler, as Goethe quotes him: "My highest wish is to become aware of God whom I find everywhere outside me, as well as inside me, within myself, so to speak." And that great heathen, Goethe, comments with emotion: "The noble man does not realize that at that very moment the Divine Being within him was in closest contact with the Divine Being in the universe."

Copernicus is more readily moved when he speaks of spherical triangles or the infinitude of the firmament than when he speaks of God.

Such was the bold man who stole the heavens from the Lord!

He was a quiet, serious and austere man! He spoke in beautiful, sublime, academic language. But when his real interests were at stake, that is, the interests of mankind or more accurately, the interests of the universe, he ruthlessly lashed out at popes and fathers of the church, Grand Masters and bishops, scholars and ignoramuses!

For the rest, he was a canon, mild-mannered, a friend of the arch-tolerant Giese.

Giordano Bruno was burned. Campanella was imprisoned. Michel Servet was burned. Galileo was forced to recant. As late as 1794 Immanuel Kant was reprimanded by the royal Prussian Cabinet for "distorting and degrading several principal and fundamental doctrines of the Holy Scriptures and Christianity."

According to Kant, God was a delusion. And according to Copernicus?

It is a good thing that he had no theological interests! With the stubbornness that was characteristic of him he might have forced his imagined circular motions upon God, and might have exclaimed triumphantly that he had encompassed the ways of the Eternal with seven circles!

Copernicus was so averse to all theology that he did not even want to suffer for the sake of the truth! He did not share the accursed pleasure of the martyrs in being slaughtered for the sake of the higher truth that was in them.

Copernicus was the most unheroic of the great revolutionaries.

Did he grow more pious or more daring as he advanced in age? Did he grow ever freer of dogma and prejudice?

Shortly before he celebrated his sixtieth birthday at Frauenburg, the pious Elbingers, who lived three miles away, performed a burlesque satirizing the man who no sooner had touched the earth with the tip of his finger than he made it whiz through space in triple motion like a dancing goddess.

Copernicus' earliest biographers: Starowolski, Broscius and Gassendi, relate that a certain schoolmaster who was egged on by Copernicus' political opponents, the "Teutonic Crossbearers," wrote this play and had it performed in order to cast ridicule upon Copernicus and his incredible new theory.

Starowolski bases this statement on letters from Copernicus' most intimate friend, the Bishop of Kulm, Tiedemann Giese.

A costumed pope mounted on a horse rode in the carnival procession through the decorated streets of the town of Elbing, a fat drunkard beat upon the drum, a tall pallid knave blew the trumpet. Because it was traditional to represent Saint Maurice as an Ethiopian, the actor impersonating Bishop Maurice of Ermland walked through the market place made up as a Moor and gave his episcopal absolution to all sinners. The comic pope also distributed blessings in the square and gave young good-for-nothings in monks' hoods letters of indulgence "empowering them to collect swine, to absolve from murder, whoredom and heresy, and to set up chapels."

It was in the course of this procession that a fellow from Elbing wearing the garb of an Ermland canon mimicked Copernicus. Did he impersonate that "new astrologer who wanted to prove that the earth was moving and revolving, rather than the heaven or the firmament, sun and moon; just as if someone in a moving carriage or on a sailing ship believed that he was motionless and in rest, but that the earth and the trees were moving. But such are the times we live in: he who wants to be clever must invent something all his own and what he makes up he naturally thinks is the best thing ever! This fool wants to turn the whole art of astronomy upside down! But as the Holy Scripture testifies, Joshua ordered the sun to stand still, not the earth!" (This is the famous passage from Luther's after-dinner speeches.)

An original at any cost, that is how the Lutherans saw Copernicus. And Luther's opinion was not sneezed at in Prussian towns like Elbing or Danzig. Luther had already been put on the stage there, and newfangled preachers and religious refugees were common. For instance, there was Wilhelm Gnapheus, who had been compelled to flee from Holland because of a theological quarrel, and who had become the first rector of the Elbing *gymnasium*. He was a writer of burlesque, and probably the author of the burlesque against Copernicus.

Intolerance soon began to kill in Ermland, Prussia and Poland. In 1523 Copernicus had the office of general administrator of Ermland. The new bishop, Moritz Ferber, former custodian at Frauenburg, in contrast to his predecessor, the tolerant (and syphilitic) Fabian von Lossainen, went on the hunt for heretics.

Moritz had not had an ordinary life. He devoted his first forty years to the love of a girl who in the end took another man. He devoted the rest of his life to hatred, in the name of the God of love, Christ. Sadists usually move in the company of the two gods of love, Jesus and Amor.

Moritz was the son of a wealthy merchant from Danzig. Like his fathers before him he became a merchant. Like his fathers he fell in love with a wealthy heiress. The girl in question was called Anna, and she did not want Moritz. The parents at first accepted the ardent wooer, but finally yielded to their daughter's aversion. The infatuated Moritz went before an ecclesiastical court and sued for breach of promise. He litigated for ten years. Finally he went to Rome in order to win his love suit at the Curia, and was about to achieve his end, for the whole Curia loved him—when Anna took another man into her marital bed, and Moritz resolved to become a bishop, if not the pope.

He did become a bishop. At first he was a priest; at the age of forty he began to study ecclesiastical law; three years later he obtained his doctor's degree, became bishop of Ermland, and in order at last to unburden his full heart, issued an edict against the "Lutheran pest."

Luther read Moritz's pamphlet against him and had it printed together with another Prussian edict, that of the Bishop of Samland, who again admonished his clergy in the sharpest terms to read Luther's works diligently and to preach in the national language. Luther coupled his enemy and his friend in the same book, wrote brief notes to both and immortalized both of the bishops. The faithful editors, out of respect for Luther's notes, reprinted the two pamphlets in all the editions of Luther's collected works.

A great writer is so powerful that he unwittingly immortalizes even his enemies.

Tiedemann Giese, Copernicus' most intimate friend, made himself the spokesman for a group of liberal tolerant men who wanted to mediate between the old-believers and the new-believers.

Giese expressed his evangelic feelings in a pamphlet directed against the pro-Lutheran writing of the Bishop of Samland. As the latter's work was entitled "110 little flowers . . ." etc., Giese called his pamphlet "Anthelogikon," the anti-little-flower. At first Giese circulated it only in manuscript; but in the end he had it printed, upon the insistence of three of his colleagues, the canons Felix Reich, Leonard Niederhoff and, especially, Nicolaus Copernicus.

Copernicus had authorized Giese to quote him publicly as a supporter of his friend's views.

Giese printed at the head of his pamphlet his own letter to Reich, where he wrote that he had sent copies of the manuscript to friends and adversaries, including even the author of "110 Little Flowers," the Bishop of Samland, to whom he was now also sending a printed copy, and whom he begged at the same time not to permit his judgment to be troubled by personal inclination, "as I think was the case with Nicolaus Copernicus, who advised me to publish my writing in print, although he is otherwise of discriminating taste."

Curiously enough no words of Copernicus have come down to us concerning Luther, Melanchthon and the whole Reformation, although Copernicus was involved in the movement through various people and issues. All the more significant is this indirect testimony to the "quarrel of the monks."

Giese says in the preface: *Ego omniversum pugnam detrecto* (I entirely reject the battle).

A gentle soul breathes in this little work: the true Catholic attitude.

"But now," writes Giese, "when everything proceeds in wild storm, in turmoil and rebellion, who is building? Who is seeking perfection? Is Christ's glory being heightened? Are spiritual gifts being increased? What do we find but general confusion as a result of all this ridicule, quarreling and defamation? Christian freedom is being perverted into lack of restraint, obedience into want of discipline, even if the originators of the tragedy never willed it so. Thus we are all plunged into the worst conceivable slavery; while referring constantly to the spirit of God we are estranging ourselves entirely from love. Love endureth all things, it is not eager for and does not try to inflict harm. Undeniably many things in the church come close to superstition, and abuses have slipped in. But the time of the harvest should have been awaited, so that we do not destroy the wheat in order to eradicate the weeds. And the leaders of the new movement are unable to find the wheat, they are throwing it into the fire, when they try to lead us back to spirituality by excluding all outward ritual, all symbols of the spiritual, all ornamentation in the church . . . For the sake of the weak and the simple-minded we must preserve the external service to God, not confuse their consciences, but slowly and gradually lead them to higher things, guiding them after the example of the Lord from the earthly to the heavenly . . . Christ Himself, although he could have destroyed the law, said that he had not come to destroy the law, but to fulfil it! . . .

"The two sisters, faith and love, live excellently together. How good and lovely it is, if we brothers can live in agreement, too, that is, in the one Christ! . . . Then we shall speak as with *one* breath: The peoples thank you, God, all the peoples thank you, the earth is giving its fruit.

"I was inspired by sheer love for the pure Christian doctrine," Giese wrote in his introductory letters, "and, to say it at once, anger also over the disputes which have brought more confusion than advantage to the church . . .

"A large part of my treatise is so composed that it might almost serve my opponent better than myself; I wanted to put the latter in a yielding and gentle mood so it might seem that, having put tragic seriousness aside, I wrote an appendix to his book, rather than a satire. Often I thought I followed in his footsteps, rather than pursued him; true, I wanted to have a comrade rather than an opponent . . .

"Oh, if only the Lutherans were filled with Christian spirit toward the Romans, and the Romans filled with Christian spirit toward the Lutherans, verily the tragedy would not have taken place in our churches, a tragedy of which the end is not yet in sight! . . . verily, the wild beasts behave more gently toward their like than the Christians toward theirs!"

As Bishop of Kulm he still preserved this gentleness. He was a *homo literatus, disertus et doctus* (a man of letters, eloquent and learned). A son of Danzig patricians, he was born in 1480, seven years after his friend, Copernicus. He studied at Leipzig, and became Magister, secretary to the King of Poland and canon at Frauenburg; in 1519 King Sigismund ennobled him; in 1538 he was appointed Bishop of Kulm, in 1548, Bishop of Ermland; he died in 1549.

He lived with Copernicus at Frauenburg for more than the space of a generation, a lifetime associate, a delight to his friend.

With the German reformers, too, Giese maintained friendly relations; true, his aim was to bring back the apostates to the Roman church. In 1538 he completed a three-volume work entitled *De Regno Christi* (on the Kingdom of Christ), in which he supported the dogmas of the Catholic church but welcomed some of the innovations of the reformers. He submitted the manuscript to the judgment of famous scholars, such as Erasmus of Rotterdam (in the spring of 1536). Erasmus, already quite close to death, in a trembling hand and as politely as only good writers can, wrote to apologize that he was unable to read the work. Two years later, Giese, then already Catholic Bishop of Kulm, sent his work to the Lutheran Melanchthon at Wittenberg; previously in a letter he had recommended his nephew who studied under Melanchthon at Wittenberg to the special consideration of the great humanist.

Because Giese in his book wanted to reconcile the two opposing parties, he displeased both, as is usually the case, and was never printed. Later the Counter-Reformation even destroyed his manuscript; Hosius had found "horrendous heresies" in it.

At that time gentlemen followed their principles very strictly—except when it was to their disadvantage. Great sacrifices are usually asked only of small people. A poor man sacrifices his life sooner than a rich man his money.

When the Grand Master, with the help of the Catholic King of Poland, became a Lutheran, secularized his order, called himself Duke Albrecht of Prussia and abolished the monasteries, the rich clergy in Polish Prussia and Ermland trembled lest their goods, too, be secularized.

But God and the King of Poland protected these property owners. And the Duke of Prussia, from the notorious family of Hohenzollern, preferred to strike the poor rather than the rich.

Andreas Osiander, the Nuremberg priest and infamous author of the interpolated preface to *De Revolutionibus,* the man who shortened Copernicus' life, had met the Grand Master at Nuremberg and secretly put him in touch with Luther. On his way to Berlin Albrecht looked up Luther at Wittenberg; the latter advised him to do away entirely with "the silly and perverted rule of the order," to marry, to secularize Prussia and become a Lutheran. Melanchthon advised him in the same sense.

Meanwhile the Polish Diet resolved to expel the order from Prussia, unless the Grand Master finally swore the oath of vassalage to the King of Poland. Then Albrecht rode to Cracow. There, on April 10, 1525, he knelt before the King of Poland, and swore the desired oath. And for this he received in fief from the Catholic King of Poland the land formerly held by the spiritual order, henceforth to be the worldly Lutheran Duchy of Prussia.

The Curia and the Catholic princes gnashed their teeth in horror, and cried: Shame and Stop thief! The Emperor and the Empire outlawed the infidel Hohenzollern, the insolent Albrecht. Immediately after the Peace of Cracow Albrecht openly went over to Luther and introduced the Lutheran church into Prussia all under the protection of the Catholic King of Poland.

But to assuage the clergy in Ermland and in Polish Prussia, the pious King of Poland at the same time struck the Lutherans in these provinces with fire and sword.

Yes, against the poor people, who at that time raised their restless heads, Catholics and Lutherans allied themselves. It was a fight against the slaves, by whose bloody sweat everyone lived, Catholics and Lutherans; it was a fight against the peasants!

The poor people had believed that a new master would be a better master. The poor people had pinned their hopes on Luther. But when the thralls in Southern Germany began to rebel, and all over Germany peasants refused to be enthralled and to be whipped quite so brutally, when they expressed the desire to elect their own priests and eat cheaper cabbage, that gentle-souled son of the poor, Luther, simply could not endure it. He sat down before his table of German oak wood and wrote "against the robbing and murderous peasants": "Such amazing times are these, that a prince can earn heaven by shedding blood better than others by praying . . . Therefore, dear gentlemen, rescue here, help there, have pity on the poor people, stab, strike, strangle, whoever can!"

In Prussia, too, the peasants wanted to be free. This was in September and October, 1525. They seized forks and sickles, took spears and threshing flails in their hands, and inveighed all too loudly against the secular and ecclesiastical estates, in Ermland, in Samland and in the new Duchy of Prussia.

The Duke of Prussia and Bishop Moritz of Ermland, neither of whom could bear the sight of the other because of his faith, joined forces, and in the name of the Lutheran and Catholic God took the field against their starving little peasants, against the poor people. And God was with Bishop Moritz, and God was with Duke Albrecht, both were victorious. They slaughtered their peasants including the women and children, they burned down the straw huts (and did not build any stone houses). They killed all the discontented; as for the dead, they are easily satisfied, they do not rebel.

The following spring, gentle Sigismund the Old, the kind-hearted King of Poland, came on horseback or by carriage. In all haste he burned a few gentlemen in Danzig, who believed in the same God as he did, but wanted to use different formulae of politeness in their intercourse with him. At Elbing and Torun, too, he wanted to burn the Protestants, but the distressed heretics had run away before he arrived.

Even the gentle Tiedemann Giese was sent by the zealous Bishop Moritz to Elbing, in the spring of 1527, to put a councillor to the question, because he had not confessed at Easter!

Five years later Tiedemann Giese was appointed coadjutor to the sickly Bishop Moritz Ferber; but this aroused the wrath of the King of Poland who wanted to see his favorite, Johannes Dantiscus, Bishop of Kulm, coadjutor to the Bishop of Ermland, for this office always led to the succession in Ermland.

In 1536, Giese and Dantiscus finally reached a secret agreement. Giese was to become bishop of Kulm, and Dantiscus bishop of Ermland. And this came to pass, to the great sorrow of Copernicus.

The latter, as he grew advanced in age, participated only to a limited extent in the affairs of his chapter. He was commissioned to supervise the church endowments. In 1540 he was appointed custodian, and in 1541, superintendent of the treasury of the cathedral association.

At the age of sixty, Copernicus petitioned for a coadjutor; the taking of one was a privilege of old age. Usually this was done to secure one's own prebend to a relative or friend. Copernicus wanted to bequeath his to his nephew, Johannes Lewsze. But Bishop Moritz delayed gratifying this wish.

On May 7, 1543, a few days before Copernicus' death, his nephew, Johannes Lewsze, on the basis of an apostolic writ of confirmation of his post as coadjutor, solicited to be inducted into his uncle's canonship.

At the age of sixty-five Copernicus renounced his so-called scholastry at Breslau, a prebend he had received as a young man and a sinecure. Probably, he also renounced it in favor of a friend.

According to all testimony, Copernicus was a vigorous old man. He is said to have had a mistress at an advanced age. From 1529 to 1536 (perhaps longer) he was the guardian of the children of one of his nieces who had been married to a Danzig councillor.

Copernicus also took a lively interest in politics. In 1537, for instance, a correspondent from Breslau sent him news, of the battle between King Ferdinand and the Turks, a battle at Kaschau and an alleged truce between Charles V and Francis I. Although these (partly false) reports from Breslau were dated the end of June, on August 9, 1537, Copernicus sent them to Bishop Dantiscus at Allenstein through a messenger whom Dantiscus had sent to Frauenburg. He must have thought that Bishop Dantiscus, that old diplomat and friend of emperors and chancellors, had not heard of these important political events which had happened two months before. How slowly world news travelled at that time!

The emperor and the Turks; burlesques at Elbing and starving peasants; Bishop Fabian and Bishop Moritz; Bishop Giese and Bishop Dantiscus; the Grand Master marries, the nephew Lewsze must wait, the young servant girl at home—and the stars . . .

Insignificant details? Trifles in the life of a great man?

But the eternal stars! The stars, always the stars. . . .

34

AND FAME? . . . AND THE GREAT WORKS?

Let the heavens be merciful to those who attack me!
HORACE

The barriers that separated states and nations in hostile selfishness are broken down. Today all thinking minds are united by a cosmopolitan tie.
SCHILLER: The meaning and purpose of the study of history

COPERNICUS' fame? And his great works? Not one of his contemporaries had even a remote foreboding of his future influence on the world.

Manifestly, at that time only Copernicus himself knew exactly what a great man Copernicus was.

By the power of his personality he won a handful of followers, such as the enthusiastic youth, Rheticus, and a few of his colleagues of the chapter, Sculteti, Donner, Tiedemann Giese. By the power of his book he won several followers of genius and several who were merely intelligent; among these some were fearful like Erasmus Reinhold and René Descartes, some courageous like Galileo and Kepler, some ruthless like Giordano Bruno.

When he died he had a dubious name among experts and a farcical reputation among laymen.

A hundred years later he was world famous, considered by some as the hero of a scientific millennium of the future, by most as the chief representative of one of the most interesting false doctrines of the past.

Two hundred years after his death (in many details long since outstripped, in several fundamental conceptions already ridiculous) he was the man who had given his name to an epoch. Like the Centaurs, like Prometheus, he had begun the fight against the old gods, and triumphed beyond all expectation. Like broken statues the gods lay in the dust. The old cosmogonies had burst like soap bubbles.

But at the end of the seventeenth century, in many countries of Europe, professors of astronomy were compelled to swear that they accepted the principles of Aristotle, particularly his views on the comets!

Since most of Copernicus' letters, those best of all sources, have been lost, we do not know what relations he had in the learned world. Peucer, Melanchthon's son-in-law and a friend of Rheticus', relates that as early as 1525 Copernicus was "most famous." What is the meaning of this term?

Only the Commentariolus could supply a fairly exact notion of Copernicus' system. But the Commentariolus obviously soon fell into oblivion, or perhaps it never aroused much attention.

Luther's after-dinner speech about the fool who wanted to turn the whole art of astronomy upside down, took place during the first half of the 1530's. Thus the news of the Copernican audacities must have reached Wittenberg shortly after the completion of his investigation, by the end of 1532 or 1533.

Gnapheus, the Dutch humanist, schoolmaster and burlesque writer, came to Elbing in 1531; there he made himself a name and perhaps won his post as rector by his school comedies. It was perhaps in his comedy "Morosophus," printed in 1540 in a revised form, that he ridiculed Copernicus.

Dorothy Stimson reports a story of the court of Albrecht of Prussia allegedly told by Bishop Kromer. When the ducal astrologer expounded the Copernican theory to Albrecht, an exaggeratedly witty courtier called out to the servant who was carrying the wine jug: "Be careful not to spill the jug!" and with this old-Prussian joke he won all the beaux esprits to his side.

By the end of 1533, Johannes Schoner, the Nuremberg astronomer, published a book in Nuremberg, which contained an inquiry into whether the earth was turning or not, an alleged disputation of Müller or Regiomontanus; in this work Schoner discussed the rotation of the earth and Copernicus' theory and rejected them. He jeeringly compared the sun with the fireplace and the earth with the meat on the roasting spit.

Thus, in the fall of 1533 at the latest, Schoner must have heard of Copernicus' doctrine.

In the summer of the same year, 1533, Johann Albrecht von Widmanstetter (1506-1557), the learned secretary and intimate of Pope Clement VII, lectured on Copernicus' theories before the pope, two cardinals, Bishop Petrus and the physician Curtius in the Vatican gardens. As a reward, he received a precious Greek manuscript with painted initials.

Widmanstetter was a man of extremely broad education, an expert in Oriental languages, and the owner of a famous library which later became part of the Bavarian state library. As the pope used him chiefly for handling German affairs, he was called "the privy councillor of the Germans at the Apostolic See in Rome."

From 1535 on, Widmanstetter was secretary to the very influential Cardinal Nicolaus von Schoenberg, who on November 1, 1536, wrote Copernicus that famous letter from Rome, which Copernicus placed at the beginning of *De Revolutionibus* in 1543.

Just as Alexander Sculteti, the preceptor at the Frauenburg Cathedral, a personal friend and colleague of Copernicus, may have aroused Widmanstetter's interest in the Copernican theories during his stay in Rome, so it was perhaps Widmanstetter who drew Cardinal Schoenberg's attention to Copernicus.

Or were the Northern Europeans Sculteti, Schoenberg and Widmanstetter still humanistically minded at a time when Rome was again plunged into obscurantism under the reactionary Pope Paul III?

Schoenberg was a Saxon. He came to Italy to study. He heard Savonarola preach, and out of sheer enthusiasm became a Dominican monk. In 1518 the pope sent him to Poland as a mediator between the Teutonic Order and the Poles, and in order to arouse Albrecht and Sigismund the Old against the Turks. Schoenberg might have heard of Copernicus in Poland. He was appointed Procurator General at the papal court, and in 1520, Bishop of Capua. He helped to conclude the Peace of Cambrai between Charles V and Francis I, and was made cardinal by Paul III. As he occupied one of the highest ranks in the order of the Dominicans, those censors of education, doctrine, morals and heresies, Copernicus placed Schoenberg's letter even before his dedication to Pope Paul III in his *De Revolutionibus*.

"Cardinal Nicolaus von Schoenberg, Bishop of Capua, sends Nicolaus Copernicus his greetings.

"A few years ago when I heard everyone constantly speaking of your amazing investigations, I conceived a regard for you, and congratulated our people for their wisdom in spreading your fame. For I had learned that you not only profoundly understood the teachings of the ancient astronomers, but that you had also constructed a new world system. You teach, as I have heard, that the earth is moving, and that the sun occupies the center of the world, and that the eighth heaven, the firmament, remains constant and motionless; and that the moon together with the elements of its sphere between Mars and Venus revolves about the sun in an annual orbit. You have also written explanations of this theory and composed tables of the planetary orbits, that fill everyone with the greatest admiration. Therefore may I earnestly beg you, highly-learned man, if it is not too much trouble, to communicate your discoveries to those desirous of knowledge, and to send me, as soon as possible, the result of your nightly meditations upon the universe, together with the tables and everything else pertinent to this subject.

"Dietrich von Rheden has been charged to have everything copied at my expense and to send it to me. If you do me this favor you will learn that I have your fame greatly at heart and am trying to obtain recognition for your work. Farewell!—Rome, on the first of November of the year 1536."

As can be seen the cardinal in this letter speaks with enthusiasm, and some caution. Instead of expressing the heretical idea that the earth revolves about the sun, he speaks of the motion of the moon, "together with the elements of its sphere . . ."

One year later Schoenberg was dead. Rheden, an Ermland canon and Roman agent of the chapter, did not return to Frauenburg until 1539. He, Niederhoff, Donner and Lewsze were chosen by Copernicus as executors of his will.

Thus some of the Catholic leaders at the beginning tried to promote Copernicus and his theory, while the leaders of the Reformation were strongly opposed to him.

This situation was soon reversed. Copernicus' first disciple came from Wittenberg, the university of Luther and Melanchthon, and his name was Rheticus. He and his young friend, another mathematician of Wittenberg, Erasmus Reinhold, and a few Lutheran scholars from Nuremberg became interested in Copernicus.

But the Catholic church began to persecute Copernicus, first him personally, because of his lady housekeeper, and later his book and his theory.

Incidentally, there were two men at that time, who occasionally asserted that the earth was moving. Canon Celio Calcagnini (born and died at Ferrara, 1479-1541) composed a small treatise under the provocative title *Quomodo coelum stet, terra moveatur, vel de perenni motu terrae Commentatio* (A treatise on how the heavens stand still, the earth moves, or on the constant motion of the earth). In 1544, that is to say, one year after Copernicus' death, it was published (in the edition of Calcagnini's works *Opera aliquot* in Basel). Calcagnini says: "I have just told you that this heaven which you let rotate with ineffable velocity, that this sun, and those stars which you let whirl and revolve, stand still, and, supported by their orbs, enjoy eternal rest."

But he does not speak of the earth's motion around the sun. Calcagnini finally refers to Nicholas of Cusa's views on the motion of the earth. Calcagnini was not an astronomer and Zinner considers his treatise insignificant.

Leonardo da Vinci, too, seems to have pondered over the question whether or not the earth moves. But his views wavered. Thus, he wrote in *Quaderni:* "The sun does not move!" and in 1510, in a treatise on falling bodies, he advanced the thesis that the earth rotated daily around its axis. On other occasions he assumed that the earth was the center of the world and that the sun and moon and stars revolved about it, thus his ideas were only flashes of genius, not to be compared to the methodical investigations of Copernicus.

And Copernicus' fame? A few cousins and colleagues of the clergy. And the interest shown by a handful of colleagues, mathematicians and astronomers? A lecture in the Vatican gardens? A few abusive remarks in Saxony! Some interest at Wittenberg and Nuremberg? A burlesque at Elbing! An invitation to sit on a committee for the reform of the calendar. Were these the fruits of fame in the life of a great man?

And the great works? His translation of a mediocre man of letters from Byzantium? His "panning" of a Nuremberg vicar? A few observations and computations? And a forgotten little commentary with an absurd, provocative and undemonstrated or badly demonstrated theory?

And the great works?

And fame?

In 1473 Copernicus was born. In 1543 his *De Revolutionibus* was published, and at the age of seventy, a few hours before he passed away, he felt of this book with fingers already growing cold.

Without this book probably nothing would have remained of him; if he had died a few years earlier, before Rheticus came and induced him to have it printed, his name would have died away, his theory would probably have been forgotten, he would have been merely another industrious and eccentric scientist, dead before his death, a plodding wagoner on the king's roads.

35

THE NEW AESCULAPIUS

In medicine Copernicus was celebrated as a new Aesculapius.
STAROWOLSKI, Hecatontas

But Copernicus knew remedies especially well and prepared them himself.
GASSENDI

Barbarus hic ego sum . . .
OVID

IN HIS "History of the Theory of Colors," Goethe writes: "Today we have reached a point when the divorce between ancient and modern times is becoming ever more significant. A certain connection with antiquity still continues uninterrupted and powerful; but from now on we find several men who rely upon their own strength.

"The human heart is said to be both defiant and timid. One might very well characterize the human mind in the same way. It is impatient and presumptuous, and at the same time uncertain and hesitating. It strives for experience and a more extended, purer activity, then it recoils, not unjustly so. As it progresses, it feels ever more urgently that it is bound to lose even while winning: for the necessary conditions of existence are tied to truth as well as to falsehood.

"Hence, in things scientific, what is handed down to us is defended as long as possible, and violent protracted struggles arise, theoretical as well as practical retardations. The fifteenth and sixteenth centuries give us the most striking examples of this. No sooner had the world become immeasurably extended in length by the discovery of new lands, than it must close up within itself as a round globe. No sooner had the magnetic needle pointed to definite quarters of the globe than it began to incline down to the earth just as definitely.

"In the domain of morality similar great effects and counter-effects take place. As soon as powder is invented, personal courage disappears from the world or at least takes a different direction. The ancient vigorous reliance on one's fist and God, dissolves into the blindest resignation to an unavoidably puissant, irrevocably commanding fate. Printing of books no sooner has generally spread culture than censorship becomes necessary in order to hedge in what has hitherto been free in a naturally limited circle.

"But among all the discoveries and beliefs perhaps nothing produced a greater effect on the human mind than the doctrine of Copernicus. No sooner had the world been recognized as round and closed within itself than it had to renounce the tremendous privilege of being the center of the universe. Perhaps no greater demand had ever been made upon mankind: for think of everything that went up in smoke because of this admission: a second Paradise, a world of innocence, poetry and devotion, the testimony of the senses, the conviction of a poetic-religious faith; no wonder that people refused to let go of all this, that they opposed by all possible means a doctrine which challenged and entitled those who accepted it to a hitherto unknown and even unimagined freedom of thought and breadth of vision."

Thus prodigious does Copernicus appear as astronomer and philosopher. But during his lifetime he was perhaps more famous as a physician, and certainly his medical reputation was less contested than his astronomical one.

He was manifestly regarded as a corypheus of medicine in Ermland, and even abroad. True, he was not a regular practising physician. But he was the physician of his uncle Watzelrode, and the physician of his colleagues at the Frauenburg Cathedral, who had once sent him to Italy to study medicine.

Now and then it seems that a poor man was treated by him; at least so it is reported by Gassendi, who embellishes a sentence of Starowolski's to this effect. The latter in turn seems to lean on a letter of Tiedemann Giese to Rheticus. Starowolski said that "the poor people worshipped him as a godlike being, who personally prepared special medicines and applied them felicitously."

When his uncle Watzelrode died, Copernicus, it is true, was not on the spot. And we do not know whether he tried to treat his brother Andreas for leprosy (or syphilis) and Bishop Fabian of Lossainen for syphilis.

However, his cousin, Bishop Moritz Ferber, consulted him frequently. Moritz was sickly—I might almost say was sickly with a vengeance. He had a weak stomach, suffered from colics and podagra, was not equal to the burdens of his office, hated Luther and at every little twinge in his belly summoned cousin Copernicus from Frauenburg to Heilsberg Castle for a consultation.

He summoned him in 1529, when he felt close to death. He summoned him in 1531, when again he thought his last hour had struck. By Christmas Moritz had a new colic and called three canons to his bedside, among them Doctor Copernicus, because he thought he was dying. Copernicus sent for Dr. Lorenz Wille, the physician in ordinary of the Duke of Prussia, for a consultation; this Doctor Wille happened to be in the neighborhood just then, at Rastenburg, where he had taken part in a theological disputation with some Prussian Anabaptists. Copernicus also consulted by letter the physician in ordinary of the King of Poland, the reliable Solpha. For Solpha, too, was a colleague of Copernicus', a canon at Frauenburg, he collected canonships, as a matter of fact he had six of them; he was a professor at the University of Cracow and was supposed to send preventive remedies to the bishop. King Sigismund the Old in his last hour extended his trembling right hand to the good Solpha and said: "Little Doctor, feel my pulse; we are traveling straight to God!"

Moritz wrote everyone letters full of praise for his wonder-doctor, Copernicus. The astronomer had to spend all of January, 1531, at the bishop's bedside, and February, too. In April, 1532, Bishop Moritz asked his Frauenburg Chapter to lend him Doctor Copernicus for at least one day. Copernicus came again for Moritz had another colic.

In 1533, Moritz got podagra into the bargain.

Finally, in 1534, his health manifestly improved. Then he had a stroke in 1535. With all haste the great Doctor Copernicus was called. He ordered his six horses harnessed, jumped into his carriage and consulted the physicians at Danzig and the physician in ordinary of the King of Poland by letter.

Moritz wrote that he longed for death. Death came. For in 1537 he had a second stroke and epileptic convulsions; the Chapter again sent Doctor Copernicus in all haste. He came too late and could only report the bishop's death.

Moritz was succeeded by Bishop Johannes from Danzig, surnamed Dantiscus, a friend of Copernicus' youth and the enemy of his old age. In April, 1538, Bishop Dantiscus fell ill; he called Doctor Copernicus, and later the custodian of the cathedral of Breslau, Dr. Tresler, a native of Danzig.

Dantiscus had been called to Cracow. He was supposed to celebrate the marriage of the young Sigismund August of Poland and Elisabeth of Habsburg. She was sixteen years of age, her father was heartless, her fiancé perverted, her mother-in-law, Bona, an Italian poison mixer. As though little Elisabeth's guardian angel wanted to protect her from the marriage by force, two bishops suddenly died immediately after they had been summoned to perform the wedding ceremony; first, the jovial Kricki, archbishop of Gniezno, then the good Choinski, Bishop of Cracow. Dantiscus was stronger than the guardian angel, or perhaps craftier. He performed the marriage ceremony and only came back sick. He called upon Copernicus to cure him and kept him as a companion on his tour through Ermland, which he undertook to receive the oath of allegiance.

In 1539, Tiedemann Giese, Copernicus' old friend and the new Bishop of Kulm, fell sick and summoned Doctor Copernicus to the castle of Loebau. He had been stricken by a violent tertian ague during a tour of inspection, and the physicians of Torun and Danzig were helpless. Copernicus ordered his six horses harnessed, got into his carriage and drove to the castle of Loebau. He or God or the sound constitution of the good Giese or the remedies of the Arab philosopher, Avicenna (980-1037 A.D.), the famous doctor of Bukhara, mastered the bad ague by the end of April, and Copernicus drove back to Frauenburg.

In May he went again to the castle of Loebau, with his young guest from Wittenberg, Professor Rheticus, and both remained there throughout the summer, until September. And next year, in 1540, Doctor Copernicus visited his dear patient Giese once more, cured him of his ills, departed and continued sending him advice by letter.

And once Doctor Copernicus was summoned abroad. Duke Albrecht of Prussia sent a messenger to Frauenburg, with letters to the Chapter and to Copernicus; he asked the Chapter to grant a furlough to the astronomer, and he asked Copernicus to come to Koenigsberg, as a consulting physician for the Duke's old friend, Georg von Kuhnheim, head magistrate at Tapiau, who was in danger of death, and whom the Jewish physicians in ordinary of the Duke of Prussia, Doctors Isaac May and Michael Abraham, were unable to cure.

And Copernicus, now almost seventy years old, once more ordered his six jades hitched up, got into his carriage and drove to Koenigsberg in Prussia, the "distant foreign land." He had met Kuhnheim who was the Duke of Prussia's expert on currency questions. This dignitary had attended many sessions of the Prussian diet, had behaved very unreasonably, and had acted exclusively for the Duke's local interests.

Although Copernicus came and stayed on, Kuhnheim failed to recover for a long time, and the Duke again wrote to the Frauenburg Chapter asking for the extension of the furlough of their famous medical colleague, Doctor Nicolaus Copernicus. Until the beginning of May Copernicus remained in Koenigsberg. Back at Frauenburg he even consulted his friend, Solpha, on Kuhnheim's malignant illness and transmitted to the duke "the letter . . . from which Your Princely Highness will hear the advice and opinion of the same doctor . . . If I can add anything better in order to be helpful to Y.P.H.'s head magistrate's recovery I will spare no labor and concern in order to please Your Princely Highness whose orders I diligently await. Dated Frauenburg on June in the year MDXLI.

Your Princely Highness's humble servant
Nicolaus Copernicus

To His Serene Highness Prince by the Grace of God, Albrecht, Margrave of Brandenburg, Duke of Prussians and Wendes, Duke Burgrave of Nuremberg and Prince of Rugen, my Gracious Lord."

Obviously at the age of seventy Copernicus was still physically and mentally vigorous.

He who was the greatest of revolutionaries as philosopher and astronomer, as physician followed the darkest and most reactionary traditions, as is revealed by the prescriptions which he noted in many of his books.

The notorious Gustavus Adolphus, who stole so dreadfully in the name of the Reformation, gave orders during his Polish war to remove the books and archives of Frauenburg and the library of the Jesuit College at Braunsberg to Sweden where they still are today stored in the royal archives at Stockholm or in the university library at Upsala. Among them are some books of Copernicus', signed by him, dedicated to him or marked up by his colleagues, and in addition to astronomical and mathematical works there are a few medical textbooks. They contain a number of scientific entries in Copernicus' hand.

Thus he noted recipes for medicines in "Practical Medicine" *(Philonium pharmaceuticum et chirurgicum,* edition of 1490) by Valescus de Taranta, court physician of Charles VI of France; Valescus died at the beginning of the fifteenth century, his books had new editions in 1680 and 1714 and were much used even in the eighteenth century. Copernicus also made notes in the margin of the table of contents, where were the remedies for the various parts of the body and their diseases; there he wrote: *Oculorum, Aures, Nares, Lingua, Dentes, Guttur, Cor, Stomachus, Epar, Splen, Renes, Genitales, Matrix, Gutta, Febres, Pestilentia, Apostemium* (eyes, ears, nose, tongue, teeth, throat, heart, stomach, liver, spleen, kidneys, genitals, womb, gout, fevers, pestilence, abscess).

In other medical books, too, that he had bought for his uncle Watzelrode's library in the Heilsberg Castle, Copernicus wrote down recipes; in *Chirurgia* by Peter de Largelata, in Silvaticus' (d. in 1340) medical lexicon, in the pharmacology *Hortus Sanitatis* (garden of health), in

Anglicus' *Rosa medicinae* of 1492, in *Practica Guarnerii* of 1496 and in the book compiled by Petrus de Montagana, Venice, 1500.

One recipe was noted twice by Copernicus; it runs as follows (the quantities are omitted):

Recipe: boli armenici
cinamoni
zeduarii
tormentillae radicis
diptamni
sandalorum rubrorum
rasurae eborum
croci
spodii
anthemii acetosi
corticis citri
margaritarum
smaragdi
jacinti rubri
zaphiri
os de corde cervi
carabae
cornu unicorni
coralli rubri
auri
argenti tabularum
zuccaris librae sem. vel quantum sufficit fiat pulvis.

But Copernicus knew simpler recipes, without "silver and gold, red corals and horns of unicorns, the pulp of a deer's heart, sapphires, red hyacinths and emeralds and pearls, the rind of a lemon tree and coal, vinegar and safron, ivory and red sandal wood and roots, cedar wood and cinnamon and Armenian sponge."

Thus he noted the universal remedy of Arnoldus de Villa Nova (d. about 1310), called *pilullae imperiales:* "The imperial pills may be taken at any time, without special preparation, without observing any special diet, mornings and evenings, before or after eating, by the healthy and the sick. They have a curative effect on *every* disease . . ." etc.

Copernicus also wrote down a few practical medical devices: bowel movements should be produced by external rather than internal medicaments; it is necessary to see to it that the movements are regular. He gives directions for vomiting and purgative remedies; three directions for the preparation of hair-removing remedies; one recipe for preserving the teeth, one against toothaches; one concerning urine; one against stones; and a recipe in Greek letters for dyeing the hair. He also wrote down a few directions for paralysis, colics, the plague and other current ills. In medicine he was "a child of his time." Most of his recipes come from Avicenna, the Arab king of physicians in the Middle Ages.

Copernicus, a philosopher against the authority of the Bible, an astronomer against Ptolemy and Aristotle, in medicine bowed to the authority of Avicenna.

36

THE PRODIGIOUS READER

Quis leget haec?
GAIUS LUCILIUS

MOST people live and die without ever having had a single idea of their own. Nothing is rarer than an idea.

As though following the Jesuit maxim: *Si quid fecisti nega*—If you have done anything deny it—Copernicus with passion and anguish sought in the authors of antiquity an excuse for his boldness in having thought something out for himself and for his luck in having found a new idea.

Only ignoramuses are proud of their originality or try to wipe out all traces of their own plagiarisms; either they believe they have invented everything themselves or that they have taken everything from others.

The mathematician Otho, a disciple of Rheticus', said that Copernicus owned only a few books. As is well known one need not read many books, but only the best books. However, in addition to his own books, and the library of the Frauenburg foundation with its 284 volumes of secular authors (*"Medici, historici, astronomi et geometrae, philosophi, grammatici, poetae"*) Copernicus had access to all the libraries of his humanist friends and the church libraries, as well as the library of the Franciscan monastery at Braunsberg.

He was a prodigious reader. More than anything else he sought a confirmation of his own forebodings. He read all the astronomers, mathematicians and philosophers; had they had any ideas about the structure of the universe? What were they?

He had the usual experience of all readers who ask the dead for the fundamental answers that no living author has been able to give them. At first he was disappointed. Then he found what he was looking for. Here and there he found views that resembled his own. In the last analysis, he read in order to get more than was really there in the texts.

A few of his books have been preserved and we know that they were his because he wrote his name on them. There was Euclid's Geometry in the Latin edition of 1482 based upon an Arabic translation; astronomical works by Albohaze and Aratus; the Alfonsine and Regiomontanus Tables; a selection from the rhetorician Jovianus Pontanus; three discussions of Plato's commentators by Cardinal Bessarion; Chrestonius' Greek-Latin dictionary; and Valescus de Tharanta's *Practica.*

In 1539 or later Copernicus received five books as gifts from Rheticus on the occasion of the latter's visit to him: Euclid's Geometry, in a new Latin edition, translated directly from the original Greek text; Regiomontanus' Trigonometry published by Petrejus in Nuremberg in 1533; a work on trigonometry by Petrus Apianus; Vitellio's Optics published by Petrejus in 1535; and the Greek edition of the Almagest published in 1538.

Except for the Almagest and Euclid, Copernicus studied these books received from Rheticus, and abundantly annotated them. The Nuremberg publishers replaced the quotations from Euclid in the manuscript of *De Revolutionibus* which had been made from the edition based upon the Arabic by the corresponding passages from the new edition.

In the volume of Apianus a horoscope of Copernicus is written in. This may be the work of Rheticus.

In Vitellio's Optics Copernicus noted on his bookmark a reflection that reminds us of a passage from Thomas Aquinas: "The brevity of life, the weakness of our senses, our torpid negligence and futile occupations, are responsible for the scantiness of our knowledge. And often what we have known vanishes from our minds after a lapse of time, because of our invincible forgetfulness, that deceitful enemy of science and memory."

A few of his books have been preserved, and we know that they were [illegible] because it was [illegible] on paper. There was [illegible] the Latin edition of [illegible] Arabic translation [illegible] work by [illegible] and [illegible] selection [illegible] Thus [illegible] Latin Renaissance [illegible].

In 1[illegible] or later Constantinople received [illegible] on the [illegible] in a new Latin translation [illegible] from the original Greek text [illegible] produced in Nuremberg in 15[illegible] a work [illegible] Peter Apian; Witelo's Optics published by [illegible] in 15[illegible] the Greek edition of the Almagest published in 15[illegible] except for the Almagest and Euclid [illegible] studied these books [illegible] from [illegible] The Nuremberg publishers replaced the [illegible] in the [illegible] which had been [illegible] from the [illegible] upon the Arabic [illegible] corresponding passages from the new edition.

In the volume of [illegible] horoscope of Copernicus is written in [illegible] way as the work of Rheticus.

In [illegible] Optics Copernicus noted up his [illegible] reflection that [illegible] passage from [illegible] the weakness of our senses, our [illegible] ignorance and the [illegible] of [illegible] knowledge [illegible] from [illegible]

BOOK SIX

THE TRUTH AND THE OBSCURANTS

37

THE NEW PYTHAGORAS

I have travelled 160 miles only in order to see you and speak with you!

PROFESSOR REUSS from Würzburg, to Kant in Königsberg

Pythagore, philosophe grec, dont l'existence est très problematique . . .

NOUVEAU PETIT LAROUSSE ILLUSTRÉ

WHEN Rheticus—a fiery young professor of mathematics at Wittenberg, to whom we owe the publication of the Book of Revolutions—stood before Copernicus, Copernicus was an old man, a new Pythagoras, who like the legendary master of old was determined to reveal the open secrets of the universe only to the initiated.

Sixty-six years old, learned and kindly, Nicolaus Copernicus had been living in one of the low towers within the walls of the cathedral for more than a quarter of a century. The little town of Frauenburg is situated on the Frische Haff, a fresh-water inlet of the Baltic Sea. The cathedral stands on a gently rising hill amidst elms and oaks; with its brick Gothic towers it looks like a citadel of God.

From the gallery of his tower Copernicus saw the ocean at his feet, and the hazy blue, deeper ocean, the beloved heavens, above his head. During clear nights he looked up to the kindly heavens, which, visible to all, first revealed their laws and structure to him.

By day he saw close to him the fresh waves of the inlet, the reddish sands of the narrow neck of land separating the inlet from the sea, and further on the darker waves of the Baltic. He enjoyed a view far over the land, over pastures, gently swaying clouds and trees, birches or firs. And by night he had the stars, always the stars . . .

At the foot of the cathedral he saw the little town of Frauenburg; it was so called after the Virgin. Copernicus occasionally baptized it Gynopolis, the city of women—a tiny town on a little river, the Baude.

Like all great revolutionaries Copernicus had endless patience as well as peculiar scruples. Revolutionaries, these truly fearless people, are afraid only of their own shadows; they recognize only their own conscience, and fear only the consequences of their own acts.

The manuscript of the Revolutions had been lying there—not for nine years, in accordance with Horace's rule, but perhaps now four times nine years. But he did not intend to publish it, even though now and then one of his friends urged him to do so. Was he really ready? Was the time ripe?

Copernicus had the greatest patience imaginable, the patience to wait beyond his own life and century.

At first he may have thought that everything was propitious for him. The fifteenth century that gave him birth and nurtured him until his twenty-eighth year seemed to have prepared everything for his greatness. The new century, the sixteenth, made as though especially for him, and arisen with him, seemed ready to unfold in accordance with the tremendous idea and intuition of its unknown leader, Copernicus.

Year after year, decade after decade, he had been waiting for the dreaming world finally to awaken to his thesis which heralded the greatest of all revolutions. Meanwhile he had calmly studied and thought, observed and computed, and in secrecy cautiously communicated the principles and draft of his new theory of the universe to a few chosen friends and scholars.

Amid the tenebrous conspiracy of inertia, habit, routine and ignorance, while engaged in his more exact observations and most recent computations he suddenly became aware that the century was moving backward.

The new freedom had only begun; independent living and sovereign thinking had just become fashionable. And now came the fanatical counter-revolution. The counter-reformers *and* Reformers turned into gaolers. Reason, that poor laughing jester, was again put into a great strait-jacket, and shook the little bells of her new fool's cap with desperate gaiety.

The new humanistic science; the new arts of the Rennaissance: music and painting, architecture and sculpture; the dream of freedom of the Italian cities, the French nobility, the conquistadores of America, the burghers of Spain, the German peasants; the tolerance of the Catholic Church; the Maecenas-like patience of the emperors; the stormy idealism of the reformers—all that seemed gone.

Copernicus saw his opportunity slipping, his enemies multiplying, the great powers growing hostile . . .

However tragic revolutions are, their beginnings usually appear grotesque. With the first heralds of Copernicus' distant fame, the clown, too, came on the stage, in the shape of the Dutch rector at Elbing, the fateful prophet of the imminent dark cloud that was to sweep over Europe: Wilhelm Gnapheus, the author of burlesques.

Gnapheus came from Holland and was known in Europe as a humanist. Progressives are often the first swallows of reaction; they think they can save their own skins if they auction off their ideals and are ready to sell their own friends to the enemy; but usually they only succeed in getting themselves skinned first of all.

Born in that year of the birth of freedom, when Columbus discovered America, this Wilhelm Gnapheus, since the age of thirty had been a continuous victim of religious intolerance. The Inquisition threw him into jail at Delft. He got out with difficulty—in Brussels people of his ilk were being burned at the stake. In the Hague he was interned for two years. No sooner released, than he was imprisoned in a monastery for three months and given only bread and beer for food. When the inquisitors began to set their little fires in Holland, too, he chose to flee, and for the space of a year hid in the countryside. Finally he sneaked across the border, travelled in Germany for some time, settled at Elbing, and found a "second homeland" there; but soon after he had written his burlesques and become rector of the *gymnasium,* he was again persecuted and driven out, always on account of the same little differences concerning the correct manner of communing with God.

This time he was persecuted by Johannes of Danzig, who called himself Dantiscus, the severe Bishop of Ermland. In 1541, fleeing his blows, Gnapheus came to Koenigsberg, whence he was again driven out by very severe Lutherans. Finally, still persecuted, still in exile, he came to East Friesland, close to his Dutch homeland, and died there, his eyes turned toward his native country. The world had grown too strict for this ill-advised satirist.

What irony! Had this pedantic humanist escaped from the dungeons of religious orthodoxy in order to ridicule the man who was beginning to burst asunder the greatest dungeon of all, the earth-seized house of error and pious superstition, with his wonderful numbers and words and his original idea?

Was it the place of the humanist Gnapheus to give the obscurantists weapons against the humanist Copernicus who had won the greatest victory over obscurantism?

Poor burlesque writer, poor Gnapheus, foolish schoolmaster, who believed that the voice of common sense was speaking through him and who in its name arose against Copernicus!

But after the fool came the hypocrite. On the heels of the satirist followed the persecutor.

38

BISHOP DANTISCUS

Le pauvre homme!
MOLIÈRE, Tartufe

Tantaene animis caelestibus irae!
VIRGIL, Aeneid

THE Bishop of Ermland was new. He displayed equal zeal in persecuting Gnapheus, the writer of burlesques, and his target, Copernicus.

This Polish bishop was a typical product of the sixteenth century. In his character holiness was mixed with lasciviousness; this zealous bishop had a girl in every province. He had a dozen talents but they did not go well with one another.

Johannes Flachsbinder was born in 1485, the son of a Danzig beer brewer. A soldier at the early age of seventeen, he fought against the Turks and Tartars. A veteran at eighteen, he returned to Cracow where he attended the high school and the university. He entered the service of King Alexander. Soon he set out again, this time without weapons, and went to Rome and Hellas, the Holy Land and Arabia. His gods lived everywhere; after all he was a disciple of the humanists, and a Latin poet.

Upon his return he was sponsored at court by the learned vice-Chancellor, a bishop, and found favor with the mighty; he was adroit in handling people and in business, conversant with the classics, familiar with Prussian affairs, and a Polish patriot!

The young secretary accompanied his king to Vienna, and became Polish ambassador to the Emperor, who made him poet-laureate. In the end this son of the people became a ruling prince: the Bishop of Ermland.

A worldly-minded person in his youth, an obscurantist in his old age, he was always witty. An indefatigable lover of Tyrolian and Spanish girls, he became the leader of the counter-Reformation in Poland, together with his favorite and successor Hosius.

He was a licentious poet singing of wine and women in Latin verses. In Innsbruck he loved Grinaea: in Toledo, Ysope de Galda.

"My strength is already ebbing," he confesses in his charming elegy on the Tyrolian girl, "my hair at the temples is already graying."

Half a generation later a friend of his youth, with whom he had once vied as a poet over the wine table, asked him for a copy of his love-complaint famous throughout Europe. The bishop answered that he would gladly send him, along with the copy of his elegy, his once so ardently beloved Tyrolian girl as a gift—if only he still had her!

As for the Toledo girl, he begot a child by her, who, in honor of her priestly father, was named Joanna Dantisca de Curiis. The bishop sent her a regular allowance to Spain through the Welsers and Fuggers, the Augsburg world bankers; from Spain, the emperor's ambassador sent the bishop a portrait of this daughter.

Johannes de Weze, Archbishop of Lund, wrote his colleague, Johannes Dantiscus, Bishop of Kulm: "The other day, on the Sabbath, I visited that most chaste nymph, your Ysope. I kissed her little hands, in accordance with the Spanish custom, and her little feet, in accordance with the Roman custom, and so on; and I kissed not only the little hands of the nymph and your daughter, Dantisca, but also the mouths of both of them, and we revelled abundantly in Toledan wine, and so on . . ."

Different at each period of his life, Dantiscus at each stage of his career assumed a different name. The name he was born with, Flachsbinder, was grecized by the young poet into Linodesmos; the courtier, ennobled by the emperor, called himself de Curiis—of the court. Later, to honor his native city, he called himself Dantiscus, the gentleman from Danzig.

It was natural for him to transform himself from time to time; thus he kept pace with the times. When the century was lascivious, Dantiscus was lascivious; when it was austere, he was austere, too.

The high clergy in Poland was at that time quite mundane. The church dignitaries enriched themselves at the expense of the king and their serfs. In palaces built for them by Italian architects they lived for pleasure and practised politics. They hunted prebends, as one hunts hares. Many came from the schools of the humanists; there were cynics and zealots—among them Dantiscus was both a cynic and a zealot.

What manner of men were his colleagues? The Bishop of Kujawia said: "I have marked out some from among the Prussian nobility; if they do not convert themselves, I will soon deal with them and bring them to God or the stake!"

Bishop (later Archbishop) Krzycki wrote to Bishop Tomicki: "I hear that you are ill, and I regret it. I ordered all my little priests *(sacricolas)* to ply Saint Apollonia with little prayers and sacrifices for your dear health. And I have threatened the saint that I would go over to Luther's sect if she did not do her duty."

In other letters he continuously alludes to lascivious matters. He wrote a facetious poem against the Bishop of Poznan, whose jealous housekeeper locked the door so that the bishop had to drop his paramour through the window into a net. *(Casus ridiculus quidam. De meretricula demissa in reti per fenestram etc. Acta Tomiciana VIII. No. 80.)*

For seventeen years Dantiscus travelled over Europe as Polish ambassador, accompanying the emperors from one court to another, and even to the battlefield. Although he had often worked against the emperors in the interests of Poland, he also served them. Emperor Maximilian sent him as a peace negotiator to Venice, Emperor Charles to Paris. Dantiscus allied the pope and the emperor against the Turks. To the pope and the emperor he justified first Poland's war against the Teutonic knights, then her peace with them.

One of the famous men of his century he had his hand in many deals. All Europe read his verses. He sang the "Difference between virtue and honor"; King Sigismund's bridal bed; and other battlefields. He sang the orgies of his youth:

> I went into the lairs of the prettiest cocottes
> In drunken passion.
> To love them all, I went always forward
> In drunken courage . . .

In passing he worked his way up in the church. For the space of twenty years he gathered prebends and dignities, the Golombie parish near Cracow, a canonship at Frauenburg, the highest parochial post at Danzig, the bishopric of Kulm, finally that of Ermland—all of these gifts from the King of Poland, all of them sinecures.

In his good moments, in Spain or Belgium he wrote pious little songs; because the poor people in Danzig refused to continue paying high taxes, he called Danzig the new Sodom and as supreme vicar ordered his brother to collect the money-offerings without delay.

Luther's teaching came to Prussia and Poland at the time of the peasant wars. At the imperial diet of 1519 the Polish nobility carried their point: tax collectors were punished by flogging or death if they demanded imposts from the nobles. And even peasants exempt from statute-labor had to work for the gentlemen of the nobility one day a week without pay. Peasants who stayed for three days in the city without practising a trade or finding employment were to be put in chains and dragged away to do compulsory labor.

The high nobility and clergy didn't care for God. The lower nobility demanded the confiscation of all the church estates. The craftsmen and poor burghers heard about Luther and thought that his God brought freedom from taxation or a better distribution of property. The poor people still remembered Jesus and that naturally the Son of God was a social revolutionary!

At Danzig unrest began to spread among the poor. They alone had to pay all the taxes. The people hated the burgomaster who, instead of taxing the rich, enriched them. The people cried: "Your accounts! We want to see your accounts!"

For the taxes of the poor grew increasingly heavy, and the city treasury increasingly poor. "The accounts!" cried the poor.

The burgomaster chose to flee. The people demanded a share in the government, just taxation, abolition of the monks' celibacy, closing of the monasteries, the end of the inquisition, the return to the doctrine of Christ, justice, the abolition of fast days, mass, church songs, and freedom: free hunting, free fishing, especially of sturgeon, free preaching, especially of the original words of Christ, and freedom for all to fish for amber in all the city waters and grounds . . .

The poor people wanted to realize Christianity purely and simply! This was going too far!

Runaway monks and unlearned people began to preach. "The preachers assumed the roles of councillors and judges, secular and the ecclesiastic," as Bernt Stegman wrote in his chronicle of the uprising of 1525.

Then the Bishop of Kujawia came to Danzig in the name of the King of Poland and threw a Protestant preacher into jail; but the people released him and drove out the bishop. And the Council issued an edict forbidding the monks not only to preach but even to beg! Then it came to civil war.

The Council set up the oldest pieces of artillery on the market place. The poor people of the suburbs broke the gates of the inner city. Then the Council yielded. But it was deposed by the blacksmith Peter König and his friends, who ruled in Danzig and closed all the monasteries except one, and imposed taxes on the wealthy. This could not go on.

The monastery of the black monks became a hospital, that of the gray ones, a Greek school. In the churches, preachers of the Gospels took the place of the destroyed images of the saints. A priest was sent with letters to Wittenberg; the blacksmith and a few of his friends were sent to Cracow, as a deputation to the king.

The blacksmith and his friends thought they would convince the king by means of quotations from the Bible. Perhaps, they thought, the king had never read the Sermon on the Mount. Political revolutions, the blacksmith said, are simply the consequences of the words of Christ.

The same things that took place in Danzig took place in Torun, Ermland, Elbing. King Sigismund wrote Duke Albrecht of Prussia asking him to return to the poor Polish nobles their peasants who had fled to Prussia *(Kmetones et servi illiberi);* these peasants, he explained, were not interested in their religion, but only in their freedom! And after all, the Duke of Prussia, too, was against the freedom of the poor.

At that time only Cricius (the jovial Archbishop Krzycki) and Tiedemann Giese wrote against the Lutherans in Poland.

The inquisition politely invited the heretic gentlemen to attend pyrotechnical spectacles. The King of Poland and his bishops issued edict after edict. In 1520 an edict of Torun prohibited the writings of friar Martin Luther, under penalty of confiscation of all goods and banishment.

Later edicts enjoined upon the people to break off all communications with Lutheran Silesia, to burn every Protestant preacher alive—and also every reader of Protestant writings—furthermore to set up a special tribunal of the inquisition, which at the bishop's request would be entitled to search every private home for forbidden books, and to establish a censorship. No printer was allowed to publish anything without the imprimatur of the Rector of the University of Cracow. A friend of Dantiscus' wrote him: "In our city no layman has the right to open his mouth in matters of faith; he must neither praise nor censure."

Meanwhile, the King of Poland came to Danzig with a strong force, held church celebrations and organized cross-examinations with torture, reinstated the old councillors, demanded new and heavier taxes, beheaded six and then another six or seven rebels, and finally the blacksmith who was so conversant with the Bible.

Many Protestant preachers and followers of Christ went into exile. Before his departure the king issued edicts: Lutheranism was to be exterminated; the royal burgrave was to have precedence over the council; only the freeborn were to have the right to become citizens—this stopped the influx of peasants. Popular assemblies were forbidden, as well as any demands to check the accounts of the city treasury.

A new statute in Prussia strictly separated the tribunal for nobles from the tribunals for the burghers. For the peasants, there were no tribunals at all. Their rights could be represented in court only by their owners.

By that time Dantiscus returned home. He was tired of his eternal wanderings, asked for a leave of absence and went to Löbau Castle, the residence of the Bishops of Kulm; soon afterwards he became Bishop of Ermland and the superior of the Ermland canon, Copernicus.

This amusing child of his epoch, a solid drinker and lover in seven lands, the charming author of piquant little songs, a hard-boiled diplomat and prebend-hunter, loose or strict according to the needs of the times, this Dantiscus was no sooner made Bishop of Ermland than he plagued the grand old man, the sixty-six-year-old Copernicus, on account of his young housekeeper. He was perhaps the cause of Copernicus' failure to complete his immortal work. Thus he was guilty of a really dreadful crime, a crime against genius.

Anna Schillings, a youngish person, perhaps a distant relative of the old canon, kept house for him. Bishop Dantiscus reproached him with having unbecoming feelings for or relations with this lady.

Thus a Dantiscus set himself up as a moral judge over the most pious, most innocent man of his time.

Poor obscurantist! Forgotten are your sweet elegies; today who knows the adventurous son of a Danzig beer brewer, the Knight of the Empire, the poet crowned by an emperor, the Spanish hidalgo, the Bishop of Kulm and Ermland, the ambassador of Poland, the friend of emperors and kings, the peace negotiator with France and Venice, the correspondent of a hundred celebrities? Who still knows Dantiscus? He seemed so great in his day, did Johnnie Flachsbinder of Danzig! Did he not look in contempt at the gray Copernicus whom he had met in his youth? Once Copernicus had been the respected nephew of the important Ermland bishop, Lukas Watzelrode. Now he was old and thrice suspect, what with his peculiar theories of the heavens, his Lutheran friends and visitors and his all-too-young and all-too-pretty housekeeper, Anna Schillings.

Strange, indeed, are the ways of fame! Today Dantiscus is only known as the man who persecuted Copernicus.

Dantiscus even survived Copernicus; he had erased him from the world of the living, he considered him eternally dead, and forgotten.

O immoral judge of others' morals, you Dantiscus, with your dissolute boon-companions who seem to have stepped out from the Italian or Spanish comedies—what is worthy of memory in all your exploits?

Dantiscus and Copernicus—what contemporaries! They came from the same corner of the world. They belonged to the same church. They laughed together as boys.

Did Dantiscus try to compensate for the sins of his youth by his later zeal? Or did he see the trend of the times, the new tendencies of Rome, and was he willing, in order to become an archbishop and cardinal, to make every sacrifice, that is, to sacrifice any other man? Or had he a dozen other even flimsier motives?

Compared to his, Copernicus' life was gentle and pious; only in spirit was he audacious. In spirit he was one of the greatest destroyers, a nihilist. To a zealot or Grand Inquisitor could this most pious man of the sixteenth century appear as anything but the devil himself? As Anti-christ?

Copernicus and Dantiscus—antipodes in their lives and spirit—were they not bound to clash with each other? Was it really only the wickedness of Dantiscus that aroused him against Copernicus or was it the deepest instinct of the son of his era against the austere father of the new era?

Copernicus was the inconspicuous man who studies and thinks and calmly seeks the truth rather than money, honors, pleasure or his own advantage, and for its sake goes further than he ever dreamed of going, and thus, the most gentle of men inexorably evolves, in the realm of the spirit, into a revolutionary, a radical as Christ before him. With the truth in his hands he no longer wavers. Without conceit he opposes his whole century, his time, the church, state, science, and the universities, he alone against mankind, even against religion and against God! The quiet, remote canon became the creator of a new world.

And as the superior of this man we have the jovial, sensual, pleasure-seeking, straying, wavering, cynical Dantiscus! Gifted in everything, he believed in nothing. Or when he believed, his belief was always in accord with his time, with his own advantage, with the powers that be. Every five or ten years he was different, had a new name, a new profession, a new business, a new tendency. Thus he followed every turn of his time, the slave of his century, the witty opportunist, the son of the people and idol of his contemporaries, a learned wise man according to Melanchthon, or in the words of the Nuremberg humanist and Lutheran, Eobanus Hessus: "Humanity itself."

In the conflict between the worldling and the philosopher, the opportunist and the man of character, of course the opportunist was victorious. And, of course, the philosopher was right in the end.

Just when the sixty-six-year-old prophet seemed defeated, weary, worn out and determined to keep silent, there came the first disciple, and everything changed.

39

LUTHER AND MELANCHTHON

He came and his name was Martin Luther.
HENDRIK WILLEM VAN LOON, The Story of Mankind.

THE first disciple set out to investigate the old man. His real name was Georg Joachim von Lauchen, and he was born at Feldkirch in Vorarlberg in 1514. He called himself the man of Rhaetia or Rheticus, in accordance with the custom of the learned who gave themselves a name in their youth by latinizing their father's names. Every educated man at that time spoke Latin: the pharmacist and God; no physician healed, no judge sentenced, no priest blessed, no alchemist cheated in any other language.

Even as a child Rheticus accomplished his Italian voyage (apparently with good results) and a Swiss voyage. At first he studied at Zurich; at Basel he met the miracle worker, Paracelsus; at the age of eighteen he went to Saxony and won the heart of a great man.

Philip Melanchthon, the great-nephew of Reuchlin and the teacher of the Germans, was at the age of twenty-one, precocious in a precocious century, a famous expert on classical antiquity and the first professor of Greek at the University of Wittenberg. Upon his advice Rheticus studied mathematics and at the age of twenty-two was professor at Wittenberg, thanks to Melanchthon, who introduced him at his inaugural lecture and presented him to the notables, especially to Dr. Luther, a professor of theology, and the burgomaster, who painted portraits of all his friends and of himself, managed a pharmacy and a bookshop and was a jovial fat man, Lukas Cranach.

For the space of two years Professor Rheticus lived side by side with the eccentric reformers of Germany, the meticulous theologian and the daring philologist.

These two dangerous and prodigious men, Luther and Melanchthon, were friends for twenty-five years, yet eternally as far apart as the antipodes. Their pamphlets and translations resulted in splitting Germany, in reforming the Roman Church and in creating the Janus-faced German Reformation, with its spiritual liberation and political strangulation.

What a contrast between the reformer of the Germans and their teacher!

Like all the other great revolutionaries they affected the whole European continent, all the Christian countries.

Jacques Maritain once amused himself by reproducing all the portraits of Luther, from 1520 until shortly before his death, in order to prove how idealistic the young thin Luther looked—when he was still a Catholic! —and how more and more sensual and vulgar and in the end repulsive the aging fat reformer looked—because he grew increasingly Lutheran! But actually Maritain was denouncing not Protestantism, but old age or Mrs. Luther's cuisine.

Luther is the grandiose creator of the German language, who hurled his inkpot at the devil! He is the marvelously fervent poet who with unsurpassed obscenity spoke to his table companions about his wife and the Holy Father. He is the scholastic mystic, who began as a wizened bone and ended up as a pot-belly, "the soft flesh of Wittenberg." The revolutionary who throttled the revolution that had fed him and made him great in the blood of his brothers, the poor peasants! He damned the dissoluteness of Rome and condoned the bigamy of the sensuous Philip of Hesse. He called the Pope the devil's son, and worse! Because he was a German nationalist and full of xenophobia he attempted to break Rome's influence in Germany. But he made every native princeling the lord of his Christian subjects' faith and conscience, and all in the name of the freedom of conscience necessary to a Christian. He fought the Catholic obscurantists, but at the same time hindered the Renaissance, that wellspring of European civilization. He rejected the indulgences and invented literal faith. Martin Luther was as stubborn as a bull, as cranky as a zealot, as avid for pleasure as a lansquenet, as learned as a three-score philologist, as superstitious as his own grandmother, the most perspicacious among the deluded, a know-better, do-better, world reformer, rebel and pragmatist, a poet and reformer, a real country doctor.

Compared to him how delicate seems the almost feminine humanist, Philip Melanchthon, who wrote in Latin and taught Greek, the man of the word, equally captivating as a popular orator and in the language of the learned. A thinker by nature and a cautious scholar, he was averse to political struggles. He was so learned that in 1519 Luther wrote, "This little Greek surpasses me even in theology!" He was so fascinating that ten years later Luther said he was not good enough to loosen Melanchthon's shoestrings; and for a time Luther considered himself to be only Melanchthon's prophet and that it was his function to pave the way for this master. Luther, who after all really knew Melanchthon, considered him a greater man than himself.

After Luther's death, this Melanchthon, the author of the Augsburg Confessions of 1530, became the leader of German Protestantism. As early as 1526, Albrecht Dürer, the friend of the Wittenbergers, wrote under his portrait: "Dürer who could paint Philip's living face and mind, but not his learned hands."

On this portrait, the incomparable Philip Melanchthon, with his bold aquiline nose, his soft lips, wild locks, poetic beard and pensive melancholy eyes resembles the young Schiller in an open shirt.

But Hans Holbein's drawing shows him as smoothly shaven, with sparse locks and thin ironic lips. He looks out calmly at a confused world. The pious philosopher strives to assert his reason and his measure in Germany; he is a tolerant reformer, the teacher of Germany, a sage full of errors, a limited humanistic man-of-letters!

The young professor Rheticus was quite equal in stubbornness to his two patrons. In the field where he was a master, that is, in mathematics and astronomy, he did not follow them. In the midst of zealots he preserved a free mind. Luther and Melanchthon summarily called Copernicus a fool. But Rheticus and his twenty-four-year-old colleague Reinhold, the other Wittenberg professor of astronomy, who were both bound by their office to teach the Ptolemaic system to their pupils, had some vague information about the revolutionary astronomical theory of Nicolaus Copernicus, a canon and astronomer from Torun, and had a burning desire to learn more of it, and even to see the author and investigate his theory.

Also Johannes Schoner, the old friend of Melanchthon who was known for his fondness for banter, and whom Rheticus, equipped with letters of recommendation from Melanchthon, looked up at Nuremberg in the fall of 1538 (as he did later Apian at Ingolstadt), knew of Rheticus' plan for an educational trip to Poland, approved of it, and asked him to report on it as soon as possible. It seems that Melanchthon did not oppose the trip of his protégé: Rheticus' chair despite his lengthy absence was not given to another professor, and after his return from Prussia he resumed his lectures on arithmetic and geometry.

In April, 1539, Rheticus set out from his native town of Feldkirch. He travelled via Wittenberg.

In May the nightingales are already singing in the woods of Germany and Poland. There are flowers everywhere. The laughing blue sky, the joyful green earth, the gusts of wind, the whole match-making magic of spring delights the traveller. At this season old men set out to ride against the windmills of reason and youngsters set out to release the enchanted world.

Thus Rheticus set out for distant Poland.

He defied all the hazards of the trip, the women of the town and the cutpurses, only in order to see the old man in his tower near the Baltic Sea.

This old man had a new theory of the structure of the universe. Rumors about his half-hidden, sensational discoveries had reached as far as Wittenberg, Nuremberg, Cracow and Rome. Perhaps this new system was simply ridiculous and heretical. But if it were the truth demonstrated by irrefutable syllogisms, computations and tables; if it were the truth expressed for the first time in thousands of years, it meant a revolution. It meant the overthrow of science and religion. Such were the implications of the most audacious thesis against the two basic books of mankind of that day, against the Bible and Aristotle. It meant the open overthrow of the heavens on earth!

If the thesis were correct. . . .

In the presentiment of his own genius, with the insolence of youth, and the privilege of reason Rheticus set out ready to damn or worship.

Driven by the unconquerable curiosity of a man of spirit, this first disciple (a fiery youth: a professor of mathematics!) came at the very last moment so to speak!

He came for a short time and stayed for years.

He came uninvited, unexpected, unknown, without letters of introduction—but were it not for him the Book of Revolutions might not have been published; the fateful manuscript might have been forgotten in the tumult of the religious wars. (And so there would have been no Copernican system—and our earth would have remained motionless, on Ptolemy's lap?)

As early as the middle of May Rheticus wrote to Nuremberg, to the good Schoner, teacher of mathematics at the very famous humanistic *gymnasium* in Nuremberg, of which Melanchthon was the founder, of which Hegel was the rector, and where I was once a pupil.

I am already in Poznan, he wrote. Soon I will be in Frauenburg and report in detail to my venerable teacher Schoner what I think of the man and his ideas.

He arrived in the middle of July. This was an event in that quiet provincial corner: a stranger! A scholar! A Lutheran! A professor from Wittenberg who had personally made the long trip to look up a canon from around here, the old man, Copernicus, because this old man maintains that the earth . . . —just think of it: the immense earth on which all of us live, including all of Frauenburg, and the cathedral and the Baltic Sea and the clouds in the sky—turns in fabulous haste around the allegedly fixed sun, which every day visibly moves in the sky, rises in the morning in the east, and sinks in the evening in the west!

Dantiscus had just forbidden the reading of Lutheran writings under heavy penalties. And here was a Lutheran come to town!

The sensation must have been so great that Copernicus was perhaps relieved to seize the first opportunity in order to go abroad with the young man, to his friend Giese at Lobau in the bishopric of Kulm. And there they remained from July until September. But there too the persecutor tracked him down!

40

THE OBSCURANTS

How often my heart broke down in fear and murmured to me: "Do you want to be wiser than all the others? Are then the innumerable others in error? Have they been always wrong for so many centuries? Suppose you err and through your error drag down so many people to eternal doom?

LUTHER at Wartburg, when he lived under the name of Junker Jörg and the devil approached him in the shape of a big black dog

. . . for he /the ruler/ beareth not the sword in vain.

ROMANS, XIII.4

COPERNICUS received the young stranger like a son.

For the arch-Protestant Rheticus, the favorite of Luther and Melanchthon, it was just as dangerous to spend years in the arch-Catholic bishopric, as it was dangerous for Copernicus and Giese to be the hosts of the Protestant.

The great anathema of the Church lay upon Wittenberg. In Poland people were warned against studying at this university. In 1534, King Sigismund suspended from office all those who had studied at Wittenberg.

In March, 1539, a few months before Rheticus' arrival Dantiscus had issued his sharp "Mandate against Heresy."

In 1540 the provisions of this mandate were made more severe. "Under the penalty of losing head and property, of proscription or banishment from all royal lands, no one shall possess, read or listen to the reading of Lutheran or similarly poisonous books, and all shall burn such books, booklets, songs or whatever else has come from the poisonous places in the presence of the authorities," etc. Dantiscus, the poet, beheaded the readers of other authors.

Vicar Feierabend from Elbing denied the presence of Christ at the holy communion. Dantiscus demanded that he be questioned. Feierabend escaped. Dantiscus was enraged: "This creature should have been arrested, put in chains!"

Dantiscus conveyed "fatherly admonitions" to Gnapheus; they had once sent each other their books with touching dedications. Now the writer of burlesques, scared to death, took to his heels, as though already smelling his own burning flesh.

Dantiscus denounced his native city of Danzig as a nest of heresy to the King of Poland.

Dantiscus persecuted Copernicus' friends, particularly the Frauenburg canon Alexander Sculteti, a historian and geographer.

Dantiscus, born Flachsbinder, accused Sculteti of trading in flax (a trader!), furthermore of thinking unbecoming thoughts (an atheist!) and committing impermissible acts, to wit, the breach of celibacy (a libertine!); on top of all this he called Sculteti a partisan of Zwingli and a heretic and ordered him to be removed from the Chapter, and through Hosius, to be put under the ban in Poland; he ordered that Sculteti's landed property be confiscated, and in the summer of 1541 wrote to the Danzig council ordering that Sculteti's wife and children also be persecuted!

For Sculteti had protested against the granting of a Frauenburg canonship to a friend of Dantiscus', Stanislaus Hosius.

Hosius, the king's private secretary at Cracow, was given the canonship. After Dantiscus' death he became his successor and the leader of the Polish counter-Reformation. His motto was: *Aut papista aut satanista:* either popish or devilish! He was called the "hammer of the heretics" and "the death of Luther." Queen Bona said: "This Hosius combines the simplicity of the dove with the cunning of the snake." He brought the Jesuits to Prussia; he congratulated the Holy Father on the occasion of St. Bartholomew's massacre; he wished Poland might have many such nights of blood.

Sculteti fled to Rome. Dantiscus prosecuted him before the Curia. The Holy Father acquitted Sculteti.

At that time, another of Dantiscus' friends, Emperor Charles V, suggested his candidacy to the College of Cardinals. Did the prospect of the red hat sharpen his zeal against all the clergymen who had ever broken the vow of celibacy?

Dantiscus summoned all the canons of his diocese to break off their relations and correspondence with their outlawed colleague, even before his Roman trial had been held.

Copernicus declared he would not obey, and that "he respected Sculteti more than he did many others."

In the summer of 1539, while Copernicus and Rheticus were at Lobau, a letter from Dantiscus came to Giese: "I was informed that Dr. Nic. Copernicus came to visit you, of whom you know that I love him as my own brother. He lives in close friendship with Sculteti. This is bad. Warn him that such connections and friendships harm him; but do not tell him that the warning came from me. You must surely know that Sculteti took a wife and is suspected of atheism."

Canon Alexander Sculteti actually did live with a woman and had a son, just like Bishop Lukas Watzelrode, like Bishop Dantiscus, like many popes.

Many clergymen then lived in sin. This was sometimes permitted, sometimes tolerated by their bishops.

Copernicus with "polite indignation" indirectly informed Dantiscus that in no respect did he want to hurt His Reverence's feelings, but rather to live in conformity with his enlightened will.

But Sculteti left Prussia.

Dantiscus sent spies to watch Copernicus. The moral salvation of the old man was in question. Anna Schillings was in question.

Anna seemed to the bishop too young to be the housekeeper of an old canon.

Dantiscus had no sooner become Bishop of Ermland than he asked Copernicus to dismiss Anna.

Copernicus did not comply. Dantiscus renewed his demand; he wrote Canon Reich concerning this matter. Copernicus and Reich answered on the same day (December 2, 1538). Reich wrote that he approved of the bishop's legitimate request and fatherly admonition which the other (Copernicus) would surely take to heart, so he did not need admonition from him (Reich); he feared that Copernicus would blush with shame if he learned that he, Reich, knew about it, and he enclosed his (Copernicus') letter.

This enclosed letter of Copernicus, "ex Gynopoli," from the city of women, ran as follows:

"Highly Reverend etc. etc.

"The admonition of Your Reverence is fatherly enough, and more than fatherly, as I admit; and I read its contents with all my heart. I have by no means forgotten your previous remonstrance which Your Reverence at first had sent out in general terms: I wanted to do what I was ordered; and although it was not easy to find a closely related and honest person,

I nevertheless resolved to put an end to the thing at fasting time. In order that Your Reverence will not imagine that I am looking for pretexts for postponement, I have limited the term to one month; verily it could not be shorter as Your Reverence yourself can readily understand. For I wish to the measure of my strength to prevent that I become an offense to good morals, and even less so to Your Reverence, who deserves that he be revered, respected and above all beloved by me; to which I devote myself with all my talents.

Your Reverence's
most obedient
Nicolaus Copernicus."

Finally, on January 11, 1539, Copernicus reported that the thing was done.

"Highly Reverend, Most Gracious, etc. etc.

"I have already done what I had neither power nor right to omit doing, and whereby I hope the admonitions of Your Reverence will be satisfied. As for what you wish to know about how long was the life of Lukas Watzelrode, of happy memory, the predecessor of Your Reverence, and my uncle: he lived sixty-four years, five months; he was bishop for twenty-three years; he died on the day before the last of March anno Christi 1522. With him was extinguished the family whose insignia are still to be seen on old respectable buildings and many works in Torun. I recommend my obedience to Your Reverence.

Your Reverence's most obedient
Nicolaus Copernicus."

But Dantiscus was not satisfied yet.

Plotowski, the provost of the Chapter, of which he had been a member since 1520, wrote to Bishop Dantiscus on March 23, 1539: "As for the Frauenburg females, Alexander's (Sculteti) hid for a few days at home. She will go away with her son. Alexander returned from Lobau with a joyful mien; I do not know what news he brought. He is staying at the curia with Niederhoff and the housekeeper *(focaria)* who resembles a beer waitress, befouled with all evil. Dr. Nicolaus' (Copernicus) woman must have sent her belongings in advance to Danzig, but she herself remains at Frauenburg. . . ."

Although Giese in his next letter warned Dantiscus against scandalmongers, Dantiscus did not relax. Anna had to be removed from Frauenburg. When Dantiscus heard that even after her dismissal Copernicus continued to meet her, he again wrote Giese, whom Copernicus was visiting. Copernicus was perhaps discussing his book and his heavens with Giese and Rheticus, and with a view to bishops like Dantiscus and private secretaries like Hosius, pointed repeatedly to the wise example of the hypothetical Pythagoras.

And Rheticus reminded them perhaps of the daring of his Lutheran friends who did not lose their nerve "even if the world were full of devils."

And perhaps Giese or the young Rheticus explained to the smiling Copernicus: "What can the world do to you?"

And then perhaps came the letter of Bishop Dantiscus, with Copernicus' superior complaining about his girl or his friend or his stubbornness. Once again, it seemed, Copernicus had been seen with this Anna Schillings at a third place. . . .

On September 12, 1539, Giese answered Bishop Dantiscus: ". . . With Dr. Nicolaus, in accordance with Your Reverence's desire, I have spoken seriously and put before his eyes the thing itself, as it is. He seemed no little dismayed over the fact that ill-intentioned people had again accused him of secret rendezvous, for he complied with Your Reverence's wishes without hesitation. He denies having seen again that person after he had dismissed her, except once on the market place at Königsberg where she briefly spoke to him. At any rate I have realized that he is not so much affected by this passion as many believe. This is also vouched for by his advanced age, his never-interrupted studies, and his virtue and respectability. Nevertheless I have admonished him to avoid even the appearance of wrong, and I think he will act accordingly. On the other hand I think that it might be fair if Your Reverence did not put too much faith in the scandalmonger considering that deserving men are often the target of envy and malice which do not even shrink to express suspicions against Your Reverence."

The following day Canon Achatius von der Trenck wrote Bishop Dantiscus that Alexander Sculteti's housekeeper had not been seen since her departure from Frauenburg; he added: "When his housekeeper was mentioned to Dr. Nicolaus whom I met at Löbau, he declared that he would never receive her in his home and do anything in that matter. I know that Your Reverence admonished him for behaving in this manner; as I hope not in vain. His age and wisdom will easily keep the good man away from such things." (Cf. L. A. Birkenmajer, Mikolai Kopernik, Cracow, 1900, and Prowe.)

Amid such base and ill-timed persecutions during the last years of his life, how could Copernicus find strength and leisure to complete his draft and revise it again? How painfully he must have been affected by all these remonstrances, in the face of Giese and Trenck, let alone young Rheticus!

And was Copernicus' relation to Anna punishable from the strictly ecclesiastical point of view? According to ordinary secular and ecclesiastical law any relation between a man and a woman began with contacts of the flesh and wherever materially possible involved sexual intercourse. Did Copernicus' relation fall under this definition? Only Provost Plotowski speaks of a "female." Children are nowhere mentioned.

Be that as it may, Anna was dismissed. And the work was never completed. The Book of Revolutions remained a fragment, because an obscene bishop played the moralist with Copernicus. No further back than 1538 the imperial envoy Scepper had sent Bishop Dantiscus a portrait of his daughter from Spain, the portrait of Dantisca de Curiis. Incidentally, Dantiscus planned to give his daughter, with whom his colleague, the Archbishop of Lund had flirted, a courtly education at Antwerp. Did Dantiscus forget his daughter in 1539? And did he no longer remember that he also had an illegitimate son named Fabian?

And did he not know that the new severe pope at Rome, Paul III (to whom Copernicus dedicated *De Revolutionibus*) intended to give the children he had begot as cardinal the best posts he could and to marry them into the families of the emperor and the king of France?

"True," writes Leopold Prowe, "Bishop Dantiscus must have been looking for cover because, on account of his connection with the humanists, the zealots in his entourage did not think him entirely firm in his faith, and he himself had made known the errors of his youth by his poems. Furthermore, everywhere in the Catholic Church reversals were then being prepared. The days of the Council of Trent were at hand. Finally the duty of his offices demanded that Dantiscus zealously help to preserve the assets of the Church."

Dantiscus persecuted the good girl Anna Schillings even after the death of Copernicus. In the fall of 1543 she wanted to come to Frauenburg for a few days in order to settle her affairs and sell a house. The Chapter asked Dantiscus' permission and he immediately objected.

Had this severe Catholic always carefully avoided connections with Lutherans?

In the summer of 1523 Dantiscus had come from Spain to Germany and made a trip from Leipzig to Wittenberg in order to look up Melanchthon. Full of proud joy he wrote to Justus Decius, chronicler and private secretary to the King of Poland: "I have at last met the great Melanchthon!" (Decius, too, visited Luther in 1522.) And to the Polish Chancellor

Tomicki he wrote: "Among all the German scholars I liked none better than Melanchthon!"

Dantiscus was also liked by Melanchthon and his friends.

Dantiscus asked Melanchthon to introduce him to Luther, the outlawed reformer.

In a letter to Bishop Tomicki, the Polish Chancellor, Dantiscus described his visit to Luther. He kept a draft of his letter and later wrote on it: "My opinion on Luther in 1523."

There, among other things, he tells how he rode through Germany, and went to Augsburg and Leipzig, and how, being so near Wittenberg, he did not want to pass by Luther whom he was so curious to meet, although he could not get there without difficulties, for the Elbe had overflowed its banks. And on his way he heard the peasants curse Luther and his companions. The peasants believed that God wanted to drown all of Saxony, because Luther and his companions had eaten meat on fast days. Dantiscus left his horses behind and embarked in a boat to cross to the other bank, to Wittenberg. . . .

"And there, among the most learned scholars of Hebrew, Greek and Latin, I found Philip Melanchthon, the prince of literature and learning, a young man of twenty-six, but the most humane, the purest man . . . I explained to him why I wanted to see Luther: If someone has not seen the pope in Rome and Luther at Wittenberg, it is commonly said of him that he has not seen anything; therefore I was so eager to see Luther and speak to him, I had no other intentions and no other business with him, except to say good day and farewell to him, *salve et vale*.

"It is no easy thing to approach Luther. But I had no special difficulties, and came with Melanchthon toward the end of the meal. Luther had invited a few friars of his order whom we recognized as monks by their white cowls, despite their military demeanor; without their cowls they would have looked like ordinary peasants. Luther rose, extended his hand to us and pointed at a seat. We sat down; and we conversed about many things for more than four hours into the night. I found the man keen, learned, eloquent, but full of malice, arrogance and poisonous words against the pope, emperor and other princes. A whole day would not suffice to describe everything. . . .

"Luther has such a big stomach that he swallows books. He has sharp eyes, they have something terrifying about them, as in obsessed people, like the King of Denmark (Christiern), although I do not think they were born under the same constellation. His language is vehement, spiced with coarseness and vulgarity, he behaves like a scholar; when he leaves his house that formerly was a monastery he is said to wear his monkish garb.

"As we sat with Luther we not only talked, but also gaily drank wine and beer, as is the custom here, and he seems to be a good companion to everyone, or as they say in German: *ein gutt Geselle.*

"As for his holiness that so many have praised to us, he does not differ from ordinary people; but his great pride is striking, as well as the arrogance with which he wears his fame. In eating and hard drinking and . . . he seems to be quite openly excessive. However that may be, his books reveal him entirely. He preaches and writes an enormous amount; recently he translated the books of Moses from the Hebrew into Latin, for which he mostly used Melanchthon's works."

At the Nuremberg diet, Dantiscus was Melanchthon's host, just as the latter was his host at Wittenberg for two days. They continued to exchange letters for a long time afterward. For a long time Dantiscus remained interested in the learned German, followed his studies, and kept himself up to date through many letters from other humanists.

Melanchthon wrote: "At that time—in Nuremberg—I conceived a liking for Dantiscus, not only because of his brilliant merits, but quite especially because of his humanity which befits so well a learned wise man. . . ."

If Dantiscus was "humanity itself" and persecuted Copernicus on account of an Anna, a Sculteti and other trifles, what could Copernicus expect from humanity as a whole when he was about—to be sure, in the name of truth—to deal mankind the worst blow it had ever suffered?

41

THE DISCIPLE

To perfect is not the pupil's job.
GOETHE, Wilhelm Meister's Apprenticeship

Amicus certus in re incerta cernitur . . . Est enim is qui est tamquam alter idem.
CICERO, De Amicitia

TRUE, there were the good friends and a few disciples.

"But friends, in truth, have brought me forth into the light again, though I long hesitated and am still reluctant; among these the foremost was Nicholas Schonberg, Cardinal of Capua, celebrated in all fields of scholarship. Next to him is that scholar, my very good friend, Tiedemann Giese, Bishop of Kulm, most learned in all sacred matters (as he is), and in all good sciences. He has repeatedly urged me and, sometimes even with censure, implored me to publish this book and to suffer it to see the light at last, as it has lain hidden by me not for nine years alone, but also in the fourth 'novenium.' Not a few other scholars of eminence also pleaded with me, exhorting me that I should no longer refuse to contribute my book to the common service of mathematicians on account of an imagined dread. . . . Brought to this hope, therefore, by these pleaders, I at last permitted my friends, as they had long besought me, to publish this work. . . ."

He wrote this eleven months before his death, in his dedication to the pope.

These friends whom he does not name and to whom he gave permission to publish his book are Protestants, from Wittenberg and Nuremberg, the centers of Lutheranism.

Immediately after his arrival Rheticus plunged into the study of the Book of Revolutions with "all the fiery zeal of youth." For ten weeks he studied the text and questioned his teacher. Finally he thought he had grasped the general ideas and most of the details. Thereupon he wrote the *Narratio Prima de Libris Revolutionum,* which was the first account of *De Revolutionibus.* He composed this treatise in the form of a letter to Johannes Schoner, while with his teacher at Löbau, but he sent it out only from Frauenburg; it was obviously written for the general public and intended for publication.

The Narratio Prima analyzes only the first four Books of Copernicus' work. A second account that was to take up the planetary theory in detail was not published because in the meantime Copernicus gave permission to publish his own work.

Rheticus' first account is ingenious. After briefly indicating the contents of the six Books he discusses Copernicus' new explanations of the precession, the length of the year, the eccentricity and the distance of the sun's orbit from the earth. Then follows a curious astrological digression, which is all the more abstruse because unlike other astronomers Copernicus never read horoscopes, wrote forecasts or interpreted comets or conjunctions of planets.

Then Rheticus gives six reasons for rejecting Ptolemy's system. He correctly appraises the strong points of the new doctrine, particularly emphasizing the simplified computations of the planetary theory.

(The discussion of the loop formation in the orbit of Mars made him thoughtful. It continued to occupy him for a long time. According to Kepler, Rheticus lost his mind for a time pondering over the orbit of Mars. The same passage in the Revolutions in which Copernicus discusses the orbit of Mars seems also to have strongly impressed Tycho de Brahe.)

In the fall of 1539 Rheticus seems to have gone to Danzig, in order to supervise the setting of the Narratio Prima and prepare the woodcuts for the figures. Previously the report must have circulated in manuscript among friends, as was the custom at that time. Rheticus appended to his first report an Encomium Prussiae, In Praise of Prussia. The title page speaks of "the most learned man and most brilliant mathematician, the revered Dr. Nicolaus of Torun, canon in Ermland." The name Copernicus is absent—was this an act of caution on the part of his friends? Rheticus gives his own name only on the second page. (The exact title is: Ad clarissimum virum D. Joannem Schonerum de libris revolutionum eruditissimi viri et mathematici excellentissimi, reverendi D. Doctoris Nicolai Torunnaei Canonici Varmiensis per quendam juvenem mathematicae studiosum Narratio prima." The treatise bears on the second page the inscription: To the illustrious John Schoner, as to his own revered father, G. Joachim Rheticus sends his greetings. It has thirty-eight sheets in small quarto.)

Rheticus begins by apologizing to Schoner for having let months pass without keeping his promise to give an account of Copernicus and his theory. But, he says, he has been able to devote scarcely ten weeks to studying the work of Copernicus; he had had a slight illness and gone with his teacher to visit the latter's friend Giese at Löbau.

"First of all I wish you to be convinced," he writes, "that this man whose work I am now treating is in every field of knowledge and in mastery of astronomy not inferior to Regiomontanus. I rather compare him with Ptolemy, not because I consider Regiomontanus inferior to Ptolemy, but because my teacher shares with Ptolemy the good fortune of completing, with the aid of divine kindness, the reconstruction of astronomy which he began, while Regiomontanus—alas, cruel fate—departed this life before he had time to erect his columns.

"My teacher has written a work of six Books in which, in imitation of Ptolemy, he has embraced the whole of astronomy. . . .

"The first Book contains the general description of the universe and the foundations by which he undertakes to save the appearances and the observations of all ages. . . .

"I have mastered the first three Books, grasped the general idea of the fourth, and begun to conceive the hypotheses of the rest.

". . . My teacher made observations with the utmost care at Bologna, where he was not so much the pupil as the assistant and witness of observations of the learned Dominicus Maria; at Rome, where, about the year 1500, being twenty-seven years of age more or less, he lectured on mathematics before a large audience of students and a throng of great men and experts in this branch of knowledge; then here in Frauenburg, when he had leisure for his studies."

The Narratio Prima deals chiefly with the third Book of the Revolutions, with the moon and with the Copernican planetary theory.

At the end of the scientific part of the Narratio Prima Rheticus exclaims enthusiastically: "Indeed, there is something divine in the circumstance that a sure understanding of celestial phenomena must depend on the regular and uniform motions of the terrestrial globe alone."

Rheticus had formed his style on the model of the ancients. He ornamented it with Latin and Greek quotations. He knew the Roman and Greek philosophers and the great theologians; he was well grounded in the history of astronomy, from Ptolemy to Regiomontanus. And he was a mathematician of genius.

His precise scientific account of the Copernican theory was accessible to the educated layman. He often interrupts himself and quotes Aristotle, Plato or later authors.

As for his teacher (Dominus Praeceptor) whom he never mentions by name, he praises him for his virtue, his intelligence, his kindness and his achievement in creating a world system. He praises the clarity of the new system. He speaks with approval of his master for not having sacrificed the real celestial appearances to his theory, for having, on the contrary, modified his hypotheses when his observations required it.

Incidentally, Rheticus displays little psychological or historical interest. He largely recognizes the revolutionary significance of Copernicus, but does not take the time to describe the man, does not mention him except occasionally with regard to his work; he does not say anything about him personally, about his observations, instruments, apartments, observatory! He does not even mention the Commentariolus.

Rheticus never forgets to exercise the caution necessary to avoid stirring up a host of possible enemies: organized reaction, the inquisition, scientific superstition, contemporary prejudice, the peripatetics, scholastics and all the other fools of his time. In his own and his teacher's interest he tries not to give the appearance of attacking them, but he reveals all their absurdity!

Since the scientific world clung to Ptolemy with thousand-year-old roots, Rheticus always emphasizes the fact that the Copernican system derives from the Ptolemaic and confesses "that he himself loves Ptolemy, as his teacher, with all his soul."

Against the inevitable reproach of frivolously seeking novelties Rheticus defends his teacher (and himself) in the following apostrophe to Schoner:

"Your unparalleled and, so to say, paternal affection for me has impelled me to enter this heaven not at all fearfully and to report everything to you to the best of my ability. May Almighty and Most Merciful God, I pray, deem my venture worthy of turning out well, and may He enable me to conduct the work I have undertaken along the right road to the proposed goal. If I have said anything with youthful enthusiasm (we young men are always endowed, as he says, with high, rather than useful, spirits) or inadvertently let fall any remark which may seem directed against venerable and sacred antiquity more boldly than perhaps the importance and dignity of the subject demanded, you surely, I have no doubt, will put a kind construction upon the matter and will bear in mind my feeling toward you rather than my fault.

"Furthermore, concerning my learned teacher I should like you to hold the opinion and be fully convinced that for him there is nothing better or more important than walking in the footsteps of Ptolemy and following, as Ptolemy did, the ancients and those who were much earlier than himself. However, when he became aware that the phenomena, which control the astronomer, and mathematics compelled him to make certain assumptions even against his wishes, it was enough, he thought, if he aimed his arrows by the same method to the same target as Ptolemy, even though he employed a bow and arrows of far different type of material from Ptolemy's. At this point we should recall the saying 'Free in mind must he be who desires to have understanding.' But my teacher especially abhors what is alien to the mind of any honest man, particularly to a philosophic nature; for he is far from thinking that he should rashly depart, in a lust for novelty, from the sound opinions of the ancient philosophers, except for good reasons, and when the facts themselves coerce him. Such is his time of life, such his seriousness of character and distinction in learning, such, in short, his loftiness of spirit and greatness of mind that no such thought can take hold of him. It is rather the mark of youth or of 'those who pride themselves on some trifling speculation,' to use Aristotle's words, or of those passionate intellects that are stirred and swayed by any breeze and their own moods, so that, as though their pilot had been washed overboard, they snatch at anything that comes to hand and struggle on bravely."

Elsewhere Rheticus writes:

"When I reflect on this truly admirable structure of new hypotheses wrought by my teacher, I frequently recall, most learned Schoner, that Platonic dialogue which indicates the qualities required in an astronomer and then adds 'No nature except an extraordinary one could ever easily formulate a theory.'

"When I was with you last year and watched your work and that of other learned men in the improvement of the motions of Regiomontanus and his teacher Peurbach, I first began to understand what sort of task and how great a difficulty it was to recall this queen of mathematics, astronomy, to her palace, as she deserved, and to restore the boundaries of her kingdom. But from the time that I became, by God's will, a spectator and witness of the labors which my teacher performs with energetic mind and has in large measure already accomplished, I realize that I had not dreamed of even the shadow of so great a burden of work.

". . . My teacher always has before his eyes the observations of all ages together with his own, assembled in order as in catalogues; then when some conclusion must be drawn or contribution made to the science and its principles, he proceeds from the earliest observations to his own, seeking the mutual relationship which harmonizes them all; the results thus obtained by correct inference under the guidance of Urania he then compares with the hypotheses of Ptolemy and the ancients; and having made a most careful examination of these hypotheses, he finds that astronomical proof requires their rejection; he assumes new hypotheses, not indeed without divine inspiration and the favor of the gods; by applying mathematics, he geometrically establishes the conclusions which can be drawn from them by correct inference; he then harmonizes the ancient observations and his own with the hypotheses which he has adopted; and after performing all these operations he finally writes down the laws of astronomy."

And Rheticus goes on to say that the astronomer who studies the motions of the stars is "surely like a blind man who, with only a staff to guide him, must make a great, endless, hazardous journey that winds through innumerable desolate places. What will be the result? Proceeding anxiously for a while and groping his way with his staff, he will at some time, leaning upon it, cry out in despair to heaven, earth and all the gods to aid him in his misery. God will permit him to try his strength for a period of years, that he may in the end learn that he cannot be rescued from threatening danger by his staff. Then God compassionately stretches forth His hand to the despairing man, and with His hand conducts him to the desired goal.

"The staff of the astronomer is mathematics or geometry, by which he ventures at first to test the road and press on.

"My teacher's astronomy can justly be called eternal, it is confirmed by the observations of past centuries and will without doubt be confirmed by the observations of posterity. . . .

"Hence I am convinced that Aristotle, who wrote careful discussions of the heavy and the light, circular motion, and the motion and rest of the earth, if he could hear the reasons for the new hypotheses, would doubtless honestly acknowledge what he proved in these discussions, and what he assumed as unproved principle. I can therefore well believe that he would support my teacher, inasmuch as the well-known saying attributed to Plato is certainly correct: 'Aristotle is the philosopher of the truth.'

"In my opinion, Ptolemy was not so bound and sworn to his own hypotheses that, were he permitted to return to life, upon seeing the royal road blocked and made impassable by the ruins of so many centuries, he would not seek another road over land and sea to the construction of a sound science of celestial phenomena.

". . . somehow I feel more inclined to the hypotheses of my teacher. This is so perhaps partly because I am persuaded that now at last I have a more accurate understanding of that delightful maxim which on account of its weightiness and truth is attributed to Plato: 'God ever geometrizes.'"

After having repeatedly emphasized that the new astronomy rests upon the observations of the ancient astronomers, Ptolemy and his disciples, Rheticus continues as follows: ". . . my teacher was especially influenced by the realization that the chief cause of all the uncertainty in astronomy was that the masters of this science (no offense is intended to divine Ptolemy, the father of astronomy) fashioned their theories and devices for correcting the motion of the heavenly bodies with too little regard for the rule which reminds us that the order and motions of the heavenly spheres agree in an absolute system. We fully grant these distinguished men their due honor, as we should. Nevertheless, we should have wished them, in establishing the harmony of the motions, to imitate the musicians who, when one string has either tightened or loosened, with greatest care and skill regulate and adjust the tones of all the other strings, until all together produce the desired harmony, and no dissonance is heard in any."

These requirements are completely satisfied by the new system, "which is not only self-contained, but is also in complete accord with appearances, just as a good explanation of something is a perfect equivalent for the thing explained.

". . . my teacher saw that only on this theory could all the circles in the universe be satisfactorily made to revolve uniformly and regularly about their own centers, and not about other centers—an essential property of circular motion.

"Fifthly, mathematicians as well as physicians must agree with the statements emphasized by Galen here and there: 'Nature does nothing without purpose' and 'So wise is our Maker that each of His works has not one use, but two or three or often more.' Since we see that this one motion of the earth satisfies an almost infinite number of appearances, should we not attribute to God, the creator of nature, that skill which we observe in the common makers of clocks? For they carefully avoid inserting in the mechanism any superfluous wheel or any whose function could be served better by another with a slight change of position."

And Copernicus' theory is not marred by the contradictions of the Ptolemaic system. Copernicus, Rheticus says, has liberated astronomy from a number of superfluous hypotheses required to explain the motions of the planets, and show why the earth could not possibly be in the center of the universe. This place most properly belongs to the sun, "which God placed in the center of the world stage, as his substitute in visible nature, as the king of the universe endowed with divine majesty.

". . . the sun was called by the ancients leader, governor of nature, and king. But whether it carries on this administration as God rules the entire universe, a rule excellently described by Aristotle in the De mundo, or whether, traversing the entire heaven so often and resting nowhere, it acts as God's administrator in nature, seems not yet altogether explained and settled. Which of these assumptions is preferable, I leave to be determined by geometers and philosophers (who are mathematically equipped). For in the trial and decision of such controversies, a verdict must be reached in accordance not with plausible opinions but with mathematical laws (the court in which the case is heard). The former manner of rule has been set aside, the latter adopted. My teacher, however, is convinced that the rejected method of the sun's rule in the realm of nature must be revived, but in such a way that the received and accepted method retains its place. For he is aware that in human affairs the emperor need not himself hurry from city to city in order to perform the duty imposed on him by God; and that the heart does not move to the head or feet or other parts of the body to sustain a living creature, but fulfills its function through other organs designed by God for that purpose.

". . . The planets are each year observed as direct, stationary, retrograde, near to and remote from the earth, etc. These phenomena, besides being ascribed to the planets, can be explained, as my teacher shows, by a regular motion of the spherical earth; that is, by having the sun occupy the center of the universe, while the earth revolves instead of the sun on the eccentric, which it has pleased him to name the great circle. Indeed, there is something divine in the circumstance that a sure understanding of celestial phenomena must depend on the regular and uniform motions of the terrestrial globe alone."

The main part of the Narratio Prima ends with the following words: "But may truth prevail, may excellence prevail, may the arts ever be honored, may every good worker bring to light useful things in his own art, and may he search in such a manner that he appears to have sought the truth. Never will my teacher avoid the judgment of honest and learned men, to which he plans of his own accord to submit."

After the Narratio Prima was published, Rheticus sent one copy from Danzig to Melanchthon (February 14, 1540), and later another copy to Achilles Gasser in Feldkirch. This friend of Rheticus', another enthusiastic disciple of Copernicus', in a letter written in 1540 urged his friend Vogelinus to advertise Rheticus' treatise zealously "in order to hasten the publication of the second account."

The publication of the Narratio Prima was the decisive step toward the publication of *De Revolutionibus.*

For the space of a generation Copernicus had kept his work from the eyes of humanity. Now he let himself be tempted. He made a half step —he was ready to dare if the world seemed sympathetic, but he was also ready to draw back into his solitude.

Copernicus' friends naturally helped to make known the Narratio Prima. Giese sent a copy of it to Duke Albrecht of Prussia with a letter recommending Rheticus. The latter went to Königsberg and received a "princely reward" in gold from the Duke.

At the beginning of 1540 Rheticus was again in Wittenberg and announced two lectures, on Alfraganus' astronomy and the Almagest. He did not name Copernicus in his announcement, but seems to have mentioned or discussed the new doctrine in his first lecture, for he announces his second lecture in the following terms: "I was *ordered* again to lecture on the Sphaera of Johannes de Sacrobosco."

Meanwhile Johannes Petrejus, the Nuremberg printer, had read the Narratio Prima with the greatest satisfaction and expressed the wish to see the Book of Revolutions, and eventually to print it. And the chief clergyman of Nuremberg, Andreas Osiander, began his notorious exchange of letters on scientific hypotheses with Copernicus.

In the summer of 1540 Rheticus returned to Frauenburg. From the summer of 1540 until September, 1541, he devoted his time to the Book of Revolutions.

Thus a young man without a reputation or special claims to consideration suddenly dropped in to see Copernicus and got him to do what the old man had not dared do by his own decision and what his oldest friends had not been able to get him to do.

Is this not one of the most comforting archetypes in the history of mankind: the hesitating sage and his enthusiastic disciple?

The old man is about to resign himself to seeing his science transmitted from mouth to mouth. And the disciple with his unspoiled confidence in mankind declares: There are thousands like me—a whole generation. The world is waiting. Publish your book. Today you seem absurd to the schoolmasters. Tomorrow schoolchildren will learn that the earth turns around the sun. The light of the sun surges through your work. You speak of the "revolutiones orbium celestium," the revolutions of the heavenly spheres, but you will also effect revolutions on earth.

The old man listens willingly. He knows the inquisitors. Perhaps he saw Savonarola burning at the stake? But he also feels his old age. They have forced Sculteti into exile. They have driven his Anna Schillings

IHS
POETA
LAVREATVS
DANTISCUS
ST

from his house. They will build walls a thousand feet high to veil the sun. His book can be the torch that lights a millennium, and a torch of war, too! But where will it be printed?

In Germany! says Rheticus.

Who will publish it?

My friends in Nuremberg! says Rheticus.

And so a young professor wrote the first book about the master who remained in the shadow. Was it not daring on the part of the young man to write about an unpublished book? An unknown young man came forth and told the world—the world of the scientists—that a revolution had taken place, the most peaceful and yet the most tremendous in the history of mankind—that an astronomer had appeared too great to be compared even to the greatest astronomer of the preceding centuries, the world-famous Regiomontanus, but worthy to be compared only to the unique astronomer who for the space of one thousand five hundred years had legislated that the earth was motionless and that the sun was its satellite—the unique man, the Alexandrian Ptolemy. Ptolemy was wrong and Copernicus had proved it and had worked out a better theory. This theory was true and as clear as the sun!

This work about an unpublished manuscript was successful and caused a sensation. No sooner was it printed in Danzig than it had a new edition in Basel: Achilles Gassarus, a friend and countryman of Rheticus, the young man in Lindau to whom Rheticus had sent a copy of his Narratio Prima with an enthusiastic letter, had it reprinted at once by the printer Georg Winter at Basel, for at that time Danzig was too far away from southern Germany and Switzerland to import copies from there. Gassarus wrote in the dedication that he hoped the "almost divine work of Copernicus" would be published soon. Gassarus' young friend, Georg Vogelinus of Constance, too, was so enthusiastic that he composed a Latin epigram for Gassarus to put on the title page.

Several scholars had apparently become interested as a result of Rheticus' book.

Originally Copernicus intended to publish only his planetary tables and directions for their use, not his planetary theory. But now Giese induced the old master to work out his planetary theory, too, and submit it to the judgment of the learned. Rheticus reports this achievement of Giese's in his Encomium Prussiae.

Now it was necessary to prepare a copy of the draft for the printer. Rheticus probably made this copy. In the course of this painstaking labor a few defects might have struck him: the trigonometrical treatise was not completed; the revision of some of the data in the tables begun by Copernicus had not been completed.

Copernicus himself must have undertaken all these revisions. In the draft there are only a few corrections in another hand, probably Rheticus'. Occasionally dubious numbers are underscored with dots, apparently to be checked later. Occasionally Rheticus made a mistake. He copied a passage for the printer that Copernicus had crossed out, but dropped Copernicus' introduction* because the dedication to Paul III seemed to make it superfluous. Nor did Rheticus take the poem that Dantiscus had composed for the Book of Revolutions in the summer of 1541.

At that time Copernicus had completed his trigonometrical treatise. But he did not make use of his new results concerning the motions of Mercury and Venus for the Book of Revolutions. Nor did he write the summary of his results that would have completed the work.

As late as in the spring of 1541 he was not ready. It appears from a letter of Paul Eber's (to Melanchthon, dated April 15, 1541), that Rheticus had written to him that he was waiting for the completion of the Book of Revolutions and could not return for the next fair, but only for the autumn fair. And that they had already discovered that the comets did not arise in the region of the elements, but in the region of the ether, beyond the moon!

The versatile young scholar also took part in other studies of Copernicus: thus he probably used Copernicus' preliminary geographic works to draw his map of Prussia. In 1529, Bishop Moritz had asked Alexander Sculteti and Copernicus to make such a map. It is not known whether it was finished at that time. But Copernicus' material, according to notes by Caspar Schuetz, was still accessible at the end of the sixteenth century.

In the course of his trip to Löbau, Danzig and Königsberg Rheticus became acquainted with various peoples and countries. He was invited to Danzig by a cousin of Copernicus', Burgomaster Werden. In Königsberg he saw Duke Albrecht of Prussia.

Rheticus composed a "Tabula chorographica of Prussia and a few adjacent lands" and dedicated it, together with "a little instrument to measure the length of the day throughout the year" to Duke Albrecht.

The tabula chorographica and the "little instrument" have been lost. But we have Rheticus' *Chorographica,* a treatise on the methods of drawing maps. This treatise, too, composed under Copernicus' supervision, was sent by Rheticus to Albrecht.

In order to arouse the duke's interest in Copernicus' astronomical works

* See Chapter 1.

he promised the prince who believed in astrology great advantages for astrology from his teacher's studies.

Incidentally, Rheticus also mentions Albrecht Duerer whom he might have met at Nuremberg. ("Albrecht Duerer teaches in his books how to reproduce a landscape. . . .")

He also begs that the duke intercede with the Elector of Saxony and the University of Wittenberg so that these will give him permission to publish Copernicus' work. The duke sent him the desired recommendations and a Portuguese ducat as an honorarium for the dedication. And Rheticus returned to Wittenberg.

He must have taken to Germany, together with his copy, his teacher's original draft, so now Copernicus could no longer change anything.

But it was only with the greatest effort that Copernicus had undertaken a few more revisions. His strength probably no longer sufficed for the synthesis at the end of the book and the necessary finishing touches.

42

"IN PRAISE OF PRUSSIA"

Prussia, the classical country of schools and barracks.
VICTOR COUSIN

La patrie de la pensée.
MADAME DE STAËL, De l'Allemagne

We are Prussians and Prussians we want to remain!
BISMARCK, 1849

RHETICUS begins his praise of Prussia with Pindar and ends it with Euripides. But Prussia meant for him a Baltic province, a few Hanseatic cities, Ermland, secularized East Prussia and Polish Prussia.

Here is the passage from *Encomium Borussiae* which deals with the friendship between Giese and Copernicus: (translated by Edward Rosen, Three Copernican Treatises, The Commentariolus of Copernicus, The Letter against Werner, The Narratio Prima of Rheticus, Columbia University Press, 1939.)

"In particular, I am wont to marvel at the kindness of two distinguished men toward me, since I readily recognize how slight is my scholarly equipment, measuring myself by my own abilities. One of them is the illustrious prelate whom I mentioned at the outset, the Most Reverend Tiedemann Giese, Bishop of Kulm. His Reverence mastered with complete devotion the set of virtues and doctrine, required of a bishop by Paul. He realized that it would be of no small importance to the glory of Christ if there existed a proper calendar of events in the Church and a correct theory and explanation of the motions. He did not cease urging my teacher, whose accomplishments and insight he had known for many years, to take up this problem, until he persuaded him to do so.

Since my teacher was social by nature and saw that the scientific world also stood in need of improvement of the motions, he readily yielded to the entreaties of his friend, the reverend prelate. He promised that he would draw up astronomical tables with new rules and that if his work had any value he would not keep it from the world, as was done by John Angelus, among others. But he had long been aware that in their own right the observations in a certain way required hypotheses which would overturn the ideas concerning the order of the motions and spheres that had hitherto been discussed and promulgated and that were commonly accepted and believed to be true; moreover, the required hypotheses would contradict our senses.

He therefore decided that he should imitate the Alfonsine Tables rather than Ptolemy and compose tables with accurate rules but no proofs. In that way he would provoke no dispute among philosophers; common mathematicians would have a correct calculus of the motions; but true scholars, upon whom Jupiter had looked with unusually favorable eyes, would easily arrive from the numbers set forth at the principles and sources from which everything was deduced. Just as heretofore learned men had to work out the true hypothesis of the motion of the starry sphere from the Alfonsine doctrine, so the entire system would be crystal clear to learned men. The ordinary astronomer, nevertheless, would not be deprived of the use of the tables, which he seeks and desires, apart from all theory. And the Pythagorean principle would be observed that philosophy must be pursued in such a way that its inner secrets are reserved for learned men, trained in mathematics, etc.

Then His Reverence pointed out that such a work would be an incomplete gift to the world, unless my teacher set forth the reasons for his tables and also included, in imitation of Ptolemy, the system or theory and the foundations and proofs upon which he relied to investigate the mean motions and prosthaphaereses and to establish epochs as initial points in the computation of time. The bishop further argued that such a procedure had produced great inconvenience and many errors in the Alfonsine Tables, since we were compelled to assume and to approve their ideas on the principle that, as the Pythagoreans used to say, 'The Master said so'—a principle which has absolutely no place in mathematics.

Moreover, contended the bishop, since the required principles and hypotheses are diametrically opposed to the hypotheses of the ancients, among scholars there would be scarcely anyone who would hereafter examine the principles of the tables and publish them after the tables have gained recognition as being in agreement with the truth. There was no place in science, he asserted, for the practice frequently adopted in kingdoms, conferences, and public affairs, where for a time plans are kept secret until the subjects see the fruitful results and remove from doubt the hope that they will come to approve the plans.

So far as the philosophers are concerned, he continued, those of keener insight and greater information would carefully study Aristotle's extensive discussion and would note that after convincing himself that he had established the immobility of the earth by many proofs Aristotle finally takes refuge in the following argument:

'We have evidence for our view in what the mathematicians say about astronomy. For the phenomena observed as changes take place in the figures by which the arrangement of the stars is marked out occur as they would on the assumption that the earth is situated at the centre.'

Accordingly the philosophers would then decide:

'If this concluding statement by Aristotle cannot be linked with his previous discussion, we shall be compelled, unless we are to waste the time and effort which we have invested, rather to assume the true basis of astronomy. Moreover, we must work out appropriate solutions for the remaining problems under discussion. By returning to the principles with greater care and equal assiduity, we must determine, whether it has been proved that the center of the earth is also the center of the universe. If the earth were raised to the lunar sphere, would loose fragments of earth seek, not the center of the earth's globe, but the center of the universe, inasmuch as they all fall at right angles to the surface of the earth's globe? Again, since we see that the magnet by its natural motion turns north, would the motion of the daily rotation or the circular motions attributed to the earth necessarily be violent motions? Further, can the three motions, away from the center, toward the center, and about the center, be in fact separated? We must analyze other views which Aristotle used as fundamental propositions with which to refute the opinions of the *Timaeus* and the Pythagoreans.'

They will ponder the foregoing questions and others of the same kind if they desire to look to the principal end of astronomy and to the power and the efficacy of God and nature.

But if it is to be the intention and decision of scholars everywhere to hold fast to their own principles passionately and insistently, His Reverence warned, my teacher should not anticipate a fate more fortunate than that of Ptolemy, the king of this science. Averroes, who was in other respects a philosopher of the first rank, concluded that epicycles and eccentrics could not possibly exist in the realm of nature and that Ptolemy did not know why the ancients had posited motions of rotation. His final judgment is: 'The Ptolemaic astronomy is nothing, so far as existence is concerned; but it is convenient for computing the nonexistent. As for the untutored, whom the Greeks call "Those who do not know theory, music, philosophy, and geometry," their shouting should be ignored, since men of good will do not undertake any labors for their sake.'

By these and many other contentions, as I learned from friends familiar with the entire affair, the learned prelate won from my teacher a promise to permit scholars and posterity to pass judgment on his work. For this reason men of good will and students of mathematics will be deeply grateful with me to His Reverence, the Bishop of Kulm, for presenting this achievement to the world.

In addition, the benevolent prelate deeply loves these studies and cultivates them earnestly. He owns a bronze armillary sphere for observing equinoxes, like the two somewhat larger ones which Ptolemy says were at Alexandria and which learned men from everywhere in Greece came to see. He has also arranged that a gnomon truly worthy of a prince should be brought to him from England. I have examined this instrument with the greatest pleasure, for it was made by an excellent workman who knew his mathematics. . . ."

43

THE REPUBLIC OF LETTERS

> Figaro: *Voyant à Madrid que la république des Lettres était celle des loups, toujours armés les uns contre les autres, et que, livrés au mépris où ce risible acharnement les conduit, tous les Insectes, les Moustiques, les Cousins, les Critiques, les Maringouins, les Envieûx, les Feuillistes, les Libraires, les Censeurs, et tout ce qui s'attache à la peau des malheureux Gens de Lettres, achevait de déchiqueter et sucer le peu de substance qui leur restait . . .*
>
> BEAUMARCHAIS, Barbier de Séville

> Le Comte: *Sauvons-nous!*
> Figaro: *Pourquoi?*
>
> BEAUMARCHAIS, Barbier de Séville

ALL his life Copernicus worked on one single book. With the frenzy of a megalomaniac dilettante or a genius he tried to squeeze the entire world into his manuscript—and it was the largest world a mortal had ever seen with his mind's eye. No wonder that, faced with this incomparable material, he again and again corrected his manuscript, his computations, his theory.

All his life Copernicus gazed at the stars . . . Tycho de Brahe, at the beginning of his work, *De Nova Stella* (On the New Star), describes this star-gazing habit:

"Last year (1572), in the month of November, on the eleventh day of that month, in the evening, after sunset, when, according to my habit, I was contemplating the stars in a clear sky, I noticed that a new unusual star, surpassing the other stars in brilliancy, was shining almost directly above my head; and since I had, almost from my boyhood, known all the stars of the heavens perfectly (there is no great difficulty in attaining that knowledge), it was quite evident to me that there had never before been any star in that place in the sky, even the smallest, to say nothing of a star so conspicuously bright as this. I was so astonished at this sight that I was not ashamed to doubt the trustworthiness of my own eyes. But when I observed that others, too, on having the place pointed out to them, could see that there was really a star there, I had no further doubts.

"A miracle indeed, either the greatest of all that have occurred in the whole range of nature since the beginning of the world, or one certainly that is to be classed with those attested by the Holy Oracles, the staying of the Sun in its course in answer to the prayers of Joshua, and the darkening of the Sun's face at the time of the Crucifixion. For all philosophers agree, and facts clearly prove it to be the case, that in the ethereal region of the celestial world no change, in the way either of generation or of corruption, takes place; but that the heavens and the celestial bodies in the heavens are without increase or diminution, and that they undergo no alteration, either in number or in size or in light or in any other respect, that they always remain the same, like unto themselves in all respects, no years wearing them away.

"Furthermore, the observations of all the founders of the science, made some thousands of years ago, testify that all the stars have always retained the same number, position, order, motion, and size as they are found, by careful observation on the part of those who take delight in heavenly phenomena, to preserve even in our own day. Nor do we read that it was ever before noted by any one of the founders that a new star had appeared in the celestial world, except only by Hipparchus, who, if we are to believe Pliny (Book II of his Natural History), noticed a star different from all others previously seen, one born in his own age . . ."*

Copernicus began the revolution in the heavens, and the unrest there has grown greater and greater ever since. In fact the title *De Revolutionibus orbium caelestium* is not the true one. Copernicus' title was: The Book of Revolutions!

Revolutionaries are usually pedants. Convinced that they are right in the main, they are distressed by the tiny errors of detail that their enemies cast in their teeth in order to compromise their entire system. Similarly, the tragic poet toward the end of the fifth act cheerfully massacres a dozen characters who have done him no harm, but sweats tears and blood over an epithet to describe the setting sun.

All his life Copernicus observed, studied, pondered, checked his results and rejected them, all his life he labored over one book, and in the end he was not satisfied with it.

* Translated by John H. Walden.

This profound dissatisfaction with himself also kept him from publishing his book. He was not ready—never quite ready.

He enjoyed fame among his friends, an insignificant kind of fame, but not the worst kind. He reaped scorn and hatred and contempt, as is usual for innovators of genius.

Under Paul III, Cardinal Caraffa, the future Paul IV, "the old man with a death's head," was already preparing to suppress freedom on the seven hills of Rome and in all the four corners of Europe. And the Protestants absolutely refused to live more freely! And the Index threatened!

And so Rheticus published his first account of the Revolutions. And in order to protect the master from the strict supporters of the Bible with their astronomically reactionary sun miracles in honor of the conqueror of Jericho and Him who was crucified on Golgotha, Giese and Rheticus wrote vindications. Finally they mastered Copernicus' last hesitations: on account of the Church; on account of the imperfections in the work; and on account of that Pythagorean doubt as to the comprehension of the multitude—"don't tell it to anyone except the sages, for the multitude jeers at once!"

Finally Rheticus had a copy of the work (and perhaps the original manuscript, too) in his hands. Petrejus in Nuremberg had declared himself willing to publish the great book; he was a teacher from Wittenberg who had inherited a printing shop; he had a predilection for printing mathematical works, although they brought in only a small profit. In the summer of 1540 he dedicated to Rheticus an astrological book printed in his shop; from it one learns that Petrejus knew the Narratio Prima published shortly before; in it he expresses his hope that Rheticus would soon publish Copernicus' Revolutions.

Nuremberg was the German Athens. Gassendi says: "With the great Regiomontanus all the Muses entered the gates of Nuremberg." Patricians like Bernhard Walther and Willibald Pirckheimer were scholars and patrons of the arts. In that city Peter Henlein manufactured his pocket watches, the "Nuremberg eggs." There Martin Behaim constructed his globe; he may have influenced Columbus in Portugal; he almost discovered America. There lived Albrecht Duerer, and the brothers Barthel and Hans Sebald Beham, painters and copperplate-engravers; and Peter Vischer and his son, sculptor brass-founders; and Veit Stoss, the woodcutter and sculptor who also created great works in Cracow and whom the Poles call Vitus Stwosz.

The free Imperial city was independent of princely whims. The emperors came to be crowned there; the golden imperial orb, scepter and crown were kept there, and the cobbler Sachs was considered a poet; there literature and the German reformation flourished side by side with the sciences, the sacks of pepper and the pedants.

The city was great and wealthy among all the cities of Germany, a playground for humanists and Lutheran ministers. Here lived the mathematicians Johannes Schoner, Regiomontanus, Bernhard Walter, Johannes Werner, Andreas Osiander and Georg Hartmann.

The printers also flourished. As early as Copernicus' birth-year Anton Koburger had founded a printing shop that soon became the biggest in Germany with twenty-four presses and sixteen branches. Indeed, uncle Lukas Watzelrode had published liturgical books for the Ermland church in Nuremberg as early as 1494.

Gassendi says that Johannes Schoner helped Rheticus in the publication of the Revolutions. It is true that in 1533, this adherent of Ptolemy in his *opusculum geographicum,* had ridiculed the philosophers and astronomers who turned the earth around "as on a turnspit." But perhaps he did not find his witty remark quite so witty later. Incidentally he was not only an author of mathematical works, but also an experienced editor, and was commissioned by the Nuremberg council to publish various manuscripts of Regiomontanus.

In the summer of 1542, thanks to the recommendation of Duke Albrecht of Prussia to the Elector of Saxony and the University of Wittenberg, Rheticus received permission to publish Copernicus' Revolutions.

On May 2, equipped with a recommendation from Melanchthon to an old friend of Luther's, the vicar of St. Sebald's church, he went to Nuremberg.

Petrejus must have begun setting the Revolution soon afterwards; for on June 29, 1542, T. Forsther wrote to J. Schad in Reutlingen: "Prussia has given birth to a new and marvelous astronomer whose theory is now being printed here, a work about one hundred sheets long, in which he maintains and demonstrates that the earth moves and the heavens are motionless. A month ago I saw two sheets printed; the corrector of the printing is a certain teacher from Wittenberg."

Thus by the end of May there was already a corrected proof of the first eight pages, and Rheticus was at that time the corrector. In June we find him again in his native Feldkirch, but he must have soon returned to Nuremberg; for he wrote the date on a little book printed at Petrejus' and dedicated it to the burgomaster of Feldkirch *(Orationes de Astronomia, Geographia and Physica)* during the Ides of August; in it he boasts of not having hesitated to pay the expenses of a long trip and to bear other unpleasantnesses in order to hear the new Copernican theory from the mouth of its great author himself.

Meanwhile Rheticus was appointed to the University of Leipzig. A year before he had been appointed dean of his faculty at Wittenberg, and had at the same time published the trigonometric chapters of Copernicus' main work in a separate pamphlet at Wittenberg, perhaps urged on by Osiander, in order to draw the attention of the learned men of that city, especially Melanchthon, to Copernicus' scientific merits; he had dedicated this pamphlet to one of those Nuremberg Lutherans, who were simultaneously priests and mathematicians, to wit, Georg Hartmann, vicar of St. Lawrence's, and at one time a friend of Andreas, Copernicus' unfortunate brother in Rome. But with his new ideas Rheticus no longer felt at home in his old university; perhaps he was also attracted to Leipzig by the offer of a higher salary, two thousand gulden; Melanchthon also refers in a letter to certain "rumors *(fabellae)* that could not be mentioned in a letter."

In November, Rheticus was on his way to Leipzig. He left the further supervision of the printing of Copernicus' Revolutions to a no better man than the Lutheran minister, Andreas Osiander.

By May, 1542, the printing had begun; on May 24, 1543, the day of Copernicus' death, one of the first copies reached his bed. The *editio princeps* comprises 203 pages (forty-nine sheets of eight pages each in small folio). The pages numbered 1 to 196 contain Copernicus' text. Six pages at the beginning contain the title, Osiander's preface, Cardinal Schonberg's letter, Copernicus' dedication to Paul III and the table of contents. The last page contains a list of errata. Page 1a begins with the title: Nicolai Copernici Revolutionum liber primus. The work closes at folio 196a with the words: Finis libri sexti et ultimi Revolutionum. Below there is the printer's mark: Norimbergae apud Joh. Petrejum, Anno MDXLIII. After the printing the errors were listed on a double page, the front side of which repeats the title; the errata followed. A certain Engelhart reported that he bought the book for one gulden; a certain Wolff maintains that he paid twenty-six gulden and six Kreuzer for it. Even contemporary data are utterly unreliable.

The book is illustrated by numerous woodcuts. The edition must have numbered one thousand copies. Petrejus assumed the expenses of the printing and the sale, and gave the author Copernicus and the editor Rheticus a few free copies as honoraria.

Rheticus sent his friends Achilles Gasser, Tiedemann Giese and Canon Donner one copy each with handwritten dedications.

Donner, Copernicus' friend, crossed out with red ink the words orbium caelestium and noted that Osiander's preface and Schonberg's letter did not come from Copernicus.

Tiedemann Giese immediately made a fuss, for this most scandalous book in world literature contained in its very first pages one of the most disgusting and portentous literary scandals ever perpetrated, to wit, Osiander's sacrilegious interpolated preface.

Andreas Osiander was one of the fathers of the Lutheran church. In 1522, at the age of twenty-two, he was the first Lutheran clergyman at the St. Lawrence church in Nuremberg. By the power of his sermons he won the great Nuremberg community and the Grand Master of the Teutonic Order (Margrave Albrecht of Brandenburg, later Duke Albrecht of Prussia) over to Luther's doctrine, and induced the latter to indulge in marriage and other worldly joys. Osiander was just as fond of fighting as Luther and the rest of the gang of reformers; in the end, even the Nurembergers, who are among the coarsest of the Germans, abused him so much that this "spiritual father" of Albrecht, the new Duke of Prussia, went to Königsberg to preach and teach at the university of that town.

Osiander published many theological works and edited a book by his friend Cardanus, *opus perfectum de arithmetica,* at Nuremberg.

During Rheticus' stay in Prussia, Osiander and Copernicus had exchanged letters about great fundamental problems.

Kepler, in his uncompleted *Apologia Tychonis contra Ursum* (published only in 1858) mentions such a letter from Copernicus to Osiander (dated July 1, 1540).

Ursus had referred to the *praefatiuncula* of the Revolutions (which were written by Osiander but which Ursus thought were written by Copernicus) in order to prove the worthlessness of astronomical hypotheses as aids in discovering the real motions of the heavenly bodies. In the course of his debate with Ursus about the role of hypotheses in astronomy, Kepler for the first time in print unmasked Osiander's fraud.

According to Kepler, Copernicus discussed with Osiander whether and to what extent the theory of the motions of the earth, in which Copernicus believed, should be expounded not only among the initiated and the specialists, but also publicly and among laymen, without provoking the contradiction of the scholastic philosophers, the Aristotelians and Ptolemaeans, let alone the "orthodox and other oxen" (as Heine puts it).

On April 20, 1541, Osiander replied to Copernicus that he had always believed astronomical hypotheses should not be regarded as articles of faith, but only as auxiliary means for astronomical computations. Thus the main thing was not whether they were correct or false, but only to what extent they helped to determine the astronomical phenomena. "For who could give us sure information as to whether the irregular course of the sun is produced by an epicyclic or excentric motion, if we followed the hypotheses of Ptolemy, according to which both are possible. Therefore I should think it very desirable if you contributed something on this question in the preface. Thus you might assuage the Aristotelians and the theologians whose violent opposition you apprehend."

On the same day Osiander wrote to Rheticus: "The Aristotelians and the theologians will easily let themselves be appeased if they are told that various hypotheses for the explanation of the same motion are possible, and that certain hypotheses are not advanced because they are irrefutable, but because they permit the most comfortable computation of the relevant phenomenon and this composite movement. It is quite possible to invent still other hypotheses. No matter how well adapted is one man's picture to explain a natural phenomenon, someone else can invent a picture that is still better adapted to the same purpose; anyone is free to do this, and he will even be thanked if he invents plausible explanations. By preliminary remarks of that kind, the opponents instead of severely censuring/the theory/will let themselves be seduced to the sweet attractions of reflection, and from the first will be in a milder and more conciliating mood; later, after vain attempts to find something better they will let themselves be conquered quite readily by the innovator."

Copernicus intensely disliked these cynical utterances of the all-too-politic vicar. In his eyes, hypotheses were the unshakable foundations of science. He regarded his hypotheses as correct and necessary.

Kepler says that Copernicus believed with the iron firmness of a stoic that he was bound to make known his profoundest conviction to the whole world, even if this were not momentarily to the advantage of science.

Copernicus had quite clearly expressed his views; and he must have thought that in doing so he had settled the question which Osiander raised.

To this same Osiander, Rheticus now entrusted the supervision of what remained to be printed of the Revolutions!

And Osiander who had in vain demanded that Copernicus disavow his whole theory in a well-sounding preface now undertook the dirty little business on his own account; he committed the colossal fraud of interpolating an anonymous preface he himself had contrived, in which he repeated the cynical ideas he had expressed in his letter to Copernicus and Rheticus, repeating them in a sharper and more shameless form.

Here is Mr. Osiander's masterpiece:

"To the reader, concerning the hypotheses of this work.

"Many scientists, in view of the already widespread reputation of these new hypotheses, will doubtless be greatly shocked by the theories of this book, to wit, that the earth moves, while the sun rests motionless in the center of the universe; the current opinion is doubtless that the science of which the foundations were correctly laid in antiquity should not be brought into confusion.

"However, upon maturer reflection it will be found that the author of this work has not undertaken anything that deserves censure. For the proper task of the astronomers is to establish the history of the heavenly motions according to careful and exact observations. Then he must discover the causes of these motions, or when he is absolutely unable to discover their true causes, to invent and construct hypotheses to his liking, by means of which these motions can be correctly computed both for the future and the past, according to geometrical theorems. The master has met these two requirements in an excellent manner.

"To be sure, his hypotheses are not necessarily true; they need not even be probable. It is completely sufficient that they lead to a computation that is in accordance with the astronomical observations; only those inexperienced in mathematics would regard the epicycle of Venus as probable and as causing this planet sometimes to precede the sun by forty degrees or more, and sometimes to follow it; for who does not see that the diameter of this planet in the apogee would have to appear more than four times as large, and the body itself more than sixteen times as large, than when it is in the perigee; yet the experience of all times is in contradiction with this.

"There are still other, no less important contradictions in this science, the discussion of which does not seem necessary here. It is quite well known that astronomy simply does not know the causes of the seemingly irregular motions. But if science invents such causes hypothetically—and actually it has invented a great number of such hypotheses—it does not invent them because it hopes to convince anyone that matters are like that in reality; its only purpose is to construct a correct foundation for computations.

"Furthermore, since one and the same motion is sometimes explainable by various hypotheses (as for instance the motion of the sun by the assumption of the excentricity or the epicycle), the astronomer will most readily follow those hypotheses which are most easily understood. The philosopher will perhaps demand greater probability; but neither of the two will be able to discover anything certain or to teach it, unless it has been made known to him by divine revelations.

"Therefore, let us grant that the following new hypotheses take their place beside the old ones which are not any more probable. Moreover, these are really admirable and easy to grasp, and in addition we find here a great treasure of the most learned observations.

"For the rest, let no one expect certainty from astronomy as regards hypotheses. It cannot give this certainty. He who takes everything that is worked out for other purposes, as truth, would leave this science probably more ignorant than when he came to it. And with this, farewell, reader!"

This interpolated preface with which the book begins is not signed by Osiander, its author; it does not contain any hint as to its origin, any indication that it was not written by Copernicus. It was accepted as an integral part of the Revolutions and passed unopposed and word for word into the second edition, and into the third, although it is in the sharpest contradiction with the spirit of Copernicus' work, especially with the fundamental conceptions which the great man openly and proudly expressed in the dedication to the pope. As late as 1617, the editor of the third (Amsterdam) edition, Nicolaus Mulerius, professor at Groningen, expresses in a note his agreement with Osiander's preface which he takes to be Copernicus' and cites as crown-witness the Almagest of that Ptolemy against whose theses the whole book was written. Only in 1854, did Joh. Baranowski put an end to this fraud by explicitly ascribing the preface to its real author in his edition of Copernicus' book published in Warsaw.

Not only the devout who apparently believed that God resided in the false natural laws or in the errors of Aristotle and Ptolemy, but also quite sensible philosophers shuddered at the idea that the earth could move. This deprived them of the last facts for security in life. To live on a racing earth that rotates around itself and rushes around the sun, and even, according to Copernicus, had still a third motion,—this was obviously too much!

Even the great Bacon of Verulam, in his learned work "On the Dignity and Increase of Science," still protested against Copernicus.

What an irony of fate! While Copernicus dedicated his book to the pope because he feared the Catholic zealots, he fell victim to falsifying Lutheran zealots.

While Copernicus thought only of the truth, Osiander had to consider his position as leader of the Reformation in Franconia. In order not to imperil it, he took into consideration Luther and Melanchthon who had laughed at the "astrologer in Poland."

But Copernicus was convinced of the truth of his system, he had written this to the editor in Nuremberg. What did the vicar care for that? What was the good name of one of the greatest of men to him? What did he care for the tender conscience of a septuagenarian? What did he care about science and truth?

It was necessary to accommodate oneself to the views of Melanchthon! Melanchthon's opinion, true or false, was of the greatest importance, for he had influence, power, and positions to bestow! and Melanchthon had written in his own textbook that astronomical hypotheses could not claim to be true!

Yes, Copernicus' character is cheapened in various ways by this interpolation. He is praised in it. The hasty reader—and where are there exact, slow and careful readers in this hasty world?—the hasty reader says to himself: So the author praises himself? What bad taste!

Was this foolish vicar "well intentioned"? So much the worse! The most annoying creature in the world is just such a well-intentioned ass, just such a softhearted, opportunistic, ambiguous falsifier!

Copernicus believed that the foundations of his system were unshakable. And he said so to all the world. He believed in the infallibility of his system; he saw the earth move.

For that very reason, the Holy Congregation of the Index, the censorship authorities of the Catholic church in Rome, at the beginning of the seventeenth century decided to mutilate the work of the great astronomer. With sacrilegious hands they made disgraceful cuts in his sacred book, as though, for instance, they could cut the shining star of Aldebaran out of its constellation. They corrected and "improved" those passages in which Copernicus reveals his conviction in the most decisive terms, and expresses it, divested of all hypothetical character, in divine nakedness.

Copernicus never intended to augment the long series of mathematical hypotheses that were to serve for the computation and explanation of the celestial phenomena. He sought and found and enunciated the real laws of nature.

With its censor's cuts the Inquisition would have compromised its God in this instance, if God would have been responsible for His church.

It is a proof of the longevity of most gods that they patiently survive even the attempts of their priests to mold them after their own image.

For a long time the name of the real author of this preface was unknown or known only in a restricted circle. Kepler discovered his name and branded the culprit in two passages. In his copy of the Copernican Revolutions he found a manuscript note which named Osiander as the author of this preface. The note was written by the Nuremberg astronomer, Hieronymus Schreiber. Through Kepler, Gassendi learned Osiander's name and included it in his Vita Copernici.

The two learned astronomers, Ramus and Ursus, still believed that Copernicus was the author of Osiander's preface.

Petrus Ramus, professor at the University of Paris, offered his chair to anyone who could write an astronomy without hypotheses!

Kepler wrote: "You did well, Ramus, to fulfill this pledge by giving up your chair when you gave up your life; for if you still possessed it, I would by right demand it of you . . ."

And at this point Kepler saved Copernicus' scientific integrity: "I grant that there is nothing more absurd than to try to explain nature from false causes. But this absurdity is not in Copernicus: because he himself held his hypotheses to be true, no less than those ancients of yours held their hypotheses to be true; and I give you this work as evidence, that he not only held them to be true, but also proved them to be true.

"Now you want to know precisely who was the fabricator of that absurdity which angered you so much. The Nuremberg astronomer Hieronymus Schreiber noted his name: Andreas Osiander. This Osiander when he was in charge of publishing Copernicus put at the beginning of the book the preface which you call absurd, but which he himself thought to be most clever, a fact that can be ascertained from his letters to Copernicus. At that time Copernicus himself either was already dead or lived in complete ignorance of the facts . . ."

Gassendi, quoting Kepler, explained Osiander's offense and his motives so clearly that all the subsequent authors who confused this matter must be reproached not only with superficiality, but also with unsavory motives. They deliberately ignored the known facts in order to foist their own ideas on Copernicus.

Osiander committed only a half-fraud. He marked his preface, the *praefatiuncula,* entitled *Ad Lectorem de hypothesibus hujus operis* (to the reader, concerning the hypotheses of this work) as a piece not written by the author, by explicitly placing it next to Copernicus' dedicatory preface to His Holiness, Pope Paul III *(ad sanctissimum Dominum Paulum III Pontificem Maximum) (Nicolai Copernici praefatio in libros revolutionum)* and citing the latter in the table of contents as *Praefatio Autoris* (author's preface).

The praise bestowed upon the astronomer and the addition to the title might have revealed the alien hand to the reader.

Everywhere, in the preface and in the title, the infamous Osiander cast his "hypotheses" in the reader's eyes like sand. Moreover, he printed an offensive band on the book: Igitur eme, lege, fruere—therefore buy, read and make use of it!

And even if anyone realized that Copernicus was not the author of

Osiander's preface, were not Osiander's words and his confounded hypotheses on the very first page? And was one not compelled to assume that Copernicus had at least doubted the truth of his own system and for that reason sanctioned the first preface? Or even asked for it in order to create a false impression and thus protect himself?

The devout adopted this opinion with all the candor of the devout. In 1844 Alexander von Humboldt still had to polemize against this misinterpretation in his *Cosmos:* "It is an erroneous and, alas! even in recent times still very widespread opinion that Copernicus, out of fear and in concern over persecution by priests, presented the planetary motion of the earth and the sun's position in the center of the entire planetary system as a mere *hypothesis* which fulfills the astronomical purpose of allowing us conveniently to compute the orbits of the heavenly bodies, 'but which need not be true nor even probable . . .' The founder of our present system of the world (its most important parts, the most grandiose features of our picture of the universe certainly are his), was almost even more distinguished by his courage and steadfastness than by his knowledge. He earned to a high degree the noble praise given him by Kepler who, in his introduction to the Rudolfine Tables calls him 'the man of free spirit.' . . . In the dedication to the Pope, while describing the birth of his work, Copernicus does not shrink from defining the opinion generally current among the theologians, of the immobility and central position of the earth absurd *acroama,* and from attacking the stupidity of those who cling to such an erroneous belief. Copernicus' vigorous free language arising from his innermost conviction sufficiently refutes the old assertion that he presented the system bearing his immortal name as a hypothesis convenient for the computing astronomer, and as one that might perhaps be unfounded."

If Tiedemann Giese had had his say, this literary fraud of Osiander's would have been unmasked and the purity of Copernicus' text and character would have been restored at once.

In 1615, a little, almost unknown pamphlet by Broscius contained together with a letter from Giese to Donner, the following letter from Giese to Rheticus:

"To Joachim Rheticus:

"Upon my return from the King's wedding celebrations at Cracow, I found at Löbau the two copies you sent me of the recently published work of our Copernicus, of whose demise I learned only after I crossed on to Prussian soil. I might have been able to mitigate my pain over the loss of our brother, that great man, by the study of his book which seemed to bring him back alive before my eyes. But at the very beginning I perceived the abuse of confidence and—you employ the correct expression—the impiety of Petrejus, which evoked in me a wrath that is more painful than the initial sorrow. For who would not be indignant over such a great crime committed under the cover of confidence? Yet this crime should perhaps be ascribed not so much to the printer who after all is dependent upon others, as rather to an envious person who in his irritation at having to abandon his mechanically acquired conviction, if this book achieved reputation, abused the kindness of the author in order to discredit his work.

"But in order not to let him go unpunished who let himself be bribed for another's fraud, I wrote to the Council of Nuremberg and at the same time indicated what, in my opinion, was necessary in order to restore confidence in the author. I send you this letter together with a copy of the work, so that you may decide according to the circumstances how the thing is to be arranged. For I do not know anyone who would be more suitable or more willing to take up this matter with the Council than you are, you who assumed the leading part in carrying out the printing of the work, so that, as it seems to me, the author himself could not be more interested than you in repairing the wrong that has been done to the truth. And if you have the thing at heart I beg you instantly to take it up with the greatest zeal.

"If the first pages of the book are reprinted, it seems necessary to me that you should add a short preface, so that those copies which have already gone out can also be purged of the forgery."

Rheticus sent Giese's letter to Nuremberg, and on August 29, 1543, the Council adopted the following resolution: "To send Mr. Tiedemann, Bishop of Kulm in Prussia, Johann Petrejus' written answer to his letter (in which answer the sharpness should be left out and softened), and write him in addition: that, in conformity with Petrejus' writing he cannot be held responsible for anything." (Cf. L. A. Birkenmajer. Mikolaj Kopernik. Cracow, 1900.)

Thus the Council contented itself with communicating the purged answer of the printer to the bishop.

Rheticus also forced Osiander to admit publicly that he had inserted the preface; Peter Apian reports this fact. Zinner conjectures that Petrejus printed Osiander's preface in order not to spoil his sales by Copernicus' stubbornness; possibly he was also afraid of the Lutherans, particularly of Melanchthon.—Calculation and fear were the two mortal sins of publishers then as today!

Despite all this, the book was not a financial success.

It was not until 1566 that a second edition was published in Basel, reprinted after the editio princeps; even the pages correspond in the two editions, even the errors of the first edition were repeated, and many new ones were added.

Copernicus' work did not supplant any of the standard works of the old school, neither Sacroboscos' Sphaera nor Peurbach's Planetary Theory. Even Melanchthon's *Initia doctrinae physicae* (Introduction to the Doctrine of Physics) written entirely in the old reactionary spirit had during the same interval of time (between 1543 and 1567) ten editions (three of them in 1550!).

But would not the sale of Copernicus' main work have been much better without Osiander's defamatory preface?

Only in 1617 did the third edition of the Revolutions appear at Amsterdam. But the first edition had never been exhausted!

The third edition is better than the preceding editions; many printing errors are eliminated; the editor, the Groningen professor Mulerius, made numerous scientific notes. It goes without saying that he had neither Copernicus' original text nor Rheticus' copy at his disposal.

For centuries the original manuscript of the Revolutions, like Goethe's violet, "alone with itself and unknown," lay in the dust of some library or other.

By the middle of the nineteenth century it was discovered in Count Nostiz's library in Prague. The deviations of the first editions from the original manuscript are so numerous, that M. Kurtze, a professor in the gymnasium at Torun, editor of the Torun centennial edition, reported, after having carefully compared the first edition with the original manuscript, that he had found practically no page exactly matching in the two texts.

Prowe thinks he recognizes certain peculiarities of Rheticus' editing; certain words written in the original in Latin characters appear in Greek characters in the printed text; in this text the word "heavens" is spelled *coelum,* as it was spelled in the Narratio Prima, instead of Copernicus' *caelum;* and similar other coquetries of the young scholar.

Ernst Zinner reproaches Rheticus for having done far too little in his later life in behalf of Copernicus and his theory, but he excuses him on the grounds of his chequered career and his waning interest in astronomy.

Here are a few notes on the later life of a youthful idealist.

His stay at the University of Leipzig, like that of Wittenberg, ended in conflicts and scandals.

The slow transformation of Rheticus' friendship with Reinhold into enmity must have been very painful.

Then, during the carnival of 1545, came the letter of the Wittenberg student, Mathias Lauterbach, an insolent pupil of Reinhold's. Rheticus had informed the Wittenbergers that he had observed the eclipse of the moon on December 28, 1544, and that his times agreed exactly with the values indicated on Copernicus' tables.

Lauterbach wrote to the Leipzig University professor and editor of Copernicus' Revolutions that he, the student Lauterbach, doubted the scientific exactitude of Rheticus' data. Particularly, he said, the professor had neglected to check his clock time. Then Lauterbach indicated the positions of the sun and the moon, and the time of the eclipse computed for Wittenberg, just as his teacher, Professor Reinhold, has taught him to do, appended to these data his own observations, whose times he had read from the Wittenberg church clock, and explained that he corrected these times subsequently by observing the sunrise. After taking the correction into consideration *his* computations completely agreed with the Copernican times.

Then the student Lauterbach took the liberty of pointing out to the Leipzig University professor the errors in the main work, errors partly of the typesetter, partly of the author. In particular, the young man denounced several errors in chapters twenty and twenty-nine, and asked Professor Rheticus why he had failed to correct these glaring errors. (Cf. L. A. Birkenmajer, op. cit.)

Rheticus took a furlough. In July, 1545, he was in Feldkirch, the next spring he went to see G. Cardano in Milan. In July, 1546, and on January 1, 1547, the Leipzig University vainly summoned him to return. On February 23, 1548, in a letter written from Basel, Rheticus excused himself on the ground of illness, but he seems meanwhile to have studied medicine under Konrad Gesner in Zurich; for on January 27, 1548, he dedicated to the Magisters and Professor of the Leipzig University a short essay on the advantages of the transversal sections of implements and on a new division of the wicket (published in Gesner Pandectarum Libri XXI), and in this work he praised Gesner as his teacher in medicine. At that time he must have been regarded as mentally ill, for Lucas Gauricius wrote under Rheticus' horoscope (that he had acquired from Reinhold's estate among a collection of other horoscopes, including those of Luther and Melanchthon): "Returned from Italy and gone mad, he died in April, 1547."

Kepler, too, reported that Rheticus had pondered so long over the peculiar orbit of Mars that in the end he lost his mind.

But in 1548 Rheticus returned to Leipzig in excellent health, and stayed for another two years among the Saxons.

A certain Jakob Kroeger wrote the following strange marginalia about Rheticus in his book: "Prominent mathematician who lived and taught for some time in Leipzig, but in 1550 fled from this city on account of sexual offenses *(sodomitica et Italica peccata);* I knew him."

A certain Hommel succeeded Rheticus at the Leipzig University.

On October 1, 1550, Rheticus, still in Leipzig, published a yearbook for 1551. Perhaps he was egged on by the example of Reinhold who had published yearbooks for 1550 and 1551 at the beginning of 1550; incidentally, Reinhold was busy with the printing of his Prussian Tables in which he used values for the length of the year that deviated somewhat from the Copernican values.

In the preface to his yearbook Rheticus protested against this crime of Reinhold. However, he avoided mentioning Reinhold by name. But he took this opportunity to quote a conversation in which Copernicus had complained about the slight exactitude of the ancients and his own inexactitude.

In the same text Rheticus also related how, during his Italian voyages, he had hoped to increase his knowledge of the world, but that it had been in far-off Prussia that he had learned the new theory of the greatest of astronomers, Copernicus, whose work was then published under his supervision.

At the same printer's (W. Guenther, in Leipzig) Rheticus also published a book of tables; in a preliminary notice he explained his plans in dialogue form and declared emphatically that nothing must be attacked, touched or changed in the work of Copernicus.

By the end of 1550 he seems to have turned his back on Leipzig and Germany.

From 1557 on he lived in Cracow; according to his notice on the works of Johann Werner (1557) he had chosen Cracow as his place for observations because it lies on the same meridian as Frauenburg. In order to fulfill the wish of his teacher that the positions of the stars be observed anew, he had a forty-five-foot obelisk erected, with the help of Johann Boner; for no instrument, he says, is better than the obelisk; armillary rings, wickets, astrolabes and quadrants are human inventions, while the obelisk, erected by order of God, surpasses them all.

Did he still find time to observe the stars? He was then absorbed by the computations for his important Tables which his pupil, L. V. Otho, completed and published twenty-two years after Rheticus' death: the *Opus Palatinum.*

On August 25, 1563, at 7.30 P.M., when it was found in Cracow that the conjunction of Jupiter and Saturn was in accord with the data of the Prussian Tables, Rheticus was asked by a few friends of his to explain to them the work of Copernicus.

Then, after many long years, he took up the Book of Revolutions and meditated upon it once more. On October 28, 1563, he wrote about it to Hagecius asking him for help. At that time, he also received an offer to go to Wallachia: four hundred thalers and free lodging for six years, probably as a physician; he rejected it. A few years later, in 1567, he wrote that he loved astronomy and chemistry, but lived from medicine. He had the same interests as Paracelsus.

The following year he wrote to Ramus in Paris that he had completed three Books on triangles and planned new Books on triangles and on celestial phenomena; that he was at work on the great tables to which he had already devoted twelve years of his life; but that he was hard pressed trying to solve Ramus' great problem, to wit, the liberation of astronomy from hypotheses and the establishment of its foundations on observation alone. For this purpose, he wrote, tables of the irregular motions must be drawn up, from which one could find the positions of the stars and all celestial phenomena as easily as from yearbooks. The shaky Ptolemaic theory must be replaced by the true and certain theory of the motions of the heavenly bodies, based on the obelisk that was used by the ancient Egyptians. THUS HE WOULD CREATE A GERMAN ASTRONOMY FOR HIS GERMANS. *(Germanis meis Germanicam astronomiam condo.)* He also projected a book on astrology, and seven books on chemistry; he loved chemistry with all his heart, he wrote, and had already penetrated into its deeper mysteries . . .

What a development in thirty years: from the enthusiastic disciple of Copernicus' new doctrine, in 1539, to the creator of a German astronomy, through the obelisk, in 1568!

In 1572, after the death of the last Jagellon, Rheticus was among the prophets who predicted that only seven kings would now follow, etc. He was then the personal physician of a Polish prince. Later he went to Kaschau in Hungary where he died on December 4, 1574.

Still Rheticus remains in our memory as the enthusiastic disciple who preferred sacrifices to compromises, and who staked his career and perhaps his reputation for the sake of the truth. And he is the man to whom the world owes its greatest revolution, the Copernican.

In their striving for good, and their fondness for evil, men usually act without much resolution.

It is a poor business to cast suspicion on the honesty of honest people. Naturally, the honest people often appear vulgar among great men and in the crowd. Untouched by the purest thoughts of the great man and frightened by his ruthless deeds, they usually betray him for a piece of silver or because of a tiny fear; in order to avoid discomfort they betray him as easily and as naturally as if they were doing something good and just and true.

And the great man himself? Does his constant reference to that aristocratic adversary of popular enlightenment and education, that alleged author of the theorem of Pythagoras and the harmony of the spheres, suggest only the revolutionary philosopher's contempt for mankind or—a higher wisdom?

Was then Copernicus not right?

He was completely conscious of the fact that he must appear absurd to everyone who could not follow his computations. But he appeared equally absurd to the mathematicians, also.

Is it not the beautiful privilege of the insane man to believe that the whole world is standing on its head and that he alone is walking upright, that he alone is sensible, that he alone in the whole world possesses the truth? Is it not the despair of the madman that he cannot convert mankind to his own madness?

And does not every thinking man know that moment before the intellectual abyss, when in the face of the all-too-complicated coils of the spirit or the abstract sciences he wonders: is not all this too complicated to be true? Is not the truth the simplest of all things on earth, as simple as God?

Did not Copernicus seem to the whole world, for forty or fifty years, to live in such a perpetual fit of weakness of the intellectual?

But—dream of a madman or no—he proved right against all mankind!

44

FUNERAL SONG

The beautiful, too, must die . . .
SCHILLER, *Nänie*

"I was this afternoon with Mr. Secretary at his office, and helped to hinder a man of his pardon, who was condemned for a rape. The Under-Secretary was willing to save him; but I told the Secretary he could not pardon him without a favourable report from the Judge; besides, he was a fiddler, and consequently a rogue, and deserved hanging for something else, and so he shall swing."
DEAN SWIFT to Stella

ON DECEMBER 8, 1542, friend Giese wrote to friend Donner about friend Copernicus: "Since Copernicus even in his days of good health liked retirement, only a few friends would probably stand sympathetically at the side of the gravely ill man, yet we are all his debtors on account of his pure soul, his integrity and his extensive learning. I know that he always counted you among the most faithful of his associates. Therefore I beg you to stand by him protectingly if his fate requires this, and to assume the care of the man whom together with me you have always loved, in order that he may not lack brotherly help in his affliction and that we do not appear ungrateful toward a friend who has abundantly earned our love and gratitude."

In the last years of his life Copernicus still had to experience the bitterest feelings of a man of spirit. The conflicts and torments connected with the radical decision as to whether he should publish his work or not; the dreadful pain of having to hand in an incomplete book that was the only book of his life, but that he had not had the strength to complete; the humiliations he suffered through that Tartufe named Johannes Dantiscus; his grief over his friend Anna; his sorrow over his exiled friend Sculteti; his sorrow over the degenerating century, his wrath at the darkening of the spiritual world, at the growing reaction; the great solitude of his old age; his hatred for the stupid obscurantists who spoiled and falsified his book with their prefaces about hypotheses; and the fear of death, which was heralded by illness and weakness; the infinitely painful regret of an astronomer at the tiny span of man's lifetime—at best it is eighty years, but the stars live such long days and nights!

The old man's strength was waning. Fever weakened him and he was compelled to give up his official duties (as Felix Reich wrote to Dantiscus on May 3, 1538). On September 15, 1540, in view of his old age and his frequent illnesses he arranged for his nephew to succeed him. At Easter, 1541, he made his last trip: to Königsberg, as a consultant physician.

He also began to receive the first news about the reception of his theory. The Narratio Prima, thanks to Rheticus and his friend Achilles P. Gasser, the young physician in Feldkirch, went out into the world from Danzig and Basel. Gemma Frisius in Louvain and A. Caprinus in Cracow evinced their interest. And Erasmus Reinhold perhaps sent him his commentaries on Peurbach's Planetary Theory in which he refers to the work of Copernicus without going into his theory; nor does he mention Copernicus by name, but only writes that a new Prussian scientist, on the basis of many observations, had reformed astronomy and was preparing to publish his definitive book. Reinhold's book was published in April, 1542. Melanchthon wrote a poem for it, and he surely would not have tolerated any open praise of Copernicus' theory; he had reacted to the Narratio Prima bitterly and negatively enough, in a letter to Burkard Mithobius (dated October 16, 1541): "Some think it is a distinguished achievement to construct such a crazy thing as that Prussian astronomer who moves the earth and fixes the sun. Verily, wise rulers should tame the unrestraint of men's minds!"

In June, 1542, Copernicus, perhaps provoked by Osiander's epistolary insinuations, wrote his dedication to Pope Paul III. With the same unshakable pride he had displayed against the Nuremberg Lutherans, Copernicus insists here against the head of the Catholic church on the truth and solidity of his new theory. He was not a philosopher, a man of the world in the style of Erasmus of Rotterdam who evaded, and took back, and recanted, in order, it is true, to shoot sharper arrows the next time.

At the end of May, 1542, when the first two sheets of the book were set in type by Petrejus, Copernicus received a galley proof. When he saw Osiander's arrogant forgery he fell into the most violent rage; his grief and fury may have aggravated his illness, for he had a hemorrhage followed by a paralysis of the right side and remained unconscious for several days.

At the beginning of the winter of 1542 his condition caused so much concern to his friends that Donner wrote about it to Giese, whereupon Giese wrote Donner the letter quoted above.

How alone the old man was!

We know that Dantiscus had driven Anna, the poor old man's woman-friend or housekeeper or nurse, from his home in order to save Poland or raise the morality of the world, and in the name of God.

Perhaps the Bishop of Ermland by God's grace warned the younger Frauenburg canons against having too close contact with the half-outlawed revolutionary old man? Did not Copernicus have intercourse with Lutherans, that is to say heretics, that is to say agitators? So he was a suspect, harmful to one's career, dangerous for the salvation of one's soul. And had not this old man written a book *De Revolutionibus* in which he taught that the earth was moving? In what sense? And what revolutions?

The old man was ill. A hemorrhage. A heart attack. A paralysis. The illness was protracted. Gemma Frisius, professor of Louvain, solicitously asked professor Dantiscus about the health of the famous astronomer, Copernicus. Solicitously Bishop Dantiscus, the friend of great men and all the great of the earth, replied that the end was feared within the next few days. This was at the beginning of 1543.

At that time Copernicus must have, remembering Thomas Aquinas, written with heavy fingers on a bookmark that groan: "O brevity of life, and our miserable knowledge; and most of it escapes us through the sieve of memory!"

He died on May 24, 1543. The faithful old Giese (in his letter to Rheticus of July 26, 1543) described it thus: "since I also wish that your biography of the author that you wrote so elegantly and that I once read, be put before the work freed from Osiander's falsification, and since I think that nothing is missing in your story except the end of his life—he died on the ninth day before the first of June, after a hemorrhage and the paralysis of the right side that followed; many days before he had lost his memory and intellectual vigor, and his ready book he saw only in his last hour, on the same day that he died."

He died, and so he was spared the shame of the failure of his Revolutions.

Christine Stulpawitz, the wife of the Prussian ducal army's kettle-drummer, came equipped with a letter of recommendation by Albrecht of Prussia and ran from one canon to another in Frauenburg; she wanted her inheritance, she was Copernicus' niece . . . (I am Stulpawitz, the niece, Your Reverences, and where is the cash, and there is also the unbleached linen, and. . . . I am Stulpawitz, the niece, Your Reverences, my husband is the Prussian duke's kettledrummer at Königsberg, here is the duke's letter, and there is also a night cap of fox-skin. . . . I am Stulpawitz, the niece, Your Reverences).

There was also the lovely Regina, the wife of a Stargard merchant, Copernicus' youngest niece. Her children received 550 marks at the division of the estate, a sum not to be sneezed at.

And Copernicus' tower was sold to the highest bidder. And Copernicus' successor was a canon and enjoyed a sumptuous life. And vicar Dr. Fabian Emmerich, the physician, inherited a medical textbook. And the canons inherited the library. And Tiedemann Giese, Bishop of Kulm, became Bishop of Ermland, and died. And Rheticus did not remain for long professor at Leipzig and soon had to take to his heels; he either made himself objectionable sexually, or a sexual slander was invented about him in order to discredit the Copernican; he shook the dust of Germany off his feet and went to Poland; he died in Hungary.

The old canon was buried in the Frauenburg Cathedral, beside his great uncle, Watzelrode, who after all had worked his way up to the position of bishop. Masses were said for his soul; and his freehold estates were auctioned off.

In 1581 a monument was erected next to his grave on the wall of the church.

In 1746 Copernicus' monument had to cede its place. The monument to Bishop Szembek superseded it.

In 1746, there was in all Poland and Prussia, in all the world, no better place for the great, world-famous, sublime Bishop Szembek than the very spot where Copernicus' monument stood.

Pereat Copernicus! Long live the dead bishop Szembek!

And so nothing remained of Copernicus, except a few signed books that had belonged to him, a few notes by him and about him, a few friends who died soon after he died, a few vague memories, and his book which was read rarely enough.

And naturally his Revolutions!—the Copernican system . . . the greatest intellectual revolution in the history of mankind . . . naturally.

. . . . .

". . . and so he shall swing!"

BOOK SEVEN

THE SLOW TRIUMPH

GIORDANO BRUNO
ST

45

THE READERS

St. Anthony was never guilty of washing his feet.

HOWARD W. HAGGARD, M.D.

O fie! says Adams, O fie! He is indeed a wicked man!

HENRY FIELDING, Joseph Andrews

COPERNICUS was dead. His Revolutions were published. From the publisher's point of view the greatest revolution in world history was a failure. The broad public could not read the book because it was written in Latin. The educated public did not want to read it. And what about the specialists?

A few hundred people bought the book, a few dozen studied it, a few made use of the computations contained in it. Many scientists noted its errors, errors of computation, textual errors, author's errors, typesetter's errors.

A cold admiration was bestowed upon the learned astronomer, Copernicus, the observer of the heavens was appreciated, he was called the reformer of astronomy and a second Ptolemy, for the Renaissance was always generous with pompous titles and paeans of praise.

But Copernicus the revolutionary was condemned all over Europe. Although the founder of the Copernican system was praised, the system itself was termed absurd and anti-religious. By the end of the sixteenth century it seemed discredited, liquidated, almost forgotten.

The Lutheran church, once it had come of age was, like all reform movements, extremely distrustful of reform, and especially after the tragic peasant wars, emphatically condemned Copernicus.

Calvin quoted against Copernicus, as a higher astronomical authority, Psalm 93: "The world also is established, that it cannot be moved," and he asked: "Who will venture to place the authority of Copernicus above that of the Holy Spirit?"

The Catholic church, which at first ignored Copernicus' "hypotheses," struck out when the Polish astronomer's second great herald, Giordano Bruno, made too much noise in Europe about the new doctrine. Upon the recommendation of the Inquisition Bruno was publicly burned in Rome, in 1600. And when, with Galileo, a great new defender of the Copernican system appeared on the Italian scene and put the pope's arguments against the new system in the mouth of a simpleton, thus making a fool out of the Holy Father, the Inquisition forced him to recant on his knees, and put his work and Copernicus' Revolutions on the index, in 1615.

Cardinal Baronius said: "The Holy Spirit intended to teach us how to go to Heaven, not how the heavens go."

And the Catholic church wrote one of the most curious chapters of its "science by decree": "The first proposition, that the sun is the center and does not revolve about the earth, is foolish, absurd; false in theology and heretical, because expressly contrary to Holy Scripture.

"The second proposition, that the earth revolves about the sun and is not the center, is absurd, false in philosophy and, from a theological point of view at least, opposed to the true faith."

True, Blaise Pascal commented on this as follows: "It is not the decree of Rome which will prove that the earth remains at rest; and, if we had constant observations to prove that it does turn, not all the people in the world could stop it from turning, nor could they stop themselves from turning with it."

But in the Universities, Aristotle and Ptolemy held undisputed sway. To astronomers still loyal to or fearful of the church Tycho de Brahe offered his "middle of the road" system that deviated from Ptolemy but left the earth at rest. And laymen and philosophers believed the evidence of their eyes, the teachings of "common sense" and the dogma of the theologians.

Was this the road to world fame? Was this the result of the greatest of all revolutions? And was a whole epoch to take its name from this half-forgotten, liquidated man?

We know the stations of his fame in the sixteenth century: in 1514 Rome invited him to the Lateran Council. Peucer reports that Copernicus was famous as early as 1525. In 1533 Widmanstadt explained the Copernican theory to the Pope in the Vatican gardens. In 1536 Cardinal Schoenberg asked for the manuscript of the Revolutions. In 1540 the Narratio Prima was published in Danzig and Basel. In 1543 the first edition of the Revolutions was published in Nuremberg. In 1551 Reinhold published the Prussian Tables. In 1566, the second printing of the Revolutions, unchanged, and only augmented by the Narratio Prima, was published in Basel. Only in 1617 did the third edition of the Revolutions, edited and revised by Mulerius, appear in Amsterdam.

During the second half of the sixteenth century, in addition to two editions of the Narratio Prima, only two editions of Copernicus' Revolutions were published, but there were more than a hundred editions of textbooks that taught or accepted only the Ptolemaic system.

Copernicus' new theory was rejected in almost all the great countries of Europe.

In Germany the very first editor of the Revolutions, vicar Osiander, by his forged preface, tried to make the Promethean rebel against a cosmic error seem like a lame bungler of world-hypotheses. This preface, Giordano Bruno said later, could have been composed only by an ignoramus for the use of a few other asses.

Rheticus, the first disciple, the courageous, infinitely meritorious author of the First Account, the fiery idealistic youth who is alleged to have become insane for a time pondering over the orbit of Mars, came forth as the defender of the faith against his former friend and colleague, Erasmus Reinhold, and solemnly proclaimed that Copernicus' main work could not be refuted, in fact could not be impugned in the slightest detail. Later after he was forced to flee from Leipzig, he gradually abandoned the study of astronomy and the Copernican system, only in the end to become an alchemist, a doctor, yes, a charlatan in Poland, where he planned his GERMAN astronomy. But the two editions of his preliminary report caused a stir, especially in Basel and Wittenberg.

Were not the repercussions of Copernicus' work great at least in Wittenberg? The patroness of mathematics and astronomy from which came the astronomical works of Reinhold, Melanchthon and Peucer? Between 1540 and 1561 neither Copernicus nor his theory was mentioned in a single lecture at Wittenberg, although Osiander's preface should have curbed the Lutheran agitators (as Schoenberg's printed letter had curbed the Catholic ones).

A few mathematicians or astronomers must have studied Copernicus' book between the spring of 1543 and the fall of 1544 at least enough to enable them to compute in advance certain celestial phenomena with the help of the Copernican Tables, as for instance that Wittenberg pupil of Reinhold's who in his letter to editor Rheticus so severely censured the latter and reproached him for "unpardonable errors of computation."

What did Erasmus Reinhold (the Wittenberg university professor, dean of the faculty from 1549 on and rector of the university from 1550 on) do about Copernicus' Revolutions?

At the end of 1544 he used the Tables of Copernicus' book to cast a horoscope for Martin Luther!

In general he considered the Tables inadequate for the computation of those observations on which Copernicus' main work was founded.

Between 1544 and 1549, despite the war and by dint of superhuman efforts, the same Reinhold computed new orbit elements on the basis of observations by Hipparchus, Ptolemy and Copernicus, and drew up tables according to them. He called these the Prussian Tables, in honor of Duke Albrecht of Prussia. Reinhold says that Copernicus' trigonometry is unsurpassable and that he himself had borrowed most of the famous Prussian's observations; but, he avers, calculation was not the master's forte and for that reason he himself had to compute everything anew.

Reinhold did full honor to the Ptolemaic hypotheses, but he paid no heed to the Copernican system, and did not discuss Copernicus' new conception of the cosmos at all.

For the seventy years that followed the results obtained by the observer and the mathematician were used; but the great revolutionary system of the philosopher was ignored.

As early as 1542, in his commentary on Peurbach's planetary theory Reinhold mentioned Copernicus' work then about to be published, but did not mention Copernicus' name; in the new edition of 1553 he mentioned Copernicus' name several times but not his theory; true, he promised to expound the Copernican theory in his own theory of the moon, but he died before doing this.

In Nuremberg, Johannes Schoner must have thoroughly studied Copernicus' book; in Leipzig, Johannes Hommel (Rheticus' successor at the University of Leipzig) and in Holland, Gemma Frisius admired it, but in 1555 in a letter to Stadius the latter expressed himself with reserve about the idea that the earth moved. According to Birkenmajer, Valentin Steinmetz from Gersbach asserted in his prophecy for 1552 that the Copernican numbers were more accurate than any earlier ones, and that the book interested him for that reason. This seems to be the first reference to the Revolutions that was printed in Germany.

When, soon after the publication of the main work, it became known that Osiander was the author of the preface (on the margin of the preface in copies of the first edition the word Osiander is sometimes written in, or the preface is entirely crossed out, or there is a note to the effect that Rheticus quarrelled with the printer Petrejus or that Rheticus had forced

Osiander to acknowledge his authorship)—and when a public scandal threatened, especially in Lutheran Wittenberg, over this book by a Catholic canon, Melanchthon wrote in his Introduction to Physics: ". . . But here a few, be it out of curiosity or in order to be ingenious, assert that the earth moves and assure us that neither the eighth sphere nor the sun moves, although they ascribe motion to the other heavenly bodies and list the earth among the stars. These jokes are not new. There is still Archimedes' work on the Computation of the Grains of Sand in which he relates that Aristarchus of Samos advanced the contradictory assertion that the sun is at rest and that the earth moves around the sun. And even though keen masters investigate many things in order to occupy their minds, it is, nevertheless, unbecoming publicly to defend such absurd theses, and even harmful because it sets a bad example."

Thereupon Melanchthon quotes the Psalms and enumerates the physical arguments against the motion of the earth. In his own work he expounded only Ptolemy's doctrine, but along with the numerical data of Ptolemy he named also those of Werner and Copernicus. In the second edition, Melanchthon struck out the adjective "absurd" when speaking of the Copernican system, but this adjective continued to be a favorite among Copernicus' adversaries for a long time.

Peucer, Melanchthon's son-in-law, called Copernicus the greatest astronomer since Ptolemy, but considered his theory absurd; and he said that because of its absurdity and remoteness from reality it should be excluded from the universities.

Similarly, Michael Maestlin, Johannes Kepler's teacher at the university of Tübingen, used Copernicus' numerical data in his textbook (Epitome Astronomiae) but did not publicly acknowledge his theory. But through Maestlin Kepler learned of the Copernican system.

Dasypodius ordered an original portrait of Copernicus from Danzig; between 1572 and 1574 he had a copy made of it and set it up with the new clock that he had constructed in the Strassburg cathedral; but this honor was probably meant for the astronomer, not the creator of the new cosmogony; at least there is nothing in the picture to indicate that its owner recognized Copernicus' importance as a thinker.

In 1581 Bishop Kromer ordered that a memorial to Copernicus be erected in the Frauenburg cathedral; a memorial to him was also erected in the Church of St. John at Torun.

The Jesuit Christopher Clavius called Copernicus' hypothesis absurd, but dubbed Copernicus himself the reformer of astronomy; he used the Polish astronomer's observations and catalogue of stars which latter he corrected; *his* book had nineteen editions before 1618.

In Poland, Miechow and Wapowski knew Copernicus' work. Hilarius Wislicza, professor of astronomy at Cracow, computed his yearbook of 1549 on the basis of the Copernican Tables. Master Jo Lathosius, an astronomer at the University of Cracow, computed his yearbook for 1571 on the basis of the Prussian Tables.

And Stanislaus Jacobeus, in his forecast for 1572, reports an experimental verification of the Prussian Tables (according to Birkenmajer and Samuel Dickstein, the latter in *Coup d'oeil sur l'histoire de sciences exactes en Pologne, Cracow, 1933*). On the occasion of the conjunction of Jupiter and Saturn in 1563 many professors and masters of the Cracow University gathered together (among them, Nikolaus Schadeck, Petrus Probosczowicze and Master Joh. Muscenius) and, in accordance with the Prussian Tables, found Jupiter and Saturn so close to each other, that Jupiter covered Saturn. According to the Alfonsine Tables the conjunction should have taken place on another day, but on the day indicated in these older tables the planets were 2 degrees 21 minutes distant from each other. The Cracow professors Schadeck and Probosczowicze who even before had been inclined to accept Copernicus declared that their successor too should follow the more accurate Copernican data. Thereupon Valentin Fontani, M.D. (1536-1618) lectured on astronomy three times during 1578-1580, and in these lectures advanced the Copernican system.

In Italy, Fr. Maurolico, who published his mathematical works in Venice in 1575 wrote in the preface to his chronology, Computus Ecclesiasticus: "May also Copernicus be destroyed, who makes the sun rest and the earth turn like a top and who deserves a whip, rather than a reprimand."

In 1580, Giuseppe Moleto (1531-1588), professor of mathematics at Padua, used the Copernican Tables for his Gregorian Tables of the celestial phenomena; "for the data of the Alfonsine Tables do not tally with the celestial phenomena. And we would still have been obliged to rely upon these tables, if Nicolaus Copernicus, the Hercules of our time, had not ingeniously discovered the inequalities of the motions and adapted his assumptions and numbers to them."

In 1577 Francesco Giuntini praised Copernicus' theory of the sun, but in another passage he condemned it.

G. A. Magini (1555-1617), professor of mathematics at Bologna, took over Copernicus' numerical data and observations and called him the greatest astronomer of all times, but labelled his theory absurd. In 1590 he admitted to Tycho de Brahe that he agreed with the latter's idea of the universe.

Copernicus' theory was thus occasionally mentioned in Italy, but it had no real adherents.

In 1563 Pierre Ramée (Peter Ramus) wrote to Rheticus from Paris that astronomy must at last be freed from hypotheses (Cf. Birkenmajer).

In 1567 Pierre de Mesme called Copernicus ridiculous.

The poet Guillaume du Bartas, in his famous poem *La Semaine* or *La Creation du Monde* condemns the Copernican doctrine; he describes the theory of the "learned German" *(du docte Germain)* as the dream of a proud and restless mind which cared little for the opinion of the many. In the edition of 1583 the publisher S. Goulart of Senlis attacked Copernicus' "absurd" hypothesis.

Montaigne, in his Essais (1580) after discussing the Ptolemaic and Copernican systems, writes: "What shall we reape by it, but only that we neede not care which of the two it be? And who knoweth whether a hundred years hence a third opinion will arise which happily shall overthrow these two precedent?" That is why, Montaigne goes on to say, the same skepticism should be displayed toward the new theories as toward the old (Montaigne, An Apologie of Raymonde Sebonde).

Jean Bodin (1520-1596), the philosopher of Angers, an adversary of Machiavelli and the author of the "Republic," condemned the Copernican theory in his posthumous *Universae Naturae Theatrum;* but as early as 1628 he himself was put on the Index because of his atheism.

The mathematician François Viète (1540-1603) pointed out a mathematical error in Chapter Nine of Book Three of the Revolutions.

The first printed reference to the Copernican theory in England is found in The Castle of Knowledge, an English book written by Robert Recorde (1510?-1588), physician in ordinary to Bloody Mary, as early as 1556. Recorde calls the theory absurd, but he praises its learned author.

John Dee, in his preface to the yearbook for 1557, computed by John Feild, boasts of having advised his friend Feild to use the Tables of Copernicus, "whose writings are established and based upon true, sure and authentic demonstrations."

Thomas Digges (born in 1546), the son of the mathematician Leonhard Digges, wanted to check the Copernican theory against the new star of 1572. In the new edition of his father's *Prognostication Everlasting* printed in 1576 he gave an enthusiastic description of the Copernican theory, translated passages from Book One of the Revolutions, especially from Chapters Eight and Ten, into English and added an explanatory diagram. Thus Englishmen desirous of knowledge could become acquainted with the theory (Cf. Francis R. Johnson, Astronomical Thought in Renaissance England, Baltimore, 1937, pages 98-101, 106, 165). There were six editions of Digges before 1605.

In 1579 he wanted to write commentaries to Copernicus' book, with demonstrations based on the most recent observations; but he was never able to do this task.

William Gilbert (1540-1603), physician in ordinary to Queen Elizabeth, in his book De Magnete (1600) borrowed arguments from Copernicus to prove the daily rotation of the earth.

In Sweden, the oldest Swedish textbook of astronomy was published in 1579; its author was Olof Luth, professor at Upsala; he does not mention Copernicus or his theory.

In Spain, according to Dorothy Stimson, the new regulations for the University of Salamanca, issued in 1561, required that in the three-year course of astrology and mathematics, the students should study first astrology, then Euclid, and then the Ptolemaic or the Copernican system, "ad vota audientium," according to the choice of the students. A doctor of the University of Salamanca, Pater Zuniga (Didacus à Stunica) wrote a commentary on Job, before 1579, which was published in Toledo only in 1584 and in Rome in 1596. In 1616 he was put on the Index of forbidden books with the mention *donec corrigatur* (until corrected). In his book Zuniga declared that the Copernican theory was much simpler and more plausible than the Ptolemaic. He based his assertion that the new theory could not be attacked on Job IX, 6: "which shaketh the earth out of her place, and the pillars thereof tremble."

Only one man in Europe preached the Copernican revolutions: Giordano Bruno.

46

GIORDANO BRUNO

"I have fought . . . it is much . . . Victory lies in the hands of Fate. Be that with me as it may, whoever shall prove conqueror, future ages will not deny, that I did not fear to die, was second to none in constancy, and preferred a spirited death to a craven life."

GIORDANO BRUNO, De monade

"Also he told me that ladies pleased him well; but he had not yet reached Solomon's number."

MOCENIGO, the informer, on Giordano Bruno

GIORDANO BRUNO, "citizen and servant of the world, child of the sun and mother earth," more prosaically the son of a soldier, was born near Nola in the province of Naples in 1548. His father baptized him Felipe; he attended school in Naples, and at the age of fourteen entered a Dominican monastery where Thomas Aquinas had once lived; there Felipe received the name of Giordano, after the River Jordan in Canaan, and was consecrated a priest at the age of twenty-four; there he is said to have written a bold allegory about Noah's ark; there he read for the first time the Book of Revolutions and grasped Copernicus' revolutionary world-view and bold ideas as no one before him had grasped them.

Bruno hated the intellectual dictatorship of that schoolmaster of Christianity, the great pagan Aristotle. Like Bacon he was an enthusiastic admirer of the pre-Socratics, the Stoa and the Pythagoreans, and the neo-Platonists. He studied Nicholas of Cusa, imitated Lully and worshipped Lucretius.

He was as little suited for life in a monastery as Luther. Because he doubted the reality of transubstantiation and the Immaculate Conception, because he read Erasmus' suspect remarks to St. Chrysostom and St.

Jerome, Fathers of the church prohibited by the Index, and because he did not think that Arius was as preposterous as the Catholic doctrinaires pretended he was, he was soon threatened with prosecution. At the age of twenty-eight he left his cowl, his monastery and the whole order of the Inquisitors behind him, fled to Rome, and became a wandering humanist, following the profession of an itinerant and unordained preacher of the truth; for sixteen years he travelled restlessly through Europe, across Italy, Switzerland, France, England, Germany and Bohemia. All the countries were traps for a courageous philosopher who wanted to proclaim that human reason had at last come of age, who never concealed anything, neither a joke nor the truth. Everywhere he preached his poetic cosmopolitan faith, everywhere he was persecuted by the privileged guardians of orthodoxy. By nature he was as trusting as a child, and became a skeptic only through philosophizing. He wrote: "Whoso itcheth to Philosophy must set to work by putting all things to the doubt." After sixteen years of restless wanderings he finally took an eight-year rest—in the dungeons of the Inquisition in Venice and Rome.

In 1579, after many trips through Italy, he went from Catholic Rome to Calvinist Geneva. Far from becoming a Calvinist there, as the legend and the Inquisition charged, he was cited before the Council of the Protestant stronghold because he showed in a pamphlet that a certain Geneva professor had committed twenty foolish errors. Like a Nimrod he went on the hunt for learned asses and wrote extensively on the great asininity that was as ubiquitous as the world soul. Sent before the consistory by the Council and excommunicated, he was compelled to apologize. He hastened to flee from Geneva and Calvinism which he hated, as well as from the meagre life he had eked out as a proof-reader.

At the University of Toulouse he acquired his doctor's degree, lectured on astronomy, and was driven out by the *furor scholasticus*. In 1581 he went to Paris; King Henry III had heard of the learned "artist of memory" from Italy and offered him the job of assistant (but paid) professor of philosophy, probably at the College de France (also called the College de Cambrai). Bruno lectured on the Ars Magna of Raymond Lully, the founder of the Lully Art (1234-1315), the Spaniard who undertook to transform the ocean into pure gold if only it were of mercury. Bruno was so little pampered by life and so thankful for every favor that he dedicated his first work, "On the Shadows of Ideas," to the lascivious Valois and even praised him later in Germany.

Armed with the French king's recommendation to his ambassador in London, Bruno went to England in 1583. He lectured and conducted disputations at Oxford; on one occasion he defended the Copernican theory against the reactionary Aristotelians before Adalbert Laski, a Polish prince who was trying to dissuade the English from continuing delivering arms to the Muscovites. If one is to believe Bruno, he won an easy triumph before him. In London, too, he was victorious in a similar disputation, at least so he declared in his work published shortly afterward under the title of "The Ash Wednesday Supper," in which he defended the Copernican theory and castigated the English and particularly the brutal customs prevalent among English scholars and students in Oxford, all of them just as superstitious and pedantic as the scholars in Geneva. But he liked the landscape, the climate and the handsome nimble white lambs and girls of England.

These were the happiest years, spent at the court of the maiden Queen Elizabeth and in the home of Michel de Castelnau, the French ambassador, with whom he stayed. He wrote: "I stayed in his home as his gentleman—only that." Between 1583 and 1585 he published seven books in London, among them his most important and extensive works. (The Thirty Seals and Seal of Seals—on mnemonics; The Ash Wednesday Supper; On Cause, Principle and The One—on metaphysics; The Infinite Universe and its Worlds—his pantheistic philosophy of the Infinite; The Expulsion of the Triumphant Beast, Proposed by Jove, Effected by the Council, Revealed by Mercury, Related by Sophia, Heard by Saulino, and set down by the Nolan—an attack of the churches and all blind faith; The Cabala of the Steed Like Unto Pegasus, With the Addition of the Ass of Cyllene; The Transports of Intrepid Souls, On Heroic Enthusiasm—seventy sonnets in praise of Truth and Beauty.

However, Bruno's books sold badly and his fame among his contemporaries was not very great. A heretic in Italy, an offender against the public peace in Geneva, he found indifference in England, almost whips in France, prohibitions to teach and reside in Germany, and finally the dungeon and the stake in Italy.

Bruno was the first to give public lectures in England on Copernicus and his doctrine. In London he frequented Sir Philip Sidney, a man of letters and courtier, and his friend Fulke Greville, one of Queen Elizabeth's lovers. (He may also have met Bacon; Shakespeare, however, in a few passages of Troilus and Cressida, King John and The Merry Wives of Windsor, describes the earth as motionless in the centre of the universe.)

In October, 1585, he returned to France with Castelnau, and on the way both of them were robbed down to their shirts. Travelling from one capital to another at that time was more painful and dangerous than an expedition to the savages is today; everywhere one found the plague and smallpox, bugs and religious wars; in France you were killed because of the form of your sacraments, in London because of your foreign manners, in Germany you had to share your bed and your bowl of food with every filthy tramp and on every road you met peddlers and saints, beggar monks and students. In Marburg Bruno was not allowed to teach. He stayed for a year and a half in Wittenberg where he lectured and made a farewell speech in praise of Luther. In Prague he vainly tried to obtain support from Emperor Rudolph II who later subsidized Tycho Brahe and Kepler. At Frankfort the Council forbade him to stay with his printer; he went to Zurich and then came back to Frankfort.

Giovanni Mocenigo, a thirty-four-year-old Venetian, formerly delegate of Venice at the Inquisition and now their agent provocateur, sent Bruno a letter inviting him to Venice as his teacher of mnemonics and other arts. In August, 1591, to the astonishment of learned Europe, the unfortunate Bruno went to Venice, perhaps because he was homesick for Italy. His promising pupil threatened him, denounced him, attacked him, fettered him, locked him up in his cellar and delivered him to the hangmen of the Inquisition in May, 1592.

During his trial before the Venetian Inquisition Bruno told the story of his life and his ideas. O perfume of life! O wild savor of his ideas! . . . Bruno had combated every false authority and feared no power on earth. Poverty did not disturb him, he despised censorship, he saw through the churches, he built mighty structures on his own strength and superiority. He considered himself an "awakener." He hated deification of suffering by the Christian religion. If the measure of man sank in the Copernican universe, Bruno taught that it also rose again because now man could encompass the universe. In the Ash Wednesday Supper, he wrote proudly of himself: "the Nolan liberated man's spirit and the sciences."

Bruno behaved like the founder of a religion, but he did not want to speak to the masses whom he despised, he wanted to reach the elite. Usually a man wins his heavenly kingdom on this earth. Bruno never influenced the masses, but he did influence Spinoza, perhaps Molière and Shakespeare, Leibnitz, and surely Hegel, Schelling and Goethe.

He was not a methodical mind, but half-poet and half-philosopher; he wanted to reform the people's morality. In the "Expulsion of the Triumphant Beast" he wrote: ". . . we call those virtues which by a certain trick and custom are so called and believed, though their effects and fruits are condemned by all sense and natural reason; such as open knavery and folly, the malignity of usurping laws and of possessors of meum and tuum; the strongest being the most rightful possessor, and he being the most worthy who is most solicitous, most industrious, and the first occupant of those gifts and parts of the earth which Nature, and consequently God, gives to all indifferently."

Bruno wanted to set up his universal religion, his religion of nature in the opposition to the revealed religions. He taught that "God, the infinite creator, created an infinite image of himself in the infinite universe." He called himself the lover of God, and, after his native Nola, the Nolan, and his philosophy, the Nolan philosophy. Like Cusa he cried out enthusiastically: "O altitudo!"

After three days spent in the dungeons of the Venetian Inquisition Bruno was led before his judges. The secretary of the Inquisition has left us a description of his average size, his chestnut brown beard and his appearance which corresponded to his age, then about forty. His gestures were vivacious, in a manner characteristic of Southerners.

He declared to the Inquisitors: "I hold the universe to be infinite as result of the infinite divine power; for I think it unworthy of divine goodness and power to have produced merely one finite world when it was able to bring into being an infinity of worlds. . . ."

In the fourth century the church had issued fifteen edicts against heresy; in the thirteenth century it set up its Inquisition, an organization designed to fetter Europe's thinking. The procedure of the Inquisition was secret, its victims vanished as though swallowed up by the ground and reappeared only dressed in a shirt on the way to the stake, escorted by priests brandishing torches and droning hymns.

Any imbecile could write a denunciation against anybody, the Inquisition accepted every denunciation gratefully, the accused never learned the names of the accusers and the witnesses, and usually not even the nature of his alleged or real crime.

After a period of relative mildness, Pope Paul III, at the instigation of the founder of the Society of Jesus, Don Inigo Lopez de Recalde, called Ignatius Loyola, and upon the advice of Cardinal Caraffa, set up the Roman Inquisition after the Spanish model, on July 21, 1542. Only a few months later Copernicus, as though with deliberate irony, published his Revolutions and dedicated it to that very same Pope (was this in order intimately to connect at one point at least the fathers of the new long war between religion and science?).

All the witnesses and officials of the Inquisition were bound by oath to eternal silence. The accuser was also the judge. The accused was not allowed to have any counsel. He had to prove his innocence without knowing the nature of his crime, but he was not allowed to cite witnesses or to have any contacts with the outside world; he was obliged to answer a thousand questions, to give a thousand identical answers to questions repeated a thousand times, and to avoid falling into any trap that might be set for him a thousand times. . . .

Giordano Bruno was the first, since the triumph of Christianity, open to return to the independence of the Greek thinkers. Against the theologians, he demanded the right to philosophize independently, the right to freedom of thought and speech. He took his wisdom wherever he found it, from the heathens, the Jews, the Christians, even from the Cabala.

The Inquisition charged him not only with heresy, but also with being a leader of the heretics; of having written books in which he praised Elizabeth of England and other heretical rulers and many things hostile to religion; of being a runaway monk who had spent many years abroad, in Genoa, Geneva and England and even in Wittenberg where he praised Luther; of having denied the birth of Christ from a virgin and of having published a pamphlet in London, entitled "On the triumph of the Beast," —by which name he referred to the Pope, in addition to other loathsome and highly absurd theories; of having denied transubstantiation at the age of eighteen; of having been prosecuted for heresy by the Roman Inquisition and of having escaped from it!

In September, 1592, the Roman Inquisition demanded the extradition of Bruno. At first Venice resisted but finally yielded, for after all he was not a Venetian, but only a Neapolitan. He had spent eight months in the prison at Venice. On February 27, 1593, Bruno disappeared into the torture dungeons of the Roman Inquisition. The world no longer heard anything of him. He seemed to have been buried alive. No voice came from his cell. Aside from inquisitors and torturers he was not allowed to receive any visitors. In those days prisoners were often put in irons, often tortured. Campanella was tortured twelve times, the last time for forty hours. A notary was present and recorded the confessions of the victim; if he failed to confess, he was tortured more cruelly. One of the Roman Inquisitors was Cardinal Bellarmin, the learned Jesuit who also played his evil part in the trials of Paolo Sarpi, the Venetian monk, of Galileo and of the Copernican theory. Only on February 4, 1599, did the Inquisition open Bruno's trial.

He remained unshakable. On January 20, 1600, the Pope presided at the session of the Inquisition. Bruno was determined not to recant; he swore that he had never published heretical doctrines, and that the servants of the Inquisition were slanderers.

He was condemned. As usual, the church decided to deliver him over to the secular arm. He was defrocked, excommunicated. The Bishop of

Sidonia received the considerable sum of 27 scudi "for the degradation of Giordano Bruno, the heretic." The governor of Rome was told: ". . . take him under your jurisdiction subject to your decision, so as to be punished with due chastisement; beseeching you, however, as we do earnestly beseech you, so to mitigate the severity of your sentence with respect to his body that there may be no danger of death or of the shedding of blood. So we, Cardinals, Inquisitor and General, whose names are written beneath decree!" This request was somewhat conditional only because it could not be heeded in any case.

"When all these things were done," writes Gaspar Schopp, a freshly converted Catholic and eyewitness, "he said not a word except in a menacing way, 'Perchance your fear in passing judgment on me is greater than mine in receiving it.' "

Only nine days after it had been pronounced was the sentence carried out. In the archives of the Brotherhood of Pity of St. John the Beheaded, in the journal of the Proveditore, there is the following entry: "Justice done on an impenitent heretic. At the second hour of the night information came that justice would be done on an impenitent friar in the morning. Hence, at the sixth hour of the night, the Comforters and the chaplain assembled at S. Ursula and went to the prison in the Tower of Nona, entered the chapel, and offered up the prayers. To them was consigned the man Giordano Bruno, son of Gni. Bruno, an apostate friar of Nola in the Kingdom, an impenitent. He was exhorted by our brothers in all love, and two Fathers of the Order of St. Dominic, two of the Order of Jesus, two of the new Church and one of St. Jerome were called in. These with all loving zeal and much learning, showed him his error, yet he stood firm throughout and to the end in his accursed obstinacy, setting his brain and mind to a thousand errors and vaingloryings; and he continued steadfastly stubborn while conducted by the Servants of Justice to the Campo di Fiori, and there being stripped and bound to a stake, was burned alive. Throughout, our Brotherhood sang litanies and the Consolers exhorted him to the very last to overcome his obstinacy. But thus ended his agony and his wretched life."

Bruno's highest goal was: to know the truth and declare it!

Only two and a half years later (August 7, 1603), were the writings of the hated pantheist put on the Index where they still remain. Even today the Index still prohibits many great books, although the Inquisition no longer drives poets insane, as it did poor Tasso, and no longer refutes philosophers with flaming arguments, as it refuted the good Vanini by burning him in Toulouse, seventeen years after the execution of Bruno.

(But we can comfort ourselves with the thought that new tyrants persecute poets and execute philosophers!)

On February 17, 1600, Giordano Bruno was burned at the stake in Rome because the earth moved (and he refused to keep silent about this most recently discovered secret).

Bruno burned for Copernicus. Inspired by Copernicus he created a magnificent cosmogony. At the time of the lowest ebb in the fame of Copernicus who insulted the most sacred belief of the Renaissance, to wit that man was the measure of all things, Bruno dubbed him the great liberator of mankind. With greater poetic fire and a more sacrificial heroism he repeated Rheticus' declaration that a new era of thought and science had begun with Copernicus.

Bruno also found an occasion to mention Osiander's preface, which he recognized as a forgery. He termed Osiander "an ignorant and presumptuous ass who, to be sure, alleges that he furthers the interests of the author, but permits his like to pick lettuce and vegetables from that book" (La Cena de le Ceneri).

In *De Immenso* Bruno reprinted a whole chapter from Copernicus' Revolutions.

He indulged in sweeping generalizations. He was as generous with innumerable and inconceivable infinitudes as the most modern astronomers. But unfortunately he was unable to prove what he thought. He was "God-intoxicated" like Spinoza.

He considered the universe limitless and infinite; but only the universe was eternal; his worlds decline and pass away, and their substance forms new combinations. The center of the universe, he thought, was where the observer stood; nature was alive and articulate. Bruno, the mystic, was also an animist.

According to his vision, the fixed stars were suns like our own and there were countless suns freely suspended in limitless space, all of them surrounded by planets like our own earth, peopled with living beings. The sun, he taught, was only one star among many, singled out by us because it is so close to us. The sun had no central position in the boundless infinite.

Everywhere in the universe dwelled spirit, spiritual beings, separated from one another only by physical distances.

"There is only one heaven, an immeasurable domain of light-giving and illuminated bodies."

Nothing exists outside the infinite universe and its eternal unchangeable substance. The divine universal soul permeates it. God is not outside the world but inside it, its supreme cause, principle and unity wherein all oppositions are resolved in eternal harmony.

This unity is reflected even in the smallest thing, the minimum or the monad, which is both material and psychic. Nothing in the world is lifeless. The universe and everything in it have a soul. And the world is moved by inner forces, not from without. The same spirit is active in everything, the same reason inherent in matter too, but it does not affect everything in the same manner, measure and degree; these depend on the level of organization: for the universe is ordered in a continual hierarchy from the lowest to the highest things.

The reason of the highest "organism," the Cosmos, is called by Bruno God. God is the nature of nature, the monad of monads. How can we worship Him better than by studying His laws, the laws of nature? Every discovery of a natural law is a moral deed: it increases our capacity for making our lives rational. True religion means to aspire to return to that "monad of all monads."

Art is a mediator. If man seems to be entirely lost in external infinitude, he finds himself again in internal infinitude, his ultimate destiny. Therefore the inhabitants of other worlds must not seek God in our world; for they have Him in their own world and in themselves.

This pantheist with an unquenchable thirst for the truth was condemned by almost all his contemporaries. For nearly two centuries he was ignored, until a young German F. H. Jacobi (1743-1819), a friend of Lessing's, referred to him in his letters on the doctrine of Spinoza. Some thought they could prove his influence on Descartes who, however, had probably never read him. But Bruno's astronomical theology and his imaginative metaphysics influenced Spinoza, Leibnitz, Goethe, Herder, Jacobi and Schelling. Hegel said that Bruno was a bacchic mind.

Many Copernicans rejected Bruno's views as absurd. Copernicus had pushed up the eighth heaven and the stars to an immense distance, but he let them remain fixed, and placed the sun in the center of the universe!

Giordano Bruno, while helping to spread the Copernican theory by his lectures and writings, especially in England and Germany, again dethroned the sun, making it a star among other stars!

In 1889 Bruno's monument was unveiled in Rome. 30,000 Romans assembled for the ceremony. Pope Leo XIII spent the entire day on his knees before the statue of St. Peter, fasting and praying. He denounced the runaway monk Giordano Bruno as "a man of impure and abandoned life: a double renegade, a heretic formally condemned, whose obstinacy against the Church endured unbroken even to his last breath. He possessed no remarkable scientific knowledge, for his own writings condemn him of a degraded materialism and show that he was entangled in commonplace errors. He had no splendid adornments of virtue, for as evidence against his moral character there stand those extravagancies of wickedness and corruption into which all men are driven by passions unresisted. He was the hero of no famous exploits and did no signal service to the state; his familiar accomplishments were insincerity, lying and perfect selfishness, intolerance of all who disagreed with him, abject meanness and perverted ingenuity in adulation."

In brief, Giordano Bruno was a great man and a winged messenger of the truth.

Already in "The Chandler," his only comedy which he wrote "in a few burning days" and which was published in Paris in 1582, he lashed out against the fools and pedants, especially among the clergymen. His favorite character in it was Panfurio, the fool and pedant, a personage conceived in the style of Rabelais, Plautus, Aretino and Machiavelli. Here Bruno castigates not only the scholastic, that orthodox of all orthodoxies, but also his time.

This farce is said to have influenced Cyrano de Bergerac's *Le Pedant Joué,* and through Bergerac, Molière. Molière replied to the accusation that he had plagiarized it by saying: "One takes one's goods wherever one finds them." Shakespeare's Holofernes in Love's Labours Lost is also supposed to have certain traits of Bruno's Panfurio.

47

TYCHO DE BRAHE

This phenix among astronomers . . .
KEPLER

GASSENDI and Dreyer, his biographers, termed him the greatest observer among astronomers.

On his deathbed he asked his assistant Kepler to publish the gigantic mass of astronomical observations he had collected during his life with the diligence of a bee and which, because of their accuracy, could serve as a basis for any new planetary theory; and he wanted Kepler to make them the basis of Tycho's system. But Kepler was an enthusiastic Copernican and used Tycho's immense contribution for demonstrating and developing the Copernican theory.

Tycho rejected the Copernican theory as absurd. But he had also destroyed the scholastic idea of solid crystal spheres. He had created a third cosmogony, but in accordance with the Holy Scripture had left the earth motionless.

However, against his will Tycho, by the immense weight of his observations, strengthened the Copernican system which without him might have remained an unconfirmed hypothesis.

Copernicus and Tycho de Brahe were the last great astronomers to make their computations and observations without telescopes, logarithm tables and pendulum clocks (necessary for measuring time accurately).

Tycho de Brahe was born in 1546, three years after Copernicus' death, on the Knudstrup family estate. He was the oldest son of the Dane, Otto Brahe, and his wife, Beate Bille. His twin brother was stillborn, but later he had nine brothers and sisters. He was baptized Tyge (and latinized his name into Tycho). His uncle Joergen stole him from his parents when he was barely one year old. Tyge's parents had promised his childless uncle their firstborn child; but after the tragic loss of his twin brother they were obviously unwilling to separate themselves from him.

Tyge's uncle was wealthier than his father and hired a tutor for the boy at Tostrup. At the age of seven Tyge began to study Latin; soon he was able to write Latin verses, and later he even wrote some good verses. At the age of thirteen he went to Copenhagen in order to study philosophy and law and become a statesman as his uncle desired.

However, when an eclipse of the sun forecast for August 21, 1560, occurred on that day, the fact that "men could foretell the motions of the stars so accurately, that they could prophesy their places and relative positions" struck the boy as something divine. For the sum of two thalers he bought the works of Ptolemy (in the Basel edition of 1551, with Georg Trapezunt's translation of the Almagest) and studied them for three years. Then, with his mentor, Vedel, who was only four years older than himself, he went to the Leipzig University.

Instead of studying law, he hurried to the lectures of all the professors of mathematics, bought astronomical books and instruments, and learned the names of the constellations with the help of a fist-sized celestial globe which he was compelled to conceal from his don mentor Vedel and could use only when the latter was asleep.

Tycho acquired the Alfonsine and Prussian Tables and soon discovered that the planets were not to be found at the places where they should have been according to the tables. At the age of sixteen Tycho, before any other European astronomer, realized that "only through a steadily pursued course of observations would it be possible to obtain a better insight into the motions of the planets and decide which system of the world was the correct one."

On August 17, 1563, on the occasion of a conjunction of Jupiter and Saturn, Tycho, who was then seventeen years old, made his first recorded observation and discovered that the Alfonsine Tables were wrong by a whole month, and the Prussian Tables by a few days. Kepler says correctly that "the rehabilitation of astronomy was first conceived and decided upon by Tycho, that phenix among astronomers, in 1564."

In May, 1565, Tycho returned to Denmark. By that time his uncle had jumped into the water to rescue the Danish King who had fallen in during a ride, following which the uncle caught cold and died. Tycho went to the University of Wittenberg, attended the lectures of Professor Peucer, drew up his horoscope and forecast that disaster lay in store for him, either jail or exile, and that he would be released only at the age of sixty by a certain military personality. (At that time Tycho, like everyone else, was a devotee of astrology—and in 1574, Peucer actually did lose his chair at Wittenberg and was thrown into jail, for he was suspected of being a Calvinist.)

From Wittenberg Tycho went to the University of Rostock, to study medicine and astronomy; it was believed at that time that epidemics came from the stars; only Galileo did away with Aristotle's philosophy of nature; and only Bacon taught the world to observe the mechanical causes of natural phenomena rather than their metaphysical causes.

On the occasion of an eclipse of the moon on October 28, 1566, Tycho, in a prophetic mood, posted a few Latin verses in the college, forecasting the imminent death of Sultan Soliman; a few weeks later the news of the eighty-year-old potentate's death arrived. However, he had died before the eclipse, and Tycho became a general laughingstock.

On December 19, 1566, during a little dancing party organized to celebrate the engagement of a professor's daughter, Tycho de Brahe and another Danish student of noble origin, Manderup Parsbjerg, got into an argument; according to Gassendi, they quarrelled over which of the two was the better mathematician. On December 29, they met in total darkness in a Rostock street and continued the argument with swords. Tycho lost his nose, or at least its most beautiful part; he replaced it by an alloy of silver and gold.

Willem Janszoon Blaev, a famous Amsterdam printer who in his youth spent a few years at Hveen, related to Gassendi that Tycho always carried a small box of salve in his pocket, and that he often applied it to his nose. Reymers Baer, a scientific opponent of Tycho and his theories, explained that Tycho had not lost his nose, but his head.

Tycho went from Rostock to Denmark and from Denmark back to Rostock because of a new eclipse of the moon. Then he went to Wittenberg and Basel to matriculate at the university, after which he travelled to Lauingen and visited the famous Livowski who had edited Regiomontanus' trigonometric tables (1552) and in his astrological writings prophesied the end of the world for 1584, during the next great conjunction.

Later Tycho went to Augsburg and set up a nineteen-foot-long quadrant in near-by Goeggingen and met the great Petrus Ramus, professor of philosophy at the Sorbonne, who had been compelled to leave France as a Huguenot. Out of patriotism and because he wanted to organize courses in mathematics instead of in Aristotle at the University of Paris, he later returned to his native land, and on St. Bartholomew's Night paid for both his return and his anti-Aristotelianism with his head.

In 1571 Tycho went to Denmark to bury his father and inherit half of his estate; he sent his old mentor Vedel prescriptions against fever, made his astronomical observations everywhere without fear, and went to an old uncle of his, who had recently expropriated a monastery "because an ungodly life was going on there" and made it into his castle. Together with his uncle, Tycho continued the chemical experiments he had begun at Augsburg. At that time the astrologer was also an alchemist; alchemy was a branch of astrology, every planet represented a metal; the moon stood for silver, Mercury for quicksilver, the sun for gold, Mars for iron, Jupiter for tin (or gold), Saturn for lead. The uncle and nephew probably wanted to make gold.

The appearance of the new star of 1572 that Tycho alone systematically observed and described induced him to attempt a new catalogue of the stars. He wrote a treatise about the new star without intending to publish it, for it was not becoming in a nobleman to publish books. The nonsense that German blockheads wrote about it and Oxe, his cousin, persuaded Tycho to publish his book in Copenhagen in 1573 under the title *De Nova Stella*. It was almost completely ignored.

With a sigh the Dane termed the German observers of the heavens: "O coecos coeli spectatores" ("O blind observers of the heavens!") For this star was the first new star observed since Hipparchus had found his new star, as Pliny relates in his Natural History.

Tycho, by his own admission, had not corrected his manuscript because he had been distracted by domestic affairs—the poor man was in love! In verses he told the world that he wanted to see more of the world, and learn more, and only later return to his rugged northland, in order to waste his time as other noblemen did with horses, dogs and girls, unless God had intended him for a better lot.

He now also planned a book "against the astrologers in behalf of astrology" (contra astrologos pro astrologia). He wrote: "O foolhardy astronomers, O exquisite and subtle calculators, who practice astronomy in huts and taverns, at the fireplace, in books and writings, but not in the heavens themselves (as would be fitting). For very many (O the disgrace of having to say this) do not even know the stars. And yet they would go to the stars."

And he makes fun of the madness of the astronomers who indicate minutes and even seconds when they try to state a planetary position, although in the 1563 conjunction of Saturn and Jupiter the Alfonsine Tables were wrong by a month and the Prussian Tables by days, let alone by minutes or seconds.

At that time Tycho wanted to leave Denmark. He loved a certain Christine, had eight children with her, yet did not enter into legal marriage with her because she was in bondage. He lived with this peasant girl, a serf, for twenty-six years.

In 1574, yielding to the request of the king and the students, he began to lecture at the University of Copenhagen. In his inaugural address he said that astronomy was a very ancient science which according to Flavius Josephus could be traced back to Seth; that Abraham had conceived the idea of the existence of God from contemplating the orbits of the sun, the moon and the stars; that the ancient Egyptians too had studied the sky; that we owed our knowledge above all to Hipparchus and Ptolemy and more recently to Nicolaus Copernicus who was not unjustly termed a second Ptolemy and who, having as a result of his own observations discovered that the Ptolemaic and Alfonsine Tables were inadequate for the explanation of the celestial phenomena, had restored the science of astronomy by means of new hypotheses created by his marvelous genius. No one before him had had a more accurate knowledge of the motions of the stars. And although his theory, Tycho said, was to a certain extent opposed to the physical principles, it contained nothing that contradicted the mathematical axioms, as was the case with the ancients, who had assumed that motions of the stars on epicycles and excentrics were irregular with regard to the centers of these circles, which was absurd.

Then Tycho went to Cassel to look up the most famous astronomer of his day, Landgrave Wilhelm IV of Hesse, who in 1566 had built a tower with a revolving dome at the Zwehr Gate in Cassel, because he too thought the most urgent task was the systematic observation of the sky.

Next, Tycho went to Frankfurt-on-Main and thence to Basel, where he would have liked best to remain, thence to Venice, to Augsburg and, finally, to Regensburg, to the Diet, not in order to meet kings, but the Emperor's physician in ordinary, the Bohemian Hayek or Hagecius who in 1575 presented him with a copy of the Commentariolus.

Then Tycho went to Saalfeld, then to Wittenberg, where the son of Erasmus Reinhold, author of the Prussian Tables, showed him his father's manuscripts.

Tycho returned to Denmark and envisaged removing to Basel.

Early in the morning of February 11, while he was still in bed in his house at Knudstrup, a young nobleman from the court, a cousin of Tycho's, came to see him with a written invitation from the king. On the same day Tycho and his cousin set out and by night reached the Danish King's hunting lodge. The king offered Tycho, who had been recommended to him by Wilhelm of Hesse, the island of Hveen, money to build himself a house there, and a pension for life, in order that he might devote himself to his mathematical and astronomical studies free from all worldly care.

Tycho asked for time to think the matter over. He consulted his friends, the French ambassador Dancey and Professor Pratensis; they urgently advised him to accept, and he did. The king wrote him the letter of patent. Four days later he went to Hveen and on the same night made his first observation there, of a conjunction of Mars and the moon—he was to contribute to our knowledge of the orbits of Mars and the moon more than any astronomer since the days of Ptolemy.

The island of Hveen, fourteen miles north of Copenhagen, three miles long and covering an area of two thousand acres, was fiefed to Tycho for life, with all its inhabitants and its forty farms that they cultivated in common. Tycho baptized the island "Island of Venus vulgo Hvenna." There he built his house and observatory famous throughout Europe, the Uraniborg (city of the heavens).

In 1584 he built a new observatory, which he called Stjerneborg. There was a statue of Mercury in it that was made to revolve by a mechanism in the pedestal. Tycho, the star-gazer with ruddy hair and a nose of silver and gold, possessed many such automata, and the fishermen and peasants of Hveen considered him a sorcerer. On the ceiling of the new observatory there was a representation of Tycho's system. On the wall hung the portraits of the eight greatest astronomers of the world (according to Tycho), that is to say, besides the portraits of Timocharis, Hipparchus, Ptolemy, Al Battani, King Alfonso of Castile and Copernicus, there were those of Tycho de Brahe and of Tychonides, the still unborn successor of the sublime Tycho; under the portrait of Tychonides a few verses expressed the hope that this unborn astronomer would prove worthy of Tycho! Tycho on his portrait pointed at his own world system, and a strip of paper in his hand bore the inscription *"Quid si sic?"* (What if it is that way?)

The King of Denmark presented Tycho with castles, estates, pensions and rights which according to Tycho's estimate amounted to about two thousand four hundred thalers a year. In 1588, when the king died, from drunkenness, as Vedel explained in his funeral sermon, Tycho calculated that he had incurred six thousand thalers of debts to pay for his scientific works; the government paid these debts.

In 1598, Tycho estimated his buildings and instruments to be worth seventy-five thousand thalers. He had planted gardens and built fishponds and hunted hares and set up a paper mill and a printing shop where he printed his own works, including the poetical works; he often received learned visitors and for the space of twenty years (1576 to 1597) lived with his large family and numerous disciples and assistants like a great lord on his little island.

In 1584 Tycho sent Olias Olsen, one of his assistants, to Frauenburg, because he suspected that Copernicus had made an error in determining the latitude of Frauenburg; Olsen took measurements and brought back not only a more correct figure (although it was not yet the correct figure) but also Copernicus' *triquetrum,* as a gift for Tycho from the Frauenburg canon, Johannes Hannov.

Live or Liuva, one of Tycho's serving maids, who subsequently lived with his learned sister Sophia, in later years became a quack in Copenhagen and also practised astrology; she died in 1693 at the age of 124, still unmarried.

Jep or Jeppe, Tycho's fool, sat at Tycho's feet at mealtimes and from time to time received a tasty morsel from his master. Jep was a chatterbox and had the gift of second sight. Once he suddenly said to Tycho during a meal: "Look how your men are washing themselves in the sea!" Tycho, who had sent two of his assistants to Copenhagen and was worried about them, sent a servant to the roof, who hastily returned to report that he had seen a capsized boat near the beach and two dripping men on the shore.

When Tycho was absent and his pupils wanted to have a good time, they ordered Jep to stand watch on the roof, and as soon as the dwarf saw Tycho coming, he uttered a piercing cry: "Junker paa Landet!" (the master is on land!)

When someone fell sick on Hveen, the dwarf always foretold whether he would recover or die, and he was always right.

Tycho also practised chemistry, alchemy and pharmacology; he distributed free medicines on Hveen. In 1599 he sent Emperor Rudolph the well-known imperial elixir, also noted by Copernicus, that cured all diseases, and consisted chiefly of theriac and wine spirits, but also contained sulphur, aloes, myrrh, saffron, pure gold, corals, sapphire, pomegranate, dissolved pearls, etc. When mixed with antimony this medicine cured all respiratory diseases. Tycho asked the emperor to keep this medicine a close secret.

The professor of medicine Brucaeus, who incidentally laughed at all astrology, wrote Tycho that it was difficult to accept the Copernican theory.

One of Tycho's visitors, Duncan Liddel from Aberdeen, professor at Helmstadt, was said to be the first professor in Germany to explain publicly the systems of Ptolemy, Copernicus and Tycho de Brahe.

Tycho was officially bound to send an annual astrological forecast to the Danish King, but as he grew older he believed less and less in such forecasts.

In 1587 he wrote to Heinrich Below, who was related to him by marriage: "When one reads a hundred forecasts, it is very rarely that two of them are in accord with each other. . . . These astrological prophecies are like a cothurnus that can be put on any leg, large or small, and therefore I have never attached any particular importance to them."

In 1577, as he went to his fishpond to catch a handsome fish for his supper, Tycho discovered the comet of 1577 in the sky. In Chapter VIII of his book about this comet published in Hveen in 1587, Tycho, "who took nothing on trust," described his own system of the world.

He distinguished between the elementary world within the orbit of the moon and the ethereal world; the latter had, according to him, a marvelously large dimension; the maximum distance of the most distant planet, Saturn, from the earth, was 235 times the radius of the elementary world. The distance of the moon he assumed to be 52 times the radius of the earth which he thought was 430 German miles. He estimated that the distance of the sun from the earth was 20 times that of the moon. The comet moved within this wide space. Therefore, he goes on to say, he must explain his system of the world that he had worked out four years earlier, in 1583. For the Ptolemaic system is too complicated. And the new system advanced by that great man, Copernicus (who followed in the footsteps of Aristarchus of Samos), while it does not contradict in any way the mathematical laws, is in contradiction with the laws of physics and is absurd, because the heavy and sluggish earth cannot move, and, furthermore, the Copernican system is in conflict with the authority of the Bible. Another difficulty derives from the wide space that must be assumed to exist between Saturn and the firmament in order to account for the want of annual parallaxes of the stars; and despite his careful observations Tycho was unable to discover any parallax of the stars, such as would surely exist if the earth really moved.

Therefore, Tycho explained, he tried to find a hypothesis that was in agreement with the mathematical and physical principles and would not fall victim to the censorship of the theologians. "As if by inspiration" the following idea about the motions of the planets had occurred to him:

The earth is the centre of the universe and of the orbits of the sun, the moon and the firmament that revolves about the earth with all the planets in twenty-four hours.

The sun is the center of the orbits of the five planets; the radii of the orbits of Mercury and Venus are smaller, those of the orbits of Jupiter and Saturn larger, than the radius of the sun's orbit.

Because the planets are not fixed to any solid crystal spheres it is not at all absurd to let the orbits of Mars and the sun cross each other, because these orbits have no physical reality and represent only geometrical figures.

In his book on the comet Tycho promised a more detailed account of his system on a future occasion, but he never found this occasion.

His was the third astronomical world system, and even today he has some followers.

The only two great astronomers of antiquity whose complete astronomical systems had come down to posterity were Hipparchus and Ptolemy. But the Ptolemaic system was only an ingenious mathematical representation of the phenomena—a working hypothesis; it did not claim to offer a physically true description of the reality of the universe.

When Copernicus recognized the drawbacks of this too complicated Ptolemaic system and created his own new system based on the movement of the earth around the sun, he developed a geometrical theory for each planet, so that it was possible to construct new tables for the motions of each. Copernicus created a completely new astronomical system, the first since the school of Alexandria, and the first which made it possible to determine the relative distances of the planets.

Thus far Tycho respected Copernicus as a great master and a new Ptolemy. For the rest he found the Copernican system no less complicated than the Ptolemaic.

Only Kepler supplied the explanation for the various distances and velocities in the planetary motions when he discovered that the planets moved in elliptical orbits and formulated the law that governs their velocities. Copernicus was still forced to use the epicycles and excentrics, like Ptolemy, for the explanation of this so-called first inequality; to that extent Copernicus' planetary theory only adapted Ptolemy's system to the heliocentric idea; and the motions were referred not to the real position of the sun, but to the "middle sun," that is the center of the earth's orbit; thus, for the representation of the orbit of Mercury seven circles were required; for the orbit of Venus, five circles; for the earth's orbit, three circles; for the moon's orbit, four circles, and for each of these outside planets, five circles; and with all this complicated machinery the new system did not represent the real motions in the heavens any better than the Ptolemaic system.

Copernicus said he would be enchanted like Pythagoras if his planetary theory did not lead to a worse error than a 10-minute deviation from the observed positions of the planets. But he fell far short of his ideal.

The system, as constructed by Copernicus, showed only that it was possible to compute the motions of the planets without assuming that the earth was the center of the universe.

Copernicus, who beyond any doubt believed in the physical truth of his system did not give any proofs that the earth really moved and could not give any.

As for his early partisans, it is not known whether they really believed in the motion of the earth or preferred his system only for geometrical reasons.

In the sixteenth century, the physical arguments against the motion of the earth were difficult to refute. Galileo alone grasped the principles of elementary mechanics and proved them by his experiments.

Only the invention of the telescope enabled the astronomers to make the numerous discoveries they made in the seventeenth century, such as the phases of Venus, the satellites of Jupiter, the form of the planets.

Obviously Tycho's purpose was not only to give a geometrical representation of the planetary system, but also to discover the real structure of the universe.

Tycho's system did not delay the adoption of the Copernican system; it actually served as a bridge between the Ptolemaic and Copernican systems.

Although Tycho kept his system a deep secret until 1587, when he revealed it in his book on the comet of 1577, his friend Rothmann informed him after reception of the book that the new system seemed to be the same that Landgrave Wilhelm of Hesse had ordered his instrument constructor to represent on a planetarium.

Tycho was thrown into consternation by this report.

But soon afterwards he received from Germany a recently published book by a former swineherd, the mathematician and astronomer Nicolai Reymers Baer (Fundamentum Astronomicum, Strassburg, 1588).

The author, who had also published a Latin grammar, had once visited Uraniborg in the company of a Danish alchemist. Tycho had treated him as a servant, and in the course of a discussion he once interrupted him with the words: "These German fellows are all half-cracked!" Tycho never called him anything else than "Eric's boy."

Now Tycho considered this Baer a plagiarist.

Nevertheless, it is possible that Baer invented a system similar to Tycho's. The priority dispute between the two scientists was very famous at that time; but both authors were wrong.

In 1597 at Prague, Baer published a book against Rothmann (whom he calls consistently Rotzmann—"snivelman") and against Tycho that has the following motto (from Hosea, XIII): "I will meet them like a bear bereaved of her whelps."

In this book Reymers Baer proved himself a Homeric master of abuse and an excellent mathematician. Tycho, he wrote, had only imitated the system of Apollonius of Perga. And a Mr. Roeslin had recently claimed the same system as his own. And he, Reymers Baer, was not Eric's boy but Emperor Rudolph II's mathematician. It was not he who had stolen Tycho's system at Uraniborg, but when he, Baer, had slept one night in a chamber at Uraniborg, where a pupil of Tycho's was also lodged, his manuscript had been stolen from his pocket. To top it all, Baer at great length made fun of Tycho's cut-off nose.

After the Danish King Frederick II drank himself to death in 1588, the new king (not yet of age) and his advisers began endless chicaneries against Tycho; he was deprived of his prebends and other sources of income, he was the target of lawsuits, his minister at Hveen was charged with heresy and he himself with not attending church frequently enough. His peasants on Hveen who had complained of his harshness and insolence were adjudged right after detailed investigations (and they were right!). Finally the great Dane was driven out of his native land and went into exile. Long before he had written Latin verses according to which every land is the homeland of the brave, and the heavens are above every land (omne solum forti patria est, coelum undique supra est).

Tycho published his scientific correspondence (Epistolae, 1596) which he dedicated to Wilhelm of Hesse's son; there he praised Wilhelm for not having learned astronomy from books, but from the heavens. He, too, he says, did the same. He began his observations at the age of sixteen, and continued them until his death. He spent more time observing than Ptolemy and Copernicus. In the same work Tycho mentions the length of time needed for a complete series of observations, if one wants really to rehabilitate astronomy. It is possible to study the orbit of the sun with sufficient exactitude in four years; but the intricate orbit of the moon requires many years of observation; twelve years are required to follow the opposition of Mars and Jupiter around the zodiac, and as many as thirty years to follow the course of Saturn around the sky.

Tycho dedicated his catalogue of stars to Emperor Rudolph II, on January 2, 1598. This catalogue of about one thousand stars was not published until 1600; only 777 stars were determined exactly; the rest were hurriedly and casually measured and determined by him and his assistants, for the sole purpose of not producing a catalogue inferior to Ptolemy's with its 1,028 stars, and in order to reach a full thousand *(pro complendo millenario).*

In his introduction Tycho compared the merits of all the preceding catalogues of stars, from that of Hipparchus to that of the *incomparabilis vir,* Nicolaus Copernicus, and observed that actually no astronomer after Hipparchus had observed a large number of stars. (The only existing independent catalogue of stars, by Ulugh Beg, was at that time still unknown in Europe.)

Later, Kepler published these thousand star positions in his Rudolfine Tables (1627).

Tycho went from Denmark to Rostock, then to Wandsbeck where he spent the winter of 1597/98 and wrote an account of his instruments and his work, with autobiographical notes, which he sent to the Prince of Orange and the Emperor, among others. Then he went to Dresden. Finally he settled in Prague or in Benathky castle near Prague, as astronomer, astrologer and alchemist to Emperor Rudolph II who put large sums of money at his disposal.

Tycho arrived in Prague in June, 1599. Among his assistants was the young exiled Swabian astronomer, Johannes Kepler, who for twenty months worked with him, often quarrelling with the proud and arrogant Dane.

On October 24, 1601, Tycho died at the age of fifty-four years and ten months. He had been taken ill on October 13 during a supper in the home of a Bohemian magnate; some people spoke of poison, but this seems absurd.

Kepler who completed Tycho's observations and published them in his Rudolfine Tables described Tycho's last illness.

As early as October 13 Tycho had great difficulties in urinating. Kepler describes in detail the constellations of that day, Tycho's five sleepless nights, his continued insomnia, his fevers, delirium, and the worsening of his condition. On October 24, Tycho was delirious again; his entourage wept and prayed; finally death closed the eyes that for thirty-eight years had observed the heavens more faithfully and keenly than any other human eyes before them.

On his last night of life Tycho in his delirium repeated over and over: *Ne frustra vixisse videar?* Will I not seem to have lived in vain?

His family took away his instruments, these marvels disappeared in various ways. They began a financial quarrel with Kepler and the emperor about his scientific papers.

Finally Kepler received in trust the enormous mass of Tycho's astronomical observations, really royal treasures, as Kepler said, for without them the reform of astronomy could not have come about. He believed that better and more accurate observations would never be made—for he did not foresee the invention of the telescope.

With the help of these observations—and his own genius—Kepler discovered his three famous laws which blew all the epicycles and excentrics out of the complicated Copernican system.

Thus exile proved to be Tycho's good fortune; he found his Kepler. Délambre, in his *Histoire de l'Astronomie Moderne,* says: "If Tycho had stayed on his island, Kepler would have never accepted his invitations; we would certainly not have the theory of Mars and we might be ignorant of the true system of the world."

Tycho's biographer Dreyer says in praise of him that the only astronomical datum he had taken over from his predecessors was false (". . . the unlucky solar parallax of 3 minutes which Tycho had borrowed from the ancients").

"He took into account, and determined for the first time, errors in the division of his circles and the refraction of the air. His measurements . . . give us the position of the stars with an accuracy of half a minute of arc (one sixtieth of a full moon diameter)." (Philip Lenard, Great Men of Science, New York, 1938).

He was irascible and patient, proud and in love with a peasant woman, a modern scientist and an alchemist and astrologer, red-headed and noseless, a tormentor of peasants and a great lover of animals.

Maestlin, Kepler's old teacher, wrote him shortly before Tycho's death that "Tycho had hardly left a shadow of astronomical science and that only one thing was certain, namely that men knew nothing about astronomy."

48

JOHANNES KEPLER

Sacred was Lactantius, who denyed the Earth's rotundity; Sacred was Augustine, who granted the Earth to be round, but denyed the Antipodes; Sacred is the Liturgy of our Moderns, who admit the smallnesse of the Earth, but deny its motion: But to me more sacred than all these is Truth, who with respect to the Doctors of the Church, do demonstrate from Philosophy that the Earth is both round, circumhabited by Antipodes, of a most contemptible smallnesse and in a word, that it is ranked amongst the planets.

KEPLER

ONLY ambition kept him tied to his work, wrote the "legislator of the universe" at the age of forty-eight. "I cannot observe any fixed order, I do not follow any set times and have no rules. If something orderly comes out of me, it has been begun ten times. Sometimes an error of computation made in haste holds me back for a long period. But I could let myself gush forth infinitely, if I wanted to; for even though I am not fond of reading, I have a rich store of fantasy. But I find no pleasure in such a jumble; it repels and annoys me. Therefore I cast the stuff away or put it aside until I can recheck it, that is to say, until I write something new, which is most often the case."

Johannes Kepler was born at Weilderstadt in Württemberg in 1571 and died at Regensburg in Bavaria in 1630. The son of a ruined family, he occasionally described his forbears—and himself—unsparingly. Kepler's father, Heinrich, spoke a great deal in praise of his honor and against his wife, a black-haired little spindle-shanks, uppish and querulous, who could neither read nor write. She was an innkeeper's daughter with a dowry of three thousand gulden. He had learned nothing in his life and drank constantly. One fine day when she was pregnant he left her and her little son Johannes and went off to fight under the Duke of Alba in the Netherlands. Catherine gave birth to another son, and with both her children ran after the army. Then the soldier came home to Swabia with his baggage and his family, but soon he found his wife intolerable, returned to the service of Alba, was almost hanged in the Netherlands, almost lost his life in an explosion, and lost his fortune because he went surety for a friend. Badly shaken, he came home and leased the inn "At the Sun" in Elmendingen. Johannes and his two younger brothers had to help in the beer-hall. Thus Kepler began his career as a bus boy.

Later he was sent to the monastery school at Maulbronn, where he learned Latin, Greek and the Psalms by rote. He proved every crazy thesis for the fun of it, did not get along with his comrades, and at the age of eighteen won a scholarship at the theological faculty of the University of Tübingen. His father left his inn to his creditors, the seven children he had begot with his wife, to their fate, and went off to fight with the Neapolitans in their naval war against Anthony of Portugal.

During his four and a half years at Tübingen Kepler became acquainted with the Copernican system through Michael Maestlin, a former village pastor and an excellent astronomer, and tried in vain to impart it, as well as the concept of Christian love, to his fellow-students. He displayed equal enthusiasm in trying to convince the young Swabians that the earth turned around the sun and that the Evangelists should patch up their quarrel with the Reformed; the Evangelical church never forgave him either of these endeavors. Thus, even in his youth this eccentric advocate of harmony quarrelled with everyone.

When the Styrian provincial diet asked the theological faculty of Tübingen for a teacher of mathematics to serve at the Evangelical foundation-school in Graz, Master Kepler was recommended upon Maestlin's advice.

Under the pressure of Maestlin and his own poverty, he went to Graz (on March 13, 1594) to teach poor boys Virgil, rhetorics and arithmetic for one hundred and fifty guldens a year (and free lodging and heating). For another twenty gulden he supplied an annual astrological calendar with predictions of the weather and world events to provincial believers in the stars.

Against his own expectations, his prophecies for 1595 came true; although Kepler had forecast it blindly, the Turk really did invade Austria, the winter was really cold, and the peasants in that region did really become rebellious. He earned a name as an astrologer, and money too, because many of the credulous asked him to cast their horoscopes.

He came to Graz at the age of twenty-three; at twenty-five he took a wife, a miller's daughter. She was twenty-three, and Kepler was her third husband; she had promptly buried her first, and her second had promptly divorced her. Along with a fifty-gulden raise, less dowry that had been promised him, and a daughter, Regina, from one of her previous marriages, he got six children from his wife and little pleasure; she did not know how to keep house, and he could not make ends meet; he had married in 1597; in 1598 he lost his job under the following circumstances:

When Kepler had come to Graz, Styria was Lutheran. The new despot Archduke Ferdinand (later Emperor Ferdinand II) was a pupil of the Jesuits; he had nothing to offer his new subjects but a new, that is to say, the old Catholic, religion. In 1598 he ordered all Lutheran clergymen and teachers to leave Graz and Judenburg within a week. Horrified, Kepler fled to Hungary.

A year later he came back at the express invitation of the Styrian diet to resume his teaching and official prophecies. But later it turned out that he was expected to become a Catholic; he disliked this idea. In a letter dated August 29, 1599, he wrote: "The point has been reached where citizens are burned at the stake . . . But the people at court envisage even worse . . . Whoever sings choral or reads Luther's Bible is banished . . . I myself was fined ten thalers for having ignored the local clergy; I was pardoned half of it upon my petition, but I had to pay the other half before I was allowed to bury my daughter."

Kepler began his investigations in Graz. At the age of twenty-five he published his first book entitled *Mysterium Cosmographicum* (1596), the Secret of the Universe, in which he appears as a resolute partisan of the Copernican system. He rejects Osiander's sophistic claim to build truth upon false hypotheses. The magnificent order of the Copernican world is to him the proof of its reality. He describes his first attempts to find a law valid for the entire solar system. If he could only find the law of one of the planetary orbits, he says, he would know the elements of all them. His secret of the universe was mathematical; he thought he had discovered the numerical relations that express the structure of the world. He "could not express in words the intense pleasure this discovery gave him" (incidentally this so-called discovery was not one).

Kepler sent his Secret of the Universe (which he reprinted twenty-five years later in his World Harmony) to many astronomers. Galileo, who was seven years older than Kepler, having read only the preface on the day he received the book wrote to him: "I estimate myself happy to have as great an ally as you in my search for truth . . . I will read . . . your work . . . all the more willingly because I have for many years been a partisan of the Copernican view and because it reveals to me the causes of many natural phenomena that are entirely incomprehensible in the light of the generally accepted hypotheses. To refute the latter I have collected many proofs, but I do not publish them, because I am deterred by the fate of our teacher Copernicus who, although he had won immortal fame with a few, was ridiculed and condemned by countless people (for very great is the number of the stupid). I would dare to publish my speculations if there were more people like you. But as this is not the case, I postpone doing so."

Tycho de Brahe praised the genius of the young astronomer, expressed some doubts as to his figures and regretted that Kepler had based himself on the Copernican system rather than on the Tychonic system. Kepler noted on the margin: "Everyone loves himself."

At that time the twenty-five-year-old Kepler describes himself as well-informed, vivacious, thin, abstemious in eating and drinking, contented or indifferent in his behavior. He said he labored to win his master's good will like a domestic dog, serving, never grumbling when criticized, and trying to win favor by all means. Impatient in conversations, he snarled at his guests. If anyone wanted to take the slightest thing away from him, he would get angry and growl like a dog. He was stingy, jeered at those who were clumsy, quarrelled easily, was sharp in speech and quick to give unpleasant answers. Hated by most, he was avoided by many; only his masters liked him, as they like a dog. . . . He avoided baths, plungings and washings—like a dog. His disorderliness was very great. He feared for his life at the slightest provocation and lost all courage in danger. His good qualities, if any, were piety, honesty, loyalty, respectability and decency. Fatal were his curiosity and his vain striving for the highest.

Kepler had dark hair and eyes, and a long nose. A frail seven-months child, he had smallpox at the age of two, particularly on his hands; since puberty he had suffered from boils, which sometimes even prevented him from sitting; later he was afflicted with headaches, fever and rashes. At the age of thirty-five, in Prague, he wrote: "You ask me about my illness. It was a lingering fever which came from the gall and returned four times because I often committed dietary indiscretions. On May 29, my wife ruthlessly compelled me at last to wash my body; she thinks baths are dangerous. She plunged me in a basin full of very warm water; the warmth did not agree with me and gave me cramps in my bowels. On May 31, I took a light purgative as usual. On June 1, I was bled also out of habit; I was not induced to do this by any illness nor even a suspicion of illness. Nor did I do it on account of any astrological prescription, as you can easily understand. After I had lost blood I felt very well for a few hours; at night a bad sleep threw me on my bed against my will; I felt cramps in the bowels. For the gall must have got to my head, past the bowels . . . I think I am one of those whose gall bladder has an opening into the stomach; such people are usually shortlived."

With the Counter-Reformation threatening at Graz, Kepler hoped "for any philosophic professorship he could find." Maestlin, to whom he appealed for a recommendation, answered after five months: "my complete inexperience in these matters . . . I beg you urgently . . . to address yourself to others. . . ."

Poor Kepler was threatened with torture and prison. Amidst all this persecution two of his children died, and then came a long letter from Tycho de Brahe (dated December 9, 1599) asking him to come to Prague and be his assistant.

Kepler went to Prague and worked tentatively for Tycho. It was not easy, for both men considered themselves unique and irreplaceable; Tycho was world famous, Kepler was proud of his "secret of the universe." After a few months he handed a memorandum to Tycho which read:

"The conditions under which I can offer my services to the esteemed Tycho de Brahe in his works:

(1) I will carry out every astronomical task, in so far as is compatible with my health. . . .

(2) My eyes are too weak for observation, and I have no skill for mechanical works, my curious and excitable nature disturbs me in domestic and political affairs, I feel too weak for long sitting (particularly beyond a correct and moderate length of banquets), especially as this is also injurious to one's health. I must frequently get up and walk around, for reasons of health.

(3) Since astronomical matters often turn up that prevent concentration on some work that interests me, Mr. Tycho will grant me philosophical liberty and share the day with me. If he prefers the morning, I will pursue my own ideas in the afternoons.

(4) He will give me much free time for attending religious services and for my own affairs."

Kepler stayed at Benatky Castle until June; Tycho had promised to pay his moving expenses, give him a hundred thalers extra a year and obtain letters patent from the emperor securing Kepler's Styrian salaries for two years.

As soon as Kepler came to Graz to attend to his moving he wrote Maestlin: "and so I am supposed now (under the threat of immediate dismissal) to give up astronomy and devote myself to medicine."

Immediately afterward (August 1, 1600), more than a thousand citizens and officials of Graz were banished forever (this time Kepler, too). All of them had to emigrate within forty-five days. All the possessions of Kepler's family "consist in immovable goods and are extremely cheap, more, not even saleable. Many are hoping to get hold of them free. For the prince has decreed that no one has the right to lease to a Papist goods that he cannot sell within forty-five days."

Maestlin, whom Kepler once again asked for help, answered: "I really do not know what I can advise in these difficulties. Only the one thing you ask me at the end of your letter, I am doing as diligently as possible, I am praying for you and your family."

Kepler answered: "I would not have believed that it is so sweet to suffer injury and damage for my religion . . . in company of a few brothers, and to leave house, farm, friends, and homeland." He was unable, he said, to become a Catholic, even less to be a hypocrite. "For that reason the clergy is angry with me, and the laymen abuse me as a fool."

In September he left Graz. He left his belongings at Linz. In Prague, now only a refugee, without his Styrian salary, he offered his services to Tycho. As always, Tycho made promises. The emperor refused to pay a second astronomer. Kepler had a rash. His wife cried out in distress that living was four times as expensive in Prague as in Graz. The poor woman became dejected. She would not let Kepler sell any of her cups. She was interested only in the prayerbooks. She despised her husband because her father, the miller, had earned more money than he did. He did not even answer her when she asked him the most important questions concerning housekeeping (he was then absorbed in his computations of the orbit of Mars). The husband and wife quarrelled frequently. Kepler confessed: "When I realized that she took it to heart and was angry, too, I felt that I would rather bite my finger than continue to offend her."

The poor woman soon fell ill with the Hungarian fever, became epileptic and lost her mind.

Kepler computed the motions of Mars, Venus and Mercury. On the basis of Tycho's and his assistants' astronomical observations he reached the conclusion that the planetary orbits had been represented incorrectly in the past.

At the same time he was Tycho's literary defender and disputed the claims of the late imperial mathematician Reymers Baer (Ursus) to having discovered Brahe's system before Brahe, and Scot Craig's claims to having evolved Brahe's theory of comets.

In the fall of 1601, Tycho de Brahe died. At the age of thirty, Kepler was Tycho's intellectual heir. He was appointed imperial mathematician with the task of completing Tycho's computations and drawing up new planetary tables. At last he triumphed.

He demanded a salary of one thousand five hundred gulden. But Tengnagel, Tycho's son-in-law, obtained a pension of one thousand gulden for Brahe's heirs because of his scientific papers; Kepler's salary was reduced to five hundred gulden, and the first payment was delayed for five months. In his letters, his worries about the stars are mingled with worries about money. He always had "to beg his bread from the Emperor."

In 1610 Galileo published his first telescopic discoveries in the "Messenger of the Heavens." But one year before, in 1609, Kepler had published his first two laws (about the form and manner of the planetary motions) in a book which he proudly entitled "The New Astronomy." There he told the story of his discoveries with "invaluable thoroughness." He computed tables for the orbit of Mars (which had annoyed Copernicus and driven Rheticus insane), for which in at least forty instances he had to make the same calculations 181 times.

The systems of Ptolemy, Copernicus and Tycho de Brahe could not free themselves of the superstition that the circle was the perfect figure, and that the planets moved only in the perfect way, that is in circles. The changes in the planetary velocities, they thought, could be only an apparent irregularity (the so-called first unevenness of the astronomy of the ancients). The astronomers were supposed to discover the true uniform motions, and thus put the real motions of the planets on excentric circles. That is why Ptolemy, Copernicus and Tycho invented those confusing epicycles and excentrics, which led the planets into contortionist dances. Kepler constructed hypothesis after hypothesis in order to find a circle that would tally with Tycho's observations.

Kepler believed that the sun not only lay within the planetary orbits but also acted on the planets according to a definite law.

Copernicus had placed the sun in the center of the world; he also said that it "*dominates* the race of the stars that turn 'round it." And Rheticus says in the Narratio Prima that the sun is the principle of motion and light. But Copernicus relates the motions of the planets not to the sun itself, but to the center of the earth's orbit conceived as circular. This center is supposed to be near the sun.

Kepler had learned from Tycho's writings on the comets that there were no solid spheres for the planets; thus, according to him, the sun was the center and source of motion of the planets surrounding it. It is in the sun itself that the lines meet, which for each individual planet connect its perihelion and aphelion.

Kepler sketched a laborious geometric diagram of Tycho's observations upon the assumption that Tycho never made a mistake greater than eight arc minutes. And he explained: "Only those eight minutes led to the complete reformation of astronomy." For according to Tycho's observations, the orbit of Mars could not possibly be a circle. Therefore Kepler looked for some oval form. By the end of 1604, with truly heavenly rapture he discovered that the simplest oval curve, the perfect ellipse, was the form of the orbit of Mars.

Thus the first law of Kepler is: "The planet describes an ellipse, the sun being in one focus."

Later he observed that Mars moved faster when near the sun and slower when far from it. And the second law of Kepler is: "The straight line joining the planet to the sun sweeps out equal areas in any two equal intervals of time."

Ten years after he enunciated the first two laws he published his third law which he discovered as though in a moment of inspiration on May 15, 1618: "That the squares of the periods of the revolutions of any two planets are proportional to the cubes of their mean distances from the sun."

This is how he announced this discovery: "What I prophesied two and twenty years ago . . . what I firmly believed before I had seen the 'Harmonies' of Ptolemy; what I promised my friends in the title of this book, which I named before I was sure of my discovery; what sixteen years ago I urged as a thing to be sought; that for which I joined Tycho Brahe; for which I settled in Prague; for which I have devoted the best part of my life to astronomical contemplations;—at length I have brought to light, and have recognized its truth beyond my most sanguine expectations. . . . It is now eighteen months since I got the first glimmer of light; three months since the dawn; a very few days since the unveiled sun, most beauteous to behold, burst out upon me. Nothing holds me. I will indulge in my sacred fury. I will triumph over mankind by the honest confession that I have stolen the golden vases of the Egyptians, to rear up a tabernacle to my God far away from the confines of Egypt. If you forgive me, I rejoice; if you are angry, I can bear it. For the die is cast, the book is written, to be read now or by posterity; I care not. I can well wait a century for a reader, since God has waited six thousand years for a discoverer."

This third law is quoted in his book *Harmonia Mundi* (Linz, 1619) which deals with harmony and music, in geometric figures, in human life and in the spheres (it was inspired by one of Ptolemy's books).

Kepler also wanted to clarify the relations between matter and spirit, but was quite obscure on this question. "And I have always wanted to explore the nature of the spirit with an open mind and according to reason, and especially whether there is not a world soul at the heart of the world, a soul which is more profoundly connected with the natural processes."

In certain passages of this book Kepler, an animist like Giordano Bruno, describes the earth as a big animal, with a heart, lungs and desires.

About the same time he published his "Outline of Copernican Astronomy" (*Epitome Astronomiae Copernicanae,* Linz 1618, 1620 and 1621) which was the strongest defense of the new doctrine, and which for that reason was promptly placed on the Index. Here he deals with astronomy as a whole. In his preface he says: "I base all my astronomy on Copernicus' hypotheses, on Tycho de Brahe's observations and finally on the magnetic philosophy of the Englishman William Gilbert." Under the latter's influence (*De Magnete,* London, 1600), Kepler wrote: "What is it then that drives the planets around the sun? What else is it but a magnetic emanation of the sun? But what is it that makes the planets excentric with regard to the sun, that compels them to come close to it and move away from it? Nothing but a magnetic emanation from the planets themselves, as well as the direction of their magnetic axes."

In this book Kepler also states that his laws were valid not only for all the planets and the moon, but also for the satellites of Jupiter discovered by Galileo. Kepler placed the firmament at a distance of 420,000 million miles; he still believed that the fixed stars were attached to a solid sphere which had its center in the sun and was "two German miles thick."

In 1619 he also published his treatise on the comets, where new ideas were mingled with astrology. In contrast to his teacher Maestlin who contemptuously refused to cast horoscopes, Kepler cast them industriously, but he criticized himself for it: "I have been obliged to compose a vile, prophesying almanac which is scarcely more respectable than begging, unless from its saving the Emperor's credit, who abandons me entirely, and would suffer me to perish with hunger."

Thanks to his three laws Kepler could happily complete his elaboration of Brahe's observations. In 1627, the Rudolfine Tables (named thus in honor of Emperor Rudolf) were published at Ulm. The archduke of Tuscany, perhaps upon Galileo's suggestion, sent Kepler a golden chain.

Thus Kepler fulfilled the requirements he formulated at the age of thirty: "He who predicts as completely as possible the motions and positions of the heavenly bodies, fulfills his duty as an astronomer; but he who in addition advances true theorems about the form of the world achieves even more and deserves even greater praise. For the former reveals the truth in so far as it can be perceived by the senses; the latter satisfies not only the senses by his deductions, but also reveals the innermost essence of nature."

As Kepler himself put it, he discovered the concealed riches of the Copernican doctrine. He proved that only it could exactly represent the planetary motions. With his three laws and his presentiment of the force active in the solar system he paved the way for Newton. (He was also Newton's forerunner in the science of optics.)

At the age of forty Kepler lost his wife, a favorite son and his emperor: In 1611 Rudolf was compelled to abdicate and a year later he died. Rudolf had prevented Kepler from accepting a professorship at Linz in order to keep him as court astrologer. Mathias, the new emperor, who did not need an astrologer let him go. Kepler retained the title of imperial mathematician, but his salary was reduced to three hundred and fifty gulden. His old claims on the imperial treasury were converted into municipal obligations: Memmingen and Kempten gave him debt certificates; Nuremberg, recently looted by Wallenstein, declared itself bankrupt. In the end, the emperor transmitted Kepler's total claims, to the amount of 11,817 gulden, to Wallenstein; the latter did not pay them either; thus Kepler died without ever collecting his money.

From his fortieth to his fifty-seventh year he was mathematician at Linz with a salary of four hundred gulden a year. Among his other duties, he was charged with drawing the map of Upper Austria; sometimes he also had to accompany the imperial court or the emperor on official journeys.

Soon after the death of his wife, Kepler took another. He examined all the women he knew in a businesslike manner. Then he considered eleven of the most likely ones; of these one was too old, another too fat (as he described in detail in a letter to a friend), a third so unattractive that she would be stared at in the street, another of ill repute, still another lazy, or noisy, or stupid. Finally he chose Susanne, the daughter of a carpenter from Efferdingen; a Countess Stahremberg had paid for the schooling of this orphaned girl for twelve years. Of her Kepler wrote: "Her person and manner are convenient to me. She has strength for work. She is middle-aged, and willing and able to acquire whatever she wants." On October 13, 1613, they celebrated their nuptials. He had seven children with her. Altogether he had thirteen children. None of them inherited his genius.

Johannes Kepler, the famous defender of the hated Copernican system, the heretic who made the planets move in elliptical curves instead of in circles, was the target of religious persecution in Linz, too. Hitzler, an evangelical clergyman, refused him the sacraments, thus excluding him from the community and branding him publicly as a heretic. Now the inhabitants of Linz threatened to drive him out.

Incidentally, the more gentle souls among his countrymen described the only great Swabian scientist as "a swindling little brain."

In Linz he was also approached by the Jesuit Guldin who promised him the greatest imperial favors if only he would accept Catholicism.

In reality Kepler was a deeply pious man, who saw in God the loving Creator of the universe, the Father of men, who warns His children through the positions of the stars, but who can decide to act differently if He so pleases. Kepler composed edifying writings for his household which expressed his unshakable faith.

When Emperor Ferdinand extended the Counter-Reformation to Upper Austria, there were peasant riots and Linz was besieged. Kepler's library was locked up and sealed and he was attacked by the Jesuits.

Kepler travelled a great deal through the country trying to find a new post and printers for his books. He refused invitations to go abroad, to England and Bologna.

To Bologna where he was invited to succeed the famous astronomer Magini, he wrote in 1617: "I am a German by origin and by inclination, grown accustomed to German habits . . . Even though fame tempts me, and the hope of a better post beckons me . . . the period of my life in which one might be stimulated by new living conditions and might wish for the beauties of Italy and expect long enjoyment from them is past. Moreover, from my youth until the present time, as a German among Germans, I have enjoyed a freedom in behavior and speech, whose use, if I went to Bologna, might easily, if it did not endanger me, at least expose me to insults, suspicion and denunciation by giddy minds.

I hope you will not take it amiss if I . . . have persuaded myself to practice a perhaps superfluous caution."

In brief, Kepler told the Bolognese almost in so many words that he wanted to spare them the trouble of burning him as the Romans burned Giordano Bruno or handing him over to the Jesuits, as the Florentines had done with Galileo a year before.

Nevertheless, at the same time it cost him the greatest efforts to prevent his old mother from being burned as a witch in Swabia. In the summer of 1617, in order to defend her, he had to write the following letter to the Vice-Chancellor in Stuttgart:

". . . Since witches have been apprehended in the Leonberg region and their harmful arts have gradually spread there among the unintelligent and superstitious people, a woman named Ursula Reinhold appeared in Leonberg, who was not quite right in her mind and was ill-reputed because she had been punished for public lechery. Before then, she had got into a quarrel with my brother, a tinsmith, for reasons of business, and as always in such cases, first my brother and then also my mother reproached her for her shameful deeds. Since that time she has had an irreconcilable hatred for them. Driven by this passion and remembering confessions made by witches about similar evil doings, she began to accuse my mother of mixing poison, and asserted that the elderly lady had once handed her a drink which had immediately given her a disease of the head. Rumor is an evil that spreads faster than any other. Among the highly superstitious people this suspicion spread immediately in secret. Confirmation of it was sought in the age of my seventy-year-old mother and in a few bad qualities such as loquacity, curiosity, irritability, viciousness and querulousness, qualities which are frequent at that age in this locality.

"Hence people began to ascribe an evil meaning to meetings with my mother and to make her responsible in vague rumors for the death of a few domestic animals. On August 14, 1615, the crazy person . . . addressed herself to the bailiff, and her husband and brother, the latter a citizen of Tübingen, surgeon and barber to the young princes, with one of whom he happened to be that day in Leonberg, assisted her. My mother was summoned and the accusations against her were aired. My mother defended herself, while the barber confused the real facts and uttered evil curses and terrible threats. Finally he grazed my mother's breast with a bare sword and swore with curses that he would kill her unless she cured his sister. The bailiff looked on for a long time and then stopped the quarrel. My mother could not let this incident go unnoticed, otherwise others might have followed his example, and come forward with similar accusations. She brought proceedings against the offender."

Her witnesses were supposed to be heard before a year passed; then she was officially denounced because a certain Burga, a debtor of Mrs. Kepler, maintained that the latter had bewitched her eight-year-old daughter. Burga attacked Kepler's mother with a knife and cried out that the witch must cure her daughter. The bailiff who sent out the legal notice was promised a gift by Kepler's mother if he withdrew it. He concluded that she had a bad conscience and declared he would arrest her and put her to the torture.

"What could my brother," Kepler went on, "and my brother-in-law, pastor Binder in Heumaden, do, since they had already incurred great expenses and each had to be concerned over his own safety? They held council and persuaded my mother to come to me at Linz, whither I had previously invited her most urgently. My mother listened to them, although very reluctantly, and went as far as Ulm. Only there great colds came prematurely and she went back home. . . . My brother led her away, although she again resisted, then he set out hastily to find me and arrived at Linz on December 3/13. . . ."

In the summer of 1617 Kepler went with his mother to Württemberg to see that the trial took place without further delay, saw that the authorities only wanted to curb her spirit, and by the end of 1617 took her back to Linz.

The trial was held on November 10, 1619. Individual witnesses maintained that their cattle or they themselves had become sick through Mrs. Kepler's having touched them or after drinking drinks she had brewed. Mrs. Kepler denied this. She had only prepared medicated wines. She was also accused of having asked the sexton of Leonberg to dig up her father's skull which she allegedly intended to frame in silver and send to her son in Linz as a symbol of the transitoriness of things.

Now public opinion was against her. On August 7, 1620, she was arrested. Upon the suggestion of her son Christoph, a tinsmith who feared for his reputation in Leonberg if his mother were tortured in their own town, she was transferred to Güglingen where she was chained in the tower at the city gates. Her son Johannes faithfully stood by her and insisted on going ahead with the proceedings. The indictments were finally placed before the juridical faculty of Tübingen which rejected the state attorney's proposal that a confession be extracted from her by torture. However, in view of the number of witnesses for the prosecution, the faculty recommended that she be taken to see the instruments of torture and told their exact use in the hope that the fear of torture would induce her to confess. On September 27, 1621, the ordeal took place. The bailiff Aulber had her led to the torture chamber; she remained steadfast—a worthy mother of Kepler. She was taken back to prison; then, by order of the ducal council, a new court was summoned which acquitted her.

This acquittal did not put an end to her persecution. The municipal council of Leonberg publicly excoriated the old woman. The original accusers came forth with new accusations. Mrs. Kepler too sued again for the costs of the trial. Only her death ended the six-year-long litigation. It had consumed the mother's last years and all her remaining fortune.

In 1623 Kepler wrote: "Our family is free from danger, and all of us from abuse and shame."

Throughout his life Kepler suffered from the religious persecution mania of his century. When conditions in Linz grew hopeless and he no longer knew where to go with his wife and six children, he wrote (at the age of fifty-six) to a friend in Strassburg offering to teach at the university there; he wanted, he said, to instruct a few of the students in his Rudolfine Tables that had just been published—or in astrology.

The Strassburg Council refused a chair to Germany's most famous astronomer, but offered him the right to reside in the city.

Incidentally, why did not Kepler announce any lecture on his planetary theory? Was he not the only theoretical astronomer in Germany? But already the Bavarian Chancellor Herwart had declared that except for himself not a single man in Munich was interested in Kepler's investigations. During the Thirty Years' War Germany lost her inhabitants, her good sense, her morality, freedom, wealth and culture. She reaped only pestilence, savagery, and religious quarrels.

Since the Emperor was now unable to pay Kepler, the great scientist at the age of fifty-seven became Wallenstein's court astrologer and moved to the latter's residence at Sagan. Twenty years earlier he had cast the general's horoscope; Wallenstein sent it back to him after eighteen years to have it corrected, for none of the prophecies in it had come true.

In Sagan Kepler composed yearbooks and was again excommunicated. He refused to accept an invitation to the Wallenstein University at Rostock unless the general redeemed his promissory notes to the amount of twelve thousand gulden, in cash or certificates for goods. Although Wallenstein was supposed to be the richest man in Germany, nothing came of this invitation. Soon the imperial general fell into disfavor, and in August, 1630, was dismissed. This made Kepler's promissory notes worthless.

In the fall Kepler rode to the Electors' Diet at Regensburg by way of

Leipzig. He hoped to be able to settle his financial affairs in Regensburg. He arrived on November 3 with a fever, had a bloodletting and on November 15, 1630, died at the age of fifty-nine. The Evangelical cemetery including Kepler's tomb, was destroyed soon thereafter by armed pious men, who smelled heresy even under the gravestones.

Kepler's estate consisted of 70 ducats, 22 thalers, 13 gulden and three promissory notes for 84 gulden, 11,817 gulden and 2,500 gulden—all these notes had equal worth, that is to say they were not even worth the paper they were written on. As late as 1717 Kepler's heirs vainly sued the Austrian Emperor for their money.

Kepler had always criticized himself sharply, and at the same time had always thought highly of himself. Persecuted by many churches, left in the lurch by emperors, he fell from one private misery into the other. A terrific hypochondriac, he never bathed in his life and begot thirteen children. (Most of them died like flies.)

This professional astrologer and maker of almanacs destroyed the foundations of astrology which he himself called "this bastard of science." During his best years this nearsighted astronomer had to suffer from schoolchildren's pranks and the moods of another astronomer; while his pupils were already professors, he vainly offered his services to universities, and in his old age became the astrologer of a soldier of fortune. In his sixtieth year he was still riding after his paper fortune, a beggar and creditor of emperors. He rode from the north to the south of Germany, caught a cold and died.

One of the world's keenest calculators, he was often obscure as only a German provincial philosopher can be.

He disclosed his poverty and illness to all the world; his "secret of the universe" concerned the moon and the stars.

The adviser of emperors and generals, whose prophesies perhaps helped to shape the destinies of great empires, he now and then induced a small peasant, by means of his almanac, to plant, let us say, barely instead of oats.

He was tactful with emperors, dignified with scholars. He recognized other people's merits without envy, and his own errors with wisdom.

He occasionally refused to accept too thick flatteries, but he told Count Bianchi, who prided himself on his noble ancestry, that his great grandfather had been dubbed knight by the emperor.

His contemporaries did not value him as he deserved; posterity accepted him among the geniuses of science only after long hesitation.

In the nineteenth century, the great astronomer Arago wrote: "The glory of Kepler is written in the heavens." Kepler in a self-written epitaph had boasted:

> "I have measured the heavens, now I measure the shadows of earth,
> My spirit was of heavenly nature, my body's shadow rests here."

"He who is convinced that he is a priest of the highest God," he wrote at the age of twenty-seven referring to astronomers, "does not lightly publish anything but what he himself believes and does not impudently change the accepted hypotheses, unless he is able to explain the phenomena in another way with certainty.

"He gives in to his sacred madness . . . and will wait a hundred years for his reader . . . after all, God himself has waited six thousand years for the discoverer" (of Kepler's laws).

Throughout the decades of the Thirty Years' War, while Germany, struggling for the best religion, went to the dogs, he completed an enormous work with iron diligence, and, as it were, against his own eccentric genius.

"When a storm is raging," he wrote at the age of fifty-seven, "and shipwreck threatens the ship of state, we can do nothing more dignified than to cast the anchor of our peaceful studies in the bed of eternity."

All his life he travelled with his whole family from place to place, hated by clerics and reactionaries, and was never too tired to fight for the new doctrine. Born about a hundred years after Copernicus, Kepler was the first great Copernican, and in the name of the old canon of Torun this stubborn Lutheran wrote the laws of modern astronomy.

49

GALILEO GALILEI

> *"Yes, it moves, I will prove that by a thousand arguments!"*
> GALILEO

> *"I believe that there is no greater hatred in the world than the hatred of ignorance for knowledge."*
> GALILEO

WHEN Galileo saw the proofs of the Copernican theory in the heavens through his telescope, he lost all fear of making himself ridiculous and braved all risks, until his seventieth year when in order to escape torture he suffered worse torture, and instead of dying as a martyr sacrificed his conscience and his freedom.

Then all his books, even the future ones, were forbidden. His work was to be erased, his memory extinguished, his teaching condemned forever. He felt that he was Italy's greatest natural scientist, and feared the suppression of all his discoveries. Kneeling before ignoramuses in purple robes he was compelled to swear the famous recantation, because Rome did not want the earth to move.

"Eppur si muove!" posterity replied about 1761 (in Abbé Trailh's *Querelles Littéraires*).

Galileo was born at Pisa in 1564 and died at Arcetri in 1642. His father, a cloth merchant from Florence, set Ugolino's complaint to music and sang it in a beautiful tenor to the accompaniment of the lute. Galileo, the oldest of seven children, was sent to a monastery at the age of eleven and taken out of it at the age of fifteen so that he would not end up as a monk. He was supposed to become a cloth merchant, he wanted to become a painter, but at the age of sixteen he went to Pisa to study medicine and for that purpose naturally attended courses on Aristotle. Even as a boy he was an amateur constructor. Almost every one of his scientific discoveries is connected with the invention, rediscovery or improvement of an instrument.

In his college notebook from Pisa there are four lines about the Copernican system. Even as a young student he allegedly protested against the dictates of Aristotle and discovered the isochronism of the pendulum. At nineteen he is supposed to have observed to his surprise that at the cathedral of Pisa a chandelier which was set into motion by the sexton lighting it swung at equal intervals of time although its vibrations grew gradually smaller.

At nineteen Galileo left Pisa and medicine without passing his examinations and studied Euclid and Archimedes under Ricci, a teacher at the Art School of Florence who had a liking for practical mechanics. At twenty-two, under the influence of his studies of Archimedes, he invented a hydrostatic balance. For four years he made a living by giving private lessons, and in 1589, after many vain attempts at Rome, Padua, Bologna and Florence, he obtained a professorship at Pisa where, for a miserable sixty scudi a year, he had to teach astrology and Ptolemaic astronomy in addition to Euclid.

The young professor is said to have made his glorious discoveries in his youth at Pisa, intuitively and independently. He is also said to have climbed the leaning tower of Pisa in view of all the professors and students, and thrown down two weights, one of ten pounds, the other of one pound, at the same time, whereupon the assembled Aristotelians declared that the simultaneous arrival of the two weights was the effect of sorcery and not a refutation of Aristotle who had taught that heavy objects fall faster than light objects. But Galileo speaks of the "thousands of hours" during which he brooded over the simple problems of his theory of motion; he based himself upon his predecessors, and his development was gradual.

Galileo had no sooner left Pisa before the end of his three-year contract, probably because of his unsatisfactory position and low salary, than his father died, leaving Galileo in charge of the whole family.

"Verily, I cannot see you in this position at Pisa," wrote his patron, the wealthy geometer, Marchese dal Monte, who had himself procured it for him more than two years earlier, and now obtained a better one for him at Padua, where the university enjoyed a certain amount of intellectual freedom under the Venetian Republic. Shortly before, the Jesuits had been driven out of the university of Padua and in 1606 they were compelled to leave the territories of the Venetian Republic. The Inquisition, too, was supervised by the Republican authorities. Nevertheless, shortly after Galileo's inaugural lecture the Signoria handed the

Copernican Giordano Bruno over to the Roman Inquisition (in January, 1593).

Galileo who drew most of his income from his private pupils and boarders, lived eleven of his years in Padua with a Venetian girl, Marina Gamba, who bore him three children, Polissena, Virginia and Vincenzio; he furnished trousseaus to his sisters and procured a post of court musician at Munich for his brother.

He lived in Padua for eighteen years altogether—and in his old age he called these years his happiest. Finally he was given a life post. His salary had been raised from one hundred eighty to one thousand florins. In his mechanical workshop he built his instruments with the help of assistants. Before he left the city he had become a celebrity. His compass that he invented in 1597 is still used today. In order not to be plagiarized he published a description of it nine years later; less than six months passed when a certain Capra translated Galileo's Italian work into Latin and published it under his own name at Padua accusing Galileo of plagiarizing him. Galileo sued him through the university, had Capra's book destroyed by court order, and published a pamphlet against Capra's "frauds."

Until the age of forty-two when he published his first book, Galileo had led the quiet life of a scientist; now by one stroke his life became turbulent, there came enemies and suits for plagiarism, numerous pupils and intrigues, sensational successes and persecutions, Inquisition trials, tortures, imprisonment, conspiracy and blindness.

In Padua Galileo founded his theory of motion and his science of the strength of materials (which is of the greatest importance for the construction of buildings and of machines); he began his telescopic discoveries; he wrote Italian poems, comedies, literary criticism; he attacked Tasso's "Jerusalem Liberated"; he wrote marginal comments on the Orlando Furioso of Ariosto whom he worshipped, corrected the great poet's metrical and stylistic "errors," and purged the sensual passages from his works.

The Italian language was his proper inheritance, and suitable for the expression of his ideas. Galileo became a teacher of Europe by the power of his language no less than his discoveries.

In Padua Galileo led a double intellectual existence; compelled by the state and church he taught Aristotle and Ptolemy at the university; at home he rejected them both and followed Copernicus and his own genius. At an early date he had begun to investigate the physical causes and laws of the double motion of the earth and quietly worked on his Copernican "System of the World."

How and when did Galileo become a Copernican?

In the "Dialogue of the Two Systems of the World," one of the speakers relates his conversion to Copernicanism. "I was still very young, had barely finished my course of philosophy, then dropped it to devote myself to other occupations, when a foreigner from Rostock—I think his name was Christian Vurstisius (Wursteisen)—a partisan of Copernicus' views, happened to come to our place and delivered two or three lectures on this subject in an academy; many listeners came, I think more on account of the novelty of the thing, than for other reasons; but I did not go, because I believed that such an opinion could only be a magnificent piece of foolishness. Later when I questioned several people who had been present, I heard them all make fun of it, and only one told me that the thing was by no means ridiculous, and as I knew that he was a very intelligent and judicious man, I repented not having gone."

Galileo professed his adherence to Copernicus in his first letter to Kepler (and shortly before also in a letter to Mazzoni, 1597). When Kepler called upon him to make his views public and wrote him in order to reassure him: "For the Italians are not alone in being unable to believe that they move when they do not feel it; in Germany, too, one finds little favor with this theory," Galileo did not reply. This German always appeared alien to him; later he said: "His manner of philosophizing is not mine."

Galileo could find another Copernican in Christoph Rothmann, the director of the famous observatory of the Landgrave of Hesse in Tycho de Brahe's "Astronomical Correspondence," and he found a third Copernican in William Gilbert, author of *De Magnete:* next to Archimedes and Copernicus, Galileo praised no one as highly as this *grandissimo filosofo,* William Gilbert, who founded all scientific studies of magnetism, and discovered the magnetism of the earth. However, all these declared Copernicans were Protestants in Protestant countries. In Catholic countries, the only declared Copernican had been dubbed a heretic before thousands of people in Rome and liquidated by pyrotechnics—the unfortunate runaway monk, Giordano Bruno.

The appearance of the new star of 1604 gave Galileo the pretext and the courage for a public profession of Copernicanism. Already Tycho had seen the strongest proof against the Aristotelian thesis of the unchangeability of the firmament in the new star of 1572. The new star of 1604 too appeared among the fixed stars and did not change its position. It was greater than all the stars of the first magnitude and vanished without a trace after eighteen months.

Before the whole University of Pisa Galileo demonstrated in three lectures that the new star was high above the sphere of the moon, and even of Saturn, in the sphere of the fixed star; he declared it was a magnificent confirmation of Copernicus. (A Paduan philosopher had heard that the new star, like all fixed stars, had no parallax, and asked Galileo: What is a parallax? I want to refute it!)

Galileo was forty-six years old when he heard of an instrument "through which one could see very distant objects as distinctly as from close at hand." As he tells shortly afterwards in his "Messenger of the Heavens," letters from a Parisian scholar confirmed to him the existence of this Dutch invention. Galileo "directed all his thoughts toward investigating the causes and finding the means enabling him to invent a similar instrument, and on the basis of the theory of refraction . . . soon found it."

Shortly thereafter he came to Venice with a telescope that magnified nine times. Procurator Priuli relates in his chronicles that together with Galileo and seven *nobiles* he ascended the bell-tower of San Marco, "to see the marvels and curious effects of Mr. Galileo."

Three days later Galileo gave his telescope to the Signoria, which on the next day confirmed Galileo's Paduan professorship for life, with a thousand gold gulden a year, as a reward for his invention which he "based on the profoundest theoretical considerations of optics" and the exclusive patent for which he promised the Signoria.

This took place at the end of August, 1609. As early as October 2, 1608, the Dutch Estates General had deliberated on the telescope of Hans Lippershey, an optician from Middleburgh; on October 17, 1608, Jacob Adriaanszon, called Metius, from Alkmaar, offered them his telescope; shortly afterwards another inventor made himself known, Zacharias Jansen from Middleburgh. And in April, 1609, Parisian spectacle makers offered the new *lunettes* for sale in their stores at low prices.

Procurator Priuli writes in another passage of his chronicles: "Such an instrument had not been seen in Italy, even though others say that it was not Galileo's invention, but was invented in Flanders; it seemed a miracle of art, although later countless others were made and sold at a very low price and were in everyone's hands."

Galileo constructed a second, third and fourth telescope, each stronger than the preceding one. He directed the fourth telescope toward the sky and was the first of all human beings to see the new, but very ancient, miracles of the universe. He saw mountains and valleys in the moon, and saw that this planet was like the earth. Since people carry their prejudices, and scientists their hatreds, into the very lap of God, Galileo saw in the moon the profound errors of Aristotle, who had thought that its surface was completely smooth and round.

The moon's resemblance to the earth became Galileo's favorite argument for proving its planetary nature, and thus the truth of the Copernican system.

Amidst the intoxication of astronomical discoveries Galileo published his first account, *Sidereus nuntius* (Messenger of the Heavens). There he announces his main work, the System of the World. "We shall prove a hundred times," he declares, "that the earth moves like a planet and surpasses the moon in brilliance, but is not the motionless scum and dregs of the world."

By his sensational discoveries (and despite his enthusiastic advocacy of the Copernican system!) Galileo became a celebrity in Europe.

He saw with his own eyes the greatness of the world that Copernicus had only sensed and computed. That winter he saw through his telescope the planets like little moons, and the stars like points of light, "so numerous that it almost seemed incredible." "And the Milky Way is nothing but a mass of countless stars in clusters."

On January 7, 1610, he directed his telescope at the planet Jupiter and saw "three little stars, very bright, near the planet, two east of it, one west; on the next evening, to his great surprise, he found all three stars to the west of the planet." On January 10, he already thought that the "change in position was not that of Jupiter, but of the stars"; on the thirteenth he saw a fourth star in this region and knew that he had discovered the four moons of Jupiter.

And all these discoveries seemed to him marvelous proofs of the Copernican system.

The Aristotelians accused Galileo of error or fraud. Seven was a sacred number, there could be only seven planets. Sizzi, a Florentine astronomer, wrote: "We have only seven windows in our heads, two nostrils, two eyes, two ears, one mouth." Clavius, the famous Jesuit mathematician of the Roman College, "laughed at the idea of the four new planets that one probably had to stick in one's telescope to see. May Galileo persist in his opinions and be happy. I persist in my opinion."

When Libri, a philosopher who had refused to look through a telescope, died, Galileo wrote to a friend of his that he would perhaps see the moons of Jupiter on his way to Heaven. To Kepler he wrote: "Just as snakes close their ears, so people close their eyes to the living truth. Such types do not seek the truth in the universe or in nature, but in comparisons between texts!"

Simon Mayr (Marius) from Gunzenhausen, the physician and mathematician to the margrave of Ansbach, began a priority dispute with Galileo on the question of the moons of Jupiter.

Kepler, who at that time was living at Emperor Rudolf's court in Prague, wrote an enthusiastic letter dated April 19, 1610, and printed it in Prague together with Galileo's "Messenger of the Heavens." In his eyes, Galileo's discoveries were the most splendid confirmation of the Copernican theory of the moon (but also a refutation of Giordano Bruno's "terrible philosophy" of the plurality of the worlds, and curiously enough, a new proof of the privileged position of the earth and its inhabitants!).

At a time when the mountains of the earth had not yet been measured, Galileo measured the mountains on the moon and wrote to the court of the Medici: "I am full of infinite astonishment and also infinite gratitude to God that it has pleased Him to make me alone the first observer of such wonderful things that in all the past centuries remained hidden."

In his intoxication over his astronomical discoveries Galileo also renounced his "free" position with the Venetian Republic in order to become court philosopher to the absolutist Duke of Tuscany. For this reason he had baptized the moons of Jupiter *Sidera Medicea,* the Medici Stars. He offered his "hereditary prince and master" his future inventions if the latter would assure him one thousand scudi as an annual salary.

He was annoyed by his double intellectual bookkeeping; he did not want to go on publicly drinking the water of Ptolemy and secretly drinking the wine of Copernicus. He was fed up with doing astrological work for money; he was fed up with keeping boarders, even if they were princes; he was fed up with teaching students. He had neither enough time nor money, at Padua. From his fortieth year on he was also tormented by his "sinister companion," a malicious rheumatism.

On September 12, 1610, he moved to Florence. Experienced eroticists and Galileo's biographers have made Marina Gamba responsible for the fact that he left Padua in a manner resembling flight. Actually he did terminate his relation with her at that time; a few years later Marina married Signor Bartoluzzi, and Bartoluzzi later took money from Signor Galileo on several occasions. Galileo took his daughters to Florence to live with his mother; Marina kept the four-year-old son.

Padua and Venice were displeased at Galileo's sudden departure. In his haste he forgot to give official notice that he was abandoning his professorship. Procurator Priuli says in his chronicles that he never wanted to hear the name of Galileo again. Sagredo, a friend of Galileo's, wrote sorrowfully: "I am extremely worried that you should be in a place where the fathers of the Society of Jesus enjoy high esteem."

Then Galileo discovered "a new extraordinary marvel." On July 30 he wrote from Padua that Saturn was formed of three stars; later he saw "two handles of Saturn." (The ring of Saturn was discovered only in 1655, by Christian Huygens.)

At the beginning of 1611 Galileo published his discovery of the phases of Venus. According to the Copernican system these had to exist. But to the naked eye Venus had always appeared round. Lacking better proof, Copernicus had counted upon God's eventual help. With his telescope Galileo was able to see the sickle-like shape of Venus.

At the beginning of 1611 he discovered the spots and protuberances on the sun. Soon he deduced that the sun rotated. For the first time the rotation Copernicus ascribed to the earth appeared visibly in a heavenly body.

Christoph Scheiner, a Jesuit father at Ingolstadt, Thomas Harriot at Isleworth and Johann Fabricius at Osteel in Friesland discovered the sunspots independently of Galileo.

The entire Roman College in Rome denied Galileo's discoveries. Jesuits and Dominicans threatened to condemn the whole Copernican school. In March, 1611, Galileo went to Rome to defend the Copernican system against its threatened stigmatization as heresy. He was allowed to kiss the Pope's feet. After a conversation with Galileo about the motion of the earth, Cardinal Bellarmin, an important member of the Inquisition, said to the Tuscan ambassador: "We have the greatest regard for everything concerning the serenissime duke, but should Galileo go too far here, it will be impossible not to call him to account."

Shortly before Galileo's departure a note was published in the record of the session of the Inquisition held on May 17 to the effect that it should be checked whether the name of Galileo was mentioned in the trial of a certain professor suspected of heresy.

Such was the triumph of the scientist in papal Rome—he was immediately declared suspect by the Inquisition!

Galileo who saw only his triumph, and not the beginning of his persecution by the ecclesiastical secret police, declared (in his Discourse on the bodies that float on water, 1611) that Aristotle's authority had no validity whatsoever in physics.

In his Letters on the Sunspots in 1613, Galileo demanded the liberation of astronomy from the chaos of epicycles and excentrics. This time he had not hurried to publish his findings. Fabricius and later Scheiner had made the same discovery public as early as 1612. In these letters Galileo attacked Scheiner's priority claims and anti-Copernicanism. Thereupon the whole Society of Jesus declared war upon Galileo. It had ordered that Aristotle be strictly defended in a decree of 1593.

Thomas Campanella wrote from his dungeon in the kingdom of Naples to Galileo: "All the philosophers in the world receive their law from your pen, because it is impossible to philosophize truly without a sure system of the world structure."

Only in Italian jails did one speak so freely, and only this one imprisoned Dominican who was a martyr of freedom; he had allegedly wanted to liberate Naples from Spanish tyranny and for twenty-seven years had sat in Neapolitan dungeons; when Naples released him, the Inquisition locked him up for three more years in order to test him!

Galileo's friends admonished him to be cautious; his enemies quoted the passages in the Bible that speak against the motion of the earth. On All Souls' Day 1612, a mendicant monk named Niccolo Lorini preached from the pulpit against Galileo's theories.

Galileo, too, intervened in the struggle of the theologians against the laws of nature. At the Grand Duke's table someone asked once more whether the Medici Stars were real or an invention of Galileo's. In her own room Christine of Lorraine, the Duke's dowager, asked Pater Castelli, who was professor of mathematics at Pisa upon Galileo's recommendation, whether the Holy Scripture did not contradict the idea of the motion of the earth. Castelli defended Galileo before the Princess and informed him of the discussion.

Thereupon Galileo wrote his long letter "On bringing the Holy Scriptures into scientific discussions" (December 21, 1613). The Holy Scriptures cannot lie or err, he said. But its interpreters can err, especially the literal ones. It was blasphemy, he went on, even heresy, to believe that God had hands, feet, eyes, that He felt anger, hatred, remorse, that He sometimes forgot the past or did not know the future. The Holy Scriptures are the last place to look for a statement of the natural laws. The theologians wanted to make science a handmaiden of religion, but Galileo advised against interpreting the Scriptures in such a way that they agreed with the laws of nature. "The Holy Scripture and nature," he says, "are emanations of God's word; the former was dictated by the Holy Ghost; the latter is the executrix of God's commands."

On the fourth Sunday of Advent in 1614, Father Tommaso Caccini, like Lorini a Dominican of the Savonarola monastery, attacked Galileo and Copernicus from the pulpit. He termed mathematics a devilish art, and the mathematicians the originators of all heresies. He demanded that they be driven out of every country. It is said that his sermon began with the words from the Acts of the Apostles: "Ye men of Galilee, why stand ye gazing into Heaven?"

In view of the growing threat against free science and this denunciation of Galileo, his friends advised him to be cautious.

At this time, a copy of Galileo's letter to Father Castelli on the Bible and science fell into the hands of the Jesuits; they transmitted it to Father Lorini who sent it to the Roman Inquisition together with a denunciation. The Jesuits hoped that the Inquisition would at least condemn Copernicus' book and doctrine.

Shortly afterwards the bishop of Fiesole resumed the attacks and threats against Galileo in the cathedral in Florence.

On February 25, the Roman Inquisition deliberated on Father Lorini's denunciation. Galileo's letter, we read in the short announcement of this meeting, contains erroneous assertions about the meaning and interpretation of the Holy Scriptures.

Meanwhile Father Caccini had arrived in a Roman monastery and expressed the wish to make a deposition before the Inquisition "in order to unburden his conscience." The Pope gave orders that he be heard. On March 20, 1615, Caccini appeared before the Commissioner General of the Roman Inquisition. "I wish to inform the Holy Office of a public rumor that Galileo holds the following two propositions to be true: The earth moves as a whole with relation to itself, and also in daily motion. The sun is motionless. According to my conscience and understanding, these propositions contradict the divine Scriptures as they are interpreted by the Holy Fathers, and therefore contradict the faith." Moreover, he said, Galileo was personally suspect, because he was a good friend of and corresponded with that *terrible* Fra Paolo Sarpi of the Servite Order, who was notorious in Venice for his godlessness and had a hand in the expulsion of the Jesuits.

During the following session the Pope ordered that a copy of the record be sent to the Florentine Inquisitor and that the latter question Father Lorini and Father Ximenes, Caccini's witnesses.

Meanwhile Galileo heard vague rumors of the secret proceedings against him or Copernicus, and sent his friends in Rome his letter to Castelli, asking them to show it to Cardinal Bellarmin. In his innocence Galileo feared that he was being judged on the basis of a falsified copy. Soon his friends answered him that his letter had displeased various princes of the church, who advised him to confine himself to mathematical analyses. Monsignor Dini wrote Galileo that Cardinal Bellarmin did not think Copernicus would be prohibited, but that only a few sentences would be inserted in order to explain the hypothetical character of his theory. "Write freely," Dini wrote, "but stay outside the vestry."

Galileo immediately answered his Roman friends that it was impossible to "moderate" Copernicus, that "one had either to condemn him entirely or leave him as he was."

In the interests of the church he composed an apology of the Copernican theory against false exegetists, his "Letter to the Dowager Grand Duchess of Tuscany." Here he wrote: "If it were enough to close an individual's mouth in order to eliminate this view and doctrine from the world, this could be done extraordinarily easily; but this is not the case; in order to carry out such a decision not only Copernicus' book and the writings of other authors adhering to the same theory would have to be prohibited, but also the entire science of astronomy, and even more, the people themselves would have to be forbidden to look at the heavens."

Galileo's friends advised caution, and he postponed publication of his "Letter." He did this all the more willingly because at the same time a clever and fearless advocate of his theses came forth, who in addition to other advantages enjoyed the privilege of being a clergyman. When "The Letter of the Carmelite Monk Paolo Antonio Foscarini to Sebastian Fantoni, the General of his Order, about the view of the Pythagoreans and Copernicus" was published at Naples, its author happened to be in Rome as a preacher by order of his superiors. Foscarini believed in the truth of the Copernican theory. It had made a hundred fictions superfluous and simplified the theory of the structure of the world. And Galileo's discoveries and Kepler's laws were its most beautiful confirmations. Foscarini only wanted to eliminate its apparent contradictions with the Scriptures. "His letter could not be published at a more favorable moment," Prince Cesi wrote to Galileo.

Upon receiving his publication Cardinal Bellarmin answered Foscarini that he did not believe in the existence of proofs of the motion of the earth; that Solomon had written: the sun rises and sets and goes back to its place . . . but that concerning the sun and the earth no sensible person needs to correct an error because he clearly perceives that the earth is motionless and that the eye is not deceived when it judges that the moon and the stars are moving."

Foscarini sent a copy of this first quasi-official pronouncement in the great dispute to Galileo, who "at that time was surrounded by physicians and medicines."

Meanwhile the Florentine Inquisitor questioned Caccini's witnesses. Lorini referred to Ximenes; Ximenes referred to the priest Attavanti, saying that the latter was a pupil of Galileo's, and that in his cell he had heard Attavanti advance heretical propositions to the prior, propositions which doubtless originated with Galileo. Attavanti swore that he was neither a pupil of Galileo's nor knew him personally. The allegedly heretical propositions of Galileo that Father Ximenes had overheard were propositions from St. Thomas' disputations.

After the minutes of the Florentine proceedings were read in the palace of the Roman Inquisition, the cardinals ordered only that "certain letters of Galileo, which have been published in Rome under the title of *Delle macchie solari* / on sunspots / be investigated."

On December 3, 1615, Galileo (perhaps warned by Attavanti) went of his own free will to Rome, resolved to fight for the Copernican system. In Rome he soon realized that in this fight he stood alone.

Guicciardini, the Tuscan ambassador, who was supposed to take care of Galileo's personal needs and furnish him with an apartment in his own house, a secretary, a servant and a mule, wrote to Florence: ". . . and this is not a country in which one can dispute about the moon. . . ."

After only a few weeks in Rome Galileo realized that he was entangled in a devilish net. On February 6, 1616, he wrote: "My business is entirely settled, in so far as my own person is concerned . . . but because my private affair is connected with another one, which does not concern me more than any of the others who for the last eighty years have adhered to a certain view and theory and who are the subject of discussions, and because I may be able to be helpful in so far as the outcome depends on the knowledge of scientific truth, I cannot and must not fail to give this help, to which I am urged by my conscience as a zealous and Catholic Christian." Thus Galileo was already afraid of mentioning Copernicus' name in his letters. Galileo and the Copernican theory had already become the objects of an Inquisitorial trial.

Galileo hoped in vain "to get the better of the clerics in Rome" (as Guicciardini wrote with equal contempt for Galileo's Quixotism and the ignorance of the clergy) and ran from one cardinal to the other, even receiving the denunciator Caccini in his home (during this visit he laughed at Caccini's ignorance, and Caccini laughing at Galileo's naïveté, sounded him out). And while the famous fifty-year-old scientist vainly proved the laws of nature and the existence of the stars before the great, he became a playball for the snobs and scoffers, and his theory was declared absurd and heretical by the church.

In the last days of 1615 Galileo was still allowed to expound his views on the connection between the tides and the motion of the earth to his eminent patron, a twenty-two-year-old fop named Orsini (Cardinal Orsini!). At the young man's invitation he wrote down his explanations and they became the basis for his "Dialogue on the world systems"—a skillfully expounded error, which Galileo considered the most irrefutable proof of the motion of the earth.

In Rome Galileo's hopeless isolation in his struggle for the recognition of the Copernican theory made itself felt with increasing sharpness. Several cardinals warned him. He continued trying to enlighten them, but only succeeded in wearying them. His bold plan called for converting the Pope to Copernicanism. He induced his young friend Cardinal Orsini to speak with Paul V. On February 20, Galileo wrote a hopeful letter to Florence; on the previous day, by order of the Pope, the Inquisition submitted the following two propositions to the examination of all the theologians of the Holy Office: (1) "The sun is the center of the world and entirely motionless as regards spatial motion." (2) "The earth is not the center of the world and is not motionless, but moves with regard to itself and in daily motion."

The Inquisition took this nonsensical formulation from the informer Caccini.

The Congregatio Qualificationis sat on February 23. On February 24 the youthful Cardinal Orsini is said to have spoken on behalf of Galileo in the papal consistory. The Pope merely replied that Orsini should rather advise his protégé to renounce his opinions. When Orsini insisted, the Pope cut him short and declared that he would submit the matter to the Holy Office.

On the same day the report on the propositions that had been examined was turned in. As for the first of these, all the wise men declared that it was foolish, philosophically absurd and formally heretical, in so far as it explicitly contradicted many passages of the Holy Scriptures literally and according to the unanimous interpretation of the Holy Fathers and the theological doctors. As for the second proposition, the same authorities declared that from a philosophical point of view it was just as censurable and with regard to the theological truth was at least erroneous in religion. Eleven theologians, for the most part Dominicans, had signed this opinion.

The "Report on the Assertions of the Mathematician Galileo" was submitted to the Inquisition on February 25; it was a sword against the Copernician theory.

At first the Inquisition proceeded against Galileo, the alleged advocate of the condemned propositions (which derived neither from him nor from Copernicus, but were based on Caccini's gibberish). Immediately after the report was read, Pope Paul V ordered Cardinal Bellarmin to summon Galileo and demand that he give up the views outlined in the propositions; if he refused, the Commissioner of the Inquisition was to command him before a notary and witnesses to refrain from teaching or advocating such views or discussing them; if he did not submit to this command, he was to be thrown into jail.

On the following day, February 26, 1616, Galileo appeared in Cardinal Bellarmin's palace. In the presence of the Commissioner of the Holy Office the cardinal pointed out the errors of his views and advised him to give them up.

Galileo declared that he submitted.

Thus ended the proceedings of the Inquisition on the basis of Lorini's and Caccini's denunciations.

Now the Index Congregation proceeded against Copernicus. During the session of the Holy Office of March 3, 1616, the decree of the Congregation against the writings of Copernicus and his adherents was read and its publication ordered by the Magister of S. Palatium. The decree against Copernicus repeated the report of the theologians but left out the word "heretical." It ran as follows: "Whereas it has come to the knowledge of the Holy Congregation that the false Pythagorean theory of the motion of the earth and the immobility of the sun, which runs completely counter to the divine Scriptures and which Nicolaus Copernicus teaches in his book 'De Revolutionibus Orbium Coelestium' and Didacus à Stunica in his 'Job,' has spread and been accepted by many, as can be seen from the printed letter of a certain Carmelite monk entitled *Lettera del R. P. Maestro Paolo Antonio Foscarini Carmelitano, sopra l'opinione dei Pittagorici e del Copernico della mobilità della Terra e stabilità del Sole, e il nuovo Pittagorico Sistema del Mondo. In Napoli per Lazzaro Scorriggio, 1615,* in which the above-mentioned Father tried to show that the said theory of the immobility of the sun in the centre of the world and the mobility of the earth conforms to the truth and does not contradict the Holy Scriptures: Therefore, in order that such an opinion not continue to stalk the land and bring about the perdition of Catholic truth, the Congregation resolved that the above-named books of Copernicus 'De revolutionibus orbium' and Didacus à Stunica on 'Job' be suspended (*usque corrigatur*) until they are corrected, and entirely to forbid and condemn the book of the Carmelite P. Paulus Antonius Foscarini, and to forbid all the other books that teach the same thing, as all of them are by the present decree respectively forbidden, condemned and suspended."

This decree was preceded by an explicit reminder of the general regulations: "No one of whatever rank and position, under the penalties provided for by the Council of Trent and the Index of forbidden books, is allowed to undertake to print or publish the said writings, to possess these in any form or to read them, and, under the same penalties, those who at present possess or will in the future possess these writings, are bound, as soon as they have learned of the present decree, to deliver them to the ordinarii or Inquisitors concerned."

This decree was published on March 5, 1616, under the heading "To be published everywhere!" Copies of it were sent to all the Inquisitors and apostolic nuncios.

In a circular letter Cardinal Sfondrati emphasized that the books in question were highly dangerous. The Pope in person, he wrote, had ordered them to be prohibited; the rules of the Index must be strictly observed and the Inquisition must be informed immediately if a suspicious book was discovered anywhere.

Cardinal Gaetani was assigned the noble task of improving Copernicus.

Galileo stayed for some time in Rome in order to prove to all the world that he himself had been neither condemned nor punished, as certain rumors in Florence and Venice pretended. He was allowed to kiss the Pope's feet. He waited in Rome until the arrival of Cardinal Medici and was allowed to kiss the rim of his cloak in the garden of the Villa Medici.

Before Galileo left Rome he asked Cardinal Bellarmin for a testimonial against his slanderers. The cardinal attested "that Galileo did not abjure to him, nor, in so far as he knew, to anyone else, in Rome or elsewhere, any opinion or theory he held, and that neither salutary nor any other penance was imposed upon him; he was only informed of the declaration issued by His Holiness and published by the Index Congregation, which says that the theory ascribed to Copernicus, according to which the earth turns around the sun and the sun is in the center of the world without moving from east to west, runs counter to the Holy Scriptures and therefore must not be defended nor held to be true."

Rehabilitated as a Christian, ruined as a scientist, discredited as a man, Galileo returned. He was full of hatred, anger and contempt. A few months later he wrote in a confidential letter: "I believe that there is no greater hatred in the world than the hatred of ignorance for knowledge."

Three years after the much publicized decree of Rome against Copernicus, the third edition of the Copernican "Revolutions" prepared by Mulerius was published in Amsterdam; it does not mention Rome's prohibition.

Only in 1620 did the church publish the indispensable corrections of the "Revolutions," nine in all, to the effect that the earth was not allowed to move, that it was not a planet, and similar pious wishes of the church.

True, there was some limit to this censorship. The national, linguistic and religious fetters on science had been partially broken. Astronomy took refuge in Protestant countries. The Roman censorship stopped neither the Copernican theory nor the motion of the earth—it only succeeded in hampering the development of science in the Catholic countries, especially in Italy.

Old Maestlin exclaimed bitterly: "Are there not at least a few among the cardinals who are versed in mathematics and astronomy?" And further: "Have the authors of the censorship decree ever seen Copernicus' work or do they even know when and whether he lived? They discover in a letter of a brave Carmelite monk that Copernicus' views are beginning to spread, and then they condemn a work of truly superhuman labor. . . ." Maestlin refused to speak of Foscarini and Didacus à Stunica—he did not know them. But to correct Copernicus? "Who is supposed to do it? Copernicus himself who has not been among the living for more than seventy years? More enduring and stronger than Copernicus himself was his astronomy—Kepler's work proved this. Thus it can be justly said that the condemnation of those censors and the judgment of a blind man on colors are of equal value."

In 1618, without having heard of the Roman censorship decree, Kepler published the first part of his "Outline of the Copernican Astronomy," which was immediately suspended in Rome. Kepler learned of this only through Galileo's request to Archduke Leopold for a copy of Kepler's suspended work. Kepler at once wrote to Johannes Remus, the archduke's physician in ordinary and mathematician: "I beg you most urgently to send me a copy of that condemnation and to let me know whether it would endanger the author if he went to Italy and whether he would be asked to recant. I am also anxious to know whether this condemnation will also be valid in Austria. Should this be the case, I would not only be unable to find a printer in Austria but . . . it will also be intimated to me that I must renounce my teaching of astronomy now, that I have become almost aged lecturing on that science, without ever being opposed; finally, I will have to give up my stay in Austria if here too no room is left for the freedom of science."

Immediately after the decree of 1616 against Copernicus the Neapolitan printer of Foscarini's prohibited letter was thrown into jail. "He is being prosecuted," the cardinal of Naples wrote to the Roman Grand Inquisitor. "That is what I call well done!" the Roman Grand Inquisitor wrote to the cardinal of Naples.

The Inquisition was storming the Copernican heaven. In its left hand it held the pitch-torch with which it lighted the stake; in its right hand it brandished the clattering censorship scissors of the Index. From the wide holes of its fluttering monk's cowl peeped contented little Aristotelian gargoyles and Ptolemaic elves. All around it things stood still, the earth, the sciences and mankind.

The burning of the Copernican Giordano Bruno in 1600, the condemnation of the Copernican Foscarini in 1616, the correction of Copernicus' Revolutions which was for all practical purposes a prohibition, the attempt at intellectual assassination of the most famous Copernican, the Florentine court philosopher Galileo, all these were death sentences against intellectual life in the Catholic world.

Only from the Neapolitan jail came the solitary voice of the imprisoned martyr of freedom, Thomas Campanella, loudly protesting against the enslavement of Europe. In 1623 his *Apologia pro Galileo* printed in Germany came to Rome, and was forbidden.

The denunciator Caccini called the partisans of Galileo "prigs" (bell' ingegno). Trembling they now fell silent, and with them trembled the freedom of the mind, and the Muses, too, fell silent. With the decree against Copernicus began the intellectual vacuum, the "de-spiritualization" of Italy.

Galileo remained silent for seven years. His conscience was sick, and this made his body sick. He was a devout Catholic; he had said so often enough; he wanted to remain one.

"Ignorance, envy and malice, the too-powerful architects of my fate," he wrote twelve days before his submission in 1616. Two years later he wrote the Archduke Leopold in Innsbruck about "that Copernican theory I once deemed true, a poet's dream, a nothing, to which I clung as sometimes poets cling to their fantasies." Now he had to acquiesce in the deeper insights of his superiors!

Then again the heavens intervened and there appeared the three terrible comets of the fall of 1618, the first year of the Thirty Years' War. Christendom expected the usual terrors and interpretations. People looked to Galileo. He was silent. Finally, one of his disciples published his theory of comets. The Jesuit Father F. Grassi of the Roman College published two works against it. In the name of the College he reproached Galileo with ingratitude and error, referred maliciously to the telescope as "not his /Galileo's/ child, to be sure, but still his pupil," and threatened him with a censorship decree.

In 1623 Galileo finally replied with his "Assayer" (*Il Saggiatore*). Just as Pascal in his *Lettres Provinciales* fought against the moral dishonesty of the Jesuits, so Galileo fought here against their intellectual dishonesty.

The Dominican Father Niccolo Riccardi, the censor of the Inquisition who granted permission to print the "Assayer," wrote that he considered himself happy to be born in the age of Galileo and visited the great man in Florence.

Both Galileo and Grassi were wrong in their theories of comets. But Galileo wanted to hit the Jesuits, the enemies of modern science; he wanted to ridicule the old pedantic methods of the Aristotelians and Scholastics. In this most extensive of his pamphlets he refuted the enemy, proposition by proposition, at the cost of three years' labor. "Woe to me!" he exclaims, "and I do not even notice that the hours are flying by, and waste my time on such childish nonsense!"

In 1623 Urban VIII was elected Pope. For a long time he had been an admirer of Galileo; now he had parts of the "Assayer" read to him and graciously accepted its dedication. Galileo's friends foresaw a "regime of the arts and sciences," and a "supreme Maecenas," and Galileo finally took new hope. At the age of sixty he had not yet completed his main work "On the System of the World" for reasons of censorship; after all, he did not wish to teach against the Church, he wanted to convert the Church to Copernicanism!

To his favorite daughter in the monastery at Arcetri he sent a whole bundle of letters that the Pope had addressed to him in former times; the enthusiastic daughter who had chosen her father's name as the name of her favorite saint was enraptured when she read how the Holy Father admired her father.

Once again Galileo was determined to convert the Pope!

The Pope asked Prince Cesi: "Is Galileo coming? When will he come?" Galileo was ill, the winter was severe; in April, 1624, he finally made the trip. He kissed the Holy Father's feet. Urban VIII granted him six audiences, and gave him gifts, agnus dei tokens, commemorative medals and a pension for his son, Vincenzio.

At Galileo's suggestion, Cardinal Zollern, chief of the German mission, told the Holy Father how much harm was done to the reputation of the Catholic Church in the Lutheran countries by its prohibition of the Copernican theory. Urban replied that the Church had not condemned it as heretical and would not do so, but only as foolhardy; moreover, that there was no fear that any compelling proof of its truth would ever be found.

At the age of sixty Galileo suddenly became afraid of death. He had dined gaily with the Cavalier d'Este; three days later Este was dead; a spur, writes Galileo, a warning to me, too, that time is rapacious!

So he returned home. The Pope sent a brief to Tuscany: "For a long time we have extended our fatherly love to this great man whose fame shines in heaven and marches on earth."

Galileo who is said to have been Urban's teacher at Pisa thought he had a friend in him. In a "Letter to Francesco Ingoli," an anti-Copernican Jesuit, Galileo wrote in 1624: "In natural things man's authority is not valid. . . . Nature, Sir, scorns the orders and decrees of princes, emperors and monarchs, and will not change an iota of its laws and orders by their command. Aristotle was a man, he saw with his eyes, listened with his ears and thought with his brain. I am a man, I see with my eyes, and much more than he did; as for thinking, I believe that he thought about more things than I have; but whether he thought more or better than I about the things that were objects of thought for both of us—this will be shown by our reasoning and not by our authorities."

In 1626 Galileo bought himself a villa at Arcetri, one mile from Florence, in order to be close to his two daughters in their convent, especially his favorite, the gifted, cheerful, charming Suor Maria Celeste, who from her poor cell sent her father flowers, delicacies, little gifts and tender letters, receiving letters and little gifts in return. As his old pupils dispersed, Galileo constantly won new ones. His correspondence spread all over Europe and increasingly revealed his encyclopaedic interests.

In April, 1630, he finally completed his main work, his *Dialogo dei due massimi sistemi del mondo,* Dialogue of the two greatest world systems.

He was sixty-six years old and he thought his time had come. Until then he had published only pamphlets and occasional writings. His pupils were already university professors and were giving public lectures about him. He was the chief of the modern school in Europe. He was the great enemy of the Aristotelians, the scholastics and the reactionaries. He had become the representative man of his century, and his greatest work was still in manuscript form.

In his Dialogue three characters converse about the systems of the world: Salviati, Sagredo and Simplicio. They are in the palace of a Venetian nobleman, they sail in a gondola, they read and they argue. Salviati and Sagredo are portraits of two of Galileo's deceased friends. Salviati is the spokesman for the Copernican theory; Sagredo, with his common sense, his *buon naturale,* is the mediator between Salviati and Simplicio, the Copernican and the Aristotelian; Simplicio is so named after the famous Sicilian commentator on Aristotle, Simplicius; he is a scholastic and defends the systems of Aristotle and Ptolemy.

Galileo wrote this book in a popular manner. He wanted to prove the truth of the Copernican system and defend it against all the arguments of the old school.

These dialogues give us hardly any astronomical discoveries, in contrast to Kepler's "Outline of the Copernican Astronomy" published a few years earlier. Indeed, here, as throughout his life, Galileo ignores Kepler's planetary laws. In Kepler's eyes, these were the main things; the arguments in favor of the motion of the earth were most important in Galileo's view; Kepler produced such arguments only incidentally.

The great merit of these dialogues is that they founded the new physics. Aristotle, in his physics, determined the nature and mechanics of the heavens assuming that the earth was motionless. Galileo created the new mechanics and dynamics of the heavens assuming that the earth moved. Here he presents the new science coherently, as applied to the Copernican theory. And he taught that scientific knowledge permits human reason to partake of divine reason. The Inquisition termed this idea heretical. Indeed, this idea implied the concept of unlimited progress, although it was also responsible for the fragmentary nature of Galileo's work.

Galileo grasped the philosophical, moral and scientific revolutions initiated by Copernicus.

Urban VIII once said casually to Thomas Campanella who, finally released from thirty years' imprisonment, had come to Rome in 1629 and been graciously received by the Pope: "If it had depended upon us, that decree [of 1616] would not have been issued." And to Cardinal Zollern he said: "Out of sheer respect for the memory of Copernicus I would not have permitted his condemnation, if I had been Pope at that time!"

Galileo heard of this and went to Rome with his manuscript. He arrived on May 3, 1630, and during an audience with the Pope explained the intention of his book: he wanted to produce all the existing proofs of the Copernican theory in order to show the world that Rome had not acted from ignorance when it condemned the Copernican theory.

Urban demanded that the book contain no theological considerations; that the Copernican system be represented only as a mathematical hypothesis; that Galileo clearly stress the purpose of the dialogues, that is, to make it clear that Rome had not acted from ignorance of the Copernican proofs and that he replace the title "Dialogues About the Ebb and Flow of the Tides" by another.

Galileo found it hardest of all to renounce his title; as is often the case in such matters, he clung to his false hypotheses about the tides more passionately than to many of his correct discoveries. He submitted his manuscript to the censorship of Riccardi, Master of the Sacred Palace, who received the Pope's instructions.

Galileo was also willing to write a preface and conclusion recognizing the omniscience of the Church without reservations. Riccardi demanded only minor changes; Galileo gave his consent, and Riccardi his *imprimatur*. Since the title and certain passages still had to be modified, the permission could only be conditional.

Galileo entrusted his friend Cesi with the printing, returned home contented and soon afterward received the news of Cesi's death and a warning from his friend Castelli advising him to publish his book in Florence, "and as soon as possible . . . and for many cogent reasons that I do not wish at present to trust to paper."

On September 11, the Florentine Inquisition put its *imprimatur* under the Roman one, but to Galileo's request to Riccardi for permission from the Roman Inquisition to print the book in Florence, the Master of the Sacred Palace replied that he had to undertake a new revision and asked for the manuscript or a copy of it.

The horrified Galileo wrote that the plague and the quarantine made it almost impossible to send such a bulky manuscript to Rome and asked permission to send only the introduction and conclusion, adding that these could be changed at will.

Thanks to the tender solicitude of the wife of the Tuscan ambassador, Niccolini, Riccardi agreed to Galileo's proposal, provided that an expert theologian of the Dominican order revised the manuscript in Florence. Months went by. The introduction and conclusion did not return from Rome nor did Father Stefani, the consultant of the Florentine Inquisition, receive the order to revise the manuscript from Rome.

Meanwhile the winter passed. "And so my work is in a trap," wrote Galileo, "my life is passing away, and I spend it in constant pain."

The Grand Duke of Tuscany began to exert pressure on Riccardi. Riccardi, just as he had done before with Galileo, fed the Grand Duke with vague promises and put the matter off from one day to the next. He obviously feared unpleasantness for Galileo and himself, and said so in one of his letters.

"This is not easy to bear!" wrote Galileo. Riccardi's letters gave him the feeling that he was sailing an ocean without shore or harbor. Only the Grand Duke, he said, could still help him. He resolutely rejected a remark made by Niccolini that "his opinions were disliked." "For the opinions that are disliked," wrote Galileo, "are not my own, and my own are those which are professed by St. Augustine, St. Thomas and all the other Holy Fathers."

Finally, by the end of May, the Florentine Inquisitor received the conditions for printing the manuscript; he was allowed to proceed independently of the Roman revision and to give or refuse his *imprimatur*. He gave it. The title and a few expressions were changed. A few weeks later the printing began. But months still had to pass before Riccardi sent in the revised introduction and conclusion. Riccardi wrote the Florentine Inquisitor that according to the Pope's order this revised introduction had to tally with the conclusion, and that Mr. Galileo might add the reasons communicated to him by His Holiness and based on God's omnipotence, intended to appease the understanding, if it could not escape from the Pythagorean reasons by other means.

Urban had asked Galileo: "Cannot God, by virtue of His infinite power and wisdom, give the element of water the alternating motion that we observe in it, by any other manner than by moving the bottom of the sea?"

Galileo put this question in the mouth of Simplicio at the end of his dialogue and makes one of his characters answer him as follows: "If the assumption of a miracle is indispensable, we shall move the earth by miracle and consequently the sea in a natural manner."

In February, 1632, the book was published with the double *imprimatur* of Rome and Florence. The preface inserted upon the insistence of the Church authorities contradicted the book both in its tone and in its contents, just as Osiander's preface had contradicted the Revolutions. Copernicus had been done violence by the Nurembergers. Galileo sacrificed his conscience voluntarily. He thought he had the right to be Jesuitical with regard to the Jesuits. But his circumspection did not do him any good.

In this preface he defends the decree of 1616 as a "salutary edict"; he celebrates Italy as the homeland of dogmas and keen discoveries "for the contentment of minds."

The book at once aroused intense passions of love and hate. It made many readers feel, as Sagredo puts it in the dialogues, like liberated prisoners. Others took pleasure in the many physical experiments described, still others enjoyed the animated dialogue, the changing scenes, the comic situations, anecdotes and fairy-tales. The work gained immediate popularity and renown. Hugo Grotius declared that it could not be compared to any book of modern times while Thomas Campanella saw "the true system of the world assured."

In the dialogues Galileo again ridiculed his old enemy, the Jesuit Father, Christoph Scheiner of Ingolstadt, as a plagiarist. It was said of this man that because he was secretly convinced of the truth of the

Copernican world system, he publicly persecuted the Copernicans with particular fury. Later everyone held this Scheiner responsible for Galileo's second trial by the Inquisition.

By the end of July Galileo learned that the Pope and the Inquisition were examining his dialogues. As early as August, 1632, only a few months after their publication, the Roman Inquisition forbade Galileo and Landini, the printer, to sell copies of the book. The remaining copies were to be handed over to the Inquisition.

The Tuscan government, through its representative in Rome, immediately expressed its surprise that a book so thoroughly scrutinized before publication and approved by the Roman and Florentine Inquisitor should be suspended. Rome replied that out of regard for the Grand Duke the book had been submitted for investigation not to the Inquisition but to a special Congregation.

The Jesuits in Rome were already circulating reports that the teachings expounded in the dialogues were most reprehensible, worse than all the heresies of Luther or Calvin; that despite all the submissive pious additions the book was still Copernican; that the censors had been bluffed by the preface and conclusion; and that Galileo had only made fun of them. Worst of all, they convinced the Pope that Galileo had held him up to ridicule in the character of Simplicio. Urban was an Aristotelian; he had often argued with Galileo about the Copernican theory, and could not fail to recognize his own arguments in many of Simplicio's arguments; in fact, Simplicio refutes the proof of the earth's motion by the existence of the tides with the Pope's own words, and makes it unmistakably clear that he had adopted this counter-argument from an *eminentissima persona*.

Urban VIII now made it his own business to persecute Galileo.

On October 1 the Florentine Inquisitor summoned Galileo, and in the presence of a notary and witnesses informed him that he must appear before the Commissioner of the Inquisition in Rome before the end of the month. Galileo was horrified. He appealed to the Minister and to the Grand Duke. He was advised to obey.

To Cardinal Barberini, a relative of the Pope, Galileo wrote: "When I think that the fruit of all my work and efforts now result in a subpoena by the Holy Office, such as is issued only to those found guilty of severe crimes, I am so affected that I curse the time I have spent on these studies, by which I hoped to rise somewhat above the beaten path of science. I regret that I have communicated part of my results to the world and I feel inclined to suppress and consign to the flames what I still have on hand, thus completely satisfying the wishes of my enemies to whom my ideas are so burdensome."

Galileo asked that he be spared the trip to Rome on account of his advanced age—he had attained seventy years—and his many ailments, to which insomnia had now been added. The plague and the long quarantine, he said, would make this trip mortally dangerous for him. Could he not be granted an examination of his case by correspondence, or could he not be heard in Florence? Naturally he would travel if the authorities insisted on it, for he valued obedience to them higher than his own life.

He won only a few weeks' delay by these entreaties. He was still tarrying in Florence when a second order was followed by a third one, even more peremptory. Now Galileo sent in the report of three highly reputed physicians, according to whom the slightest accident might cause the death of the sick and aging man.

Urban VIII who was directing the proceedings against Galileo gave orders to inform the Florentine Inquisitor that His Holiness and the Holy Office could not tolerate any excuses, and that, if necessary, they would send a commissioner and a physician to examine Galileo. If they found him transportable they would bring him to Rome in chains as a prisoner. Should the trip really be dangerous for him because of his condition, "his intermittent pulse, weakened senses and humors, frequent spells of fainting, melancholies, weak stomach, insomnia, stitches in the side and severe rupture," that is, should a delay be found to be imperative, he would be brought to Rome in chains as a prisoner immediately upon his recovery or the elimination of immediate danger to his life. And Galileo himself was to pay the travelling expenses of the commissioner and the physician!

The Grand Duke is said to have been indignant at the tone of this order, but he severely admonished Galileo to submit to the Pope. In the middle of the winter (January 26, 1633) he set out on his journey.

He was surprised by the indictment. He had discussed his manuscript with the Pope and the Roman and Florentine Inquisitors, he had submitted to their revisions on every point, he had obtained a double imprimatur, his book was formally justified and protected. If it nevertheless proved dangerous later, it could after all be prohibited. But the author was guilty of no crime—except the one that had been manufactured to do him injury.

In 1812, the records of the Roman Inquisition concerning the trial of Galileo were transferred from Rome to Paris by order of Napoleon.

They lay there for thirty-five years, but the French scholars published only a few pages of them, and these were injurious to Galileo's character. In 1847 the records were returned to Rome. Marini, the director of the papal archives, published extracts that Wohlwill, Galileo's biographer, called a falsification. In 1867, the greater part of the record was published by Henri de l'Epinois. It shows that the indictment of 1633 was based on a strange prohibition dated 1616. While the above-quoted document of February 25, 1616, confirms that Cardinal Bellarmin was supposed to send for Galileo and call upon him to renounce his opinion, and only *if* he refused, to forbid him to teach, defend or discuss it, and only if he did not comply with this, to put him in jail, a sinister document dated February 26, 1616, runs, on the contrary, as follows: "Friday, February 26, 1616, in the palace of Cardinal Bellarmin, the cardinal . . . admonished the said Galileo to renounce the above-mentioned opinion, and *immediately afterward* . . . the above-named Pater Commissarius ordered Galileo in the name of His Holiness the Pope and the whole Congregation of the Holy Office to give up the above-mentioned opinion . . . wholly and entirely and furthermore never to hold it for true, or teach it or defend it in any way, in words or writings; otherwise the Holy Office would proceed against him; and Galileo accepted this order and promised to obey it. . . ."

On February 25 the Pope had ordered that the complete prohibition be made only *if* Galileo refused to accept the first admonition. The report of February 26 contradicts all the depositions of Galileo and the testimony of Cardinal Bellarmin. According to this report Galileo promised to obey *at once.*

For this reason Wohlwill assumes that this document, although dated February 26, 1616, was actually written in 1632 and interpolated into the record. The first authentic report on this dangerous document dates from September 11, 1632; on that day Niccolini wrote to Florence that he had just learned from Riccardi under the seal of secrecy that "it was found in the archives that in 1616 the order had been given Galileo in the name of the Pope and the Inquisition to renounce any discussion of the Copernican theory. This alone, the ambassador added, was sufficient to ruin Galileo."

It was sufficient. When a tangible proof of Galileo's guilt was lacking, it was—found. Now the later permission granted by the Inquisition, the double *imprimatur* lost all value. The censors had given it without knowledge of the order of 1616. According to the indictment Galileo had fraudulently concealed this order.

On February 3, 1633, after a long quarantine Galileo reached Rome in the Grand Duke's sedan chair—a mark of his favor. For the time being he was allowed to stop in the Tuscan ambassador's palace; but he was already under house arrest and forbidden to receive visitors.

Only two months later, on April 12, was he summoned for the first questioning in the palace of the Inquisition. As in all Inquisition trials, what was in question was not the defense of the accused or the clarification of the facts, but a confession of guilt. If the accused confessed his guilt the Inquisition might order him to be burned and confiscate his possessions; but if he failed to confess, he was burned and his possessions confiscated for that failure.

Galileo was supposed to confess his guilt, that is to say, the violation of the forged order dated February 26, 1616.

The technique of the Inquisition is well known. Galileo never saw the bill of indictment against him, he never saw the dubious record of the proceedings of February 26, 1616. His persecutors only alluded darkly to his dark guilt. Confess, they demanded, confess! Confess everything! What words had been used sixteen years before; which witnesses had been present at the time; what this one or that one had said according to the minutes, all these matters were discussed. At no point was Galileo's book or his theory discussed.

Urban directed the examination of the defendant, he never presided at the trial.

During the first examination Galileo declared spontaneously that his dialogues did not defend the Copernican theory, but rather refuted it; that desirous of doing everything in the proper fashion he had submitted his manuscript to the Roman and Florentine Inquisitions and humbly accepted every change they suggested. True, he had not mentioned Bellarmin's admonition, because, after all, it did not occur to him that it was applicable to this book in which he demonstrated the untenability of the Copernican arguments. And he submitted a copy of Bellarmin's testimonial of May, 1616, to the effect that no penalty had been imposed on Galileo and that only the text of the decree against Copernicus had been transmitted to him.

Now the Inquisition kept Galileo in its palace as a prisoner, from April 12 to April 30. He fell sick in jail, and appeared for the second examination completely broken. He declared that he had just reread his book for the first time in three years; that he had noticed that in certain passages he had been led astray by his pleasure in his own skill in debate, so that some arguments against Simplicio had turned out to be fairly cogent, even quite credible. But he intended, he said, to expand the book in order to make it quite clear that he did not then and did not now in any way share the condemned opinion that the earth moves. "Since on this occasion I will have to add one or two dialogues, I promise to take up again the arguments in favor of the opinion considered false and condemned and to refute them in the most conclusive manner that our merciful Lord will inspire in me. Accordingly I beg this high court to assist me in this good resolve and to enable me to carry it out."

On April 30 he was allowed to return from the jail of the Inquisition to Ambassador Niccolini's palace where he remained under house arrest. He brought a document containing his defense to his third examination on May 10. He stated that the text of the order of 1616 was entirely new to him; that he had obeyed Bellarmin's order and that he would do every penance imposed upon him by the Holy Office. He asked the cardinals "to consider his wretched health and his constant anguish of heart during the last ten months, and the discomfort of his long hard trip during the worst season, at the age of seventy, and the fact that he had already lost the greater part of the year, and that all these sufferings were already a sufficient punishment for his errors which they should ascribe to his senility. He also recommended to them his honor and reputation against the slanders of his enemies intent upon besmirching his good name."

Six weeks later he received his last summons, on June 21. Galileo expected to be acquitted. The examining magistrate made him give the usual oath that he would speak the truth. He asked Galileo whether he had anything to say. Galileo answered: "I have nothing to say."

Once again he was asked whether he held for true, had held for true and since when he had held for true that the sun was the center of the world and that the earth daily moved around it.

Once again Galileo declared that before the decree of the Index in 1616 he had held that both opinions, those of Ptolemy and of Copernicus, were worthy of consideration; after the decree "every doubt vanished from my mind, and I held and still hold Ptolemy's opinion that the earth is motionless and that the sun moves as absolutely true and incontestable."

Once again he was told that it was clear from his dialogues that even after that time he had believed in the motion of the earth; and he was asked freely to tell the truth: whether he now considered this opinion true or had considered it to be true.

Galileo reiterated that after the decision of the authorities he had not considered the condemned opinion true.

The judge reiterated that, nevertheless, the dialogues suggested that he did consider Copernicus' opinion true; and that if he did not make up his mind finally to confess the truth, the proper legal proceedings would be taken against him.

Galileo declared: "I do not consider Copernicus' opinion true and have not considered it true, since I was ordered to renounce it; for the rest, I am here in your hands, do with me what you please."

Once again the magistrate asked him to speak the truth, and said that if he did not, he would be tortured.

Galileo replied: "I am here to submit, but I have not held this opinion for true since the decision, as I have said."

According to the text of the minutes as it stands today he was thereupon sent back to his dungeon in the palace of the Inquisition. But the minutes seem to have been tampered with at this point. From the verdict against Galileo it can be inferred that at least the "first degree of torture," the *territio realis,* that is to say, a cross-examination in the torture chamber in view of the instruments of torture, was applied to him.

Thus, by order of Pope Urban, the employees of the famous international institute for torture displayed before the creator of modern mechanics their latest machines for dispensation of "justice" and explained to him in the minutest detail what parts of his flesh they would twinge and which of his bones they would break unless he finally confessed his belief in the motion of the earth. Galileo must have cast a long glance at the Church's mechanical arguments before finally admitting in the torture chamber under duress what the very next day he was compelled to recant in the monastery under the same duress, to wit, the Copernican theory of the earth's motion.

According to another record the verdict had already been prescribed on June 16, five days before its final examination, by order of the Pope. Here we read: "Sanctissimus gave orders that Galileo be questioned *de intentione,* under threat of torture, as though he were to be submitted to it, and then that he be made to recant before the full Congregation of the Holy Office, and be sentenced to imprisonment, at the discretion of the Holy Office."

On the day following his last examination the seventy-year-old Galileo who was suffering from several ailments, was compelled to kneel down in a penitential robe in the presence of seven cardinals at a solemn session of the Inquisition in the great hall of the Dominican monastery of Santa Maria Sopra Minerva in Rome; he was compelled to take a Bible in his hands to abjure the error of thinking that the earth moves by reciting a long and ignominious formula: "I recant, curse and execrate with sincere heart and non-hypocritical faith all these errors

and heresies, as well as all other errors and opinions, which are contrary to the teachings of the Holy Catholic and Roman Apostolic Church; I also swear that in the future I will neither orally nor in writing say or maintain anything that might justify a similar suspicion of heresy against me; and should I know a heretic or anyone suspect of heresy, I will report him to the Holy Office or the Inquisitor or the bishop of my diocese."

The Inquisitors then read the verdict. Galileo was condemned to formal imprisonment in the dungeons of the Holy Office for an undetermined period at the discretion of the Inquisition. For three years he was to recite the seven penitential psalms once a week; he was "extremely suspect to heresy." The Dialogues were prohibited.

These Dialogues were no more examined in 1632 than Copernicus' book had been in 1616. The Church was not interested in the truth, it was interested only in obedience.

Soon after hearing his sentence Galileo wrote to a friend of his the remark of the Jesuit Father Grienberger who was well versed in astronomy: "If Galileo had known how to win the sympathy of the Fathers and the College, he would have lived gloriously in the world, and none of these misfortunes would have befallen him; he would have been able to write freely on any subject, even about the motion of the earth." "And so you see," Galileo commented, "it is not this or that opinion that has conjured up the war against me, but only the disfavor of the Jesuits."

Galileo remained a prisoner of the Inquisition until the end of his life, for almost nine years. From June 21 to June 24 he languished in the dungeons of the Inquisition. Then he was placed in the Villa Medici. Then, from July 6 until December 1, he was imprisoned in the palace of Archbishop Ascanio Piccolomini, a pupil of a pupil of his who was courageous enough to give shelter to the outlawed scientist in his home at Siena.

Galileo left his jail in Rome "quite broken, dejected and disheartened." At Siena he "recovered his peace and freshness of mind amidst the many sufferings," and after a few days began to work again; in July, 1633, one month after his condemnation, he sent his forbidden "Dialogues" by secret channels to Bernegger at Strassburg asking him to translate them into Latin, but to conceal the fact that he had suggested this.

Matthias Bernegger, professor at Strassburg, had previously translated Galileo's treatise on the compass. In 1635, the "Dialogues," together with the Letter to the Grand Duchess Christine and Foscarini's prohibited pamphlet, were published in Holland; in the words of the preface, "without the author's foreknowledge and very much against his will." This new edition, Galileo wrote, made him feel that he had "his revenge, because now the disgrace redounded upon the traitors and the representatives of ignorance." Through the Parisian scientist, Elias Diodati, all of Galileo's works reached the circle of the faithful and were published and saved from oblivion.

By the end of 1633 Galileo received permission to live in his own villa, "Il Giojello," at Arcetri, one mile from Florence, as a prisoner of the Inquisition. Informers and spies, paid and voluntary servants of the Inquisitors watched him. He was most strictly forbidden to visit Florence or to move more than a few steps away from his villa. It took courage for anyone to visit him, for the Florentine Inquisitor watched all those who came to his house.

Galileo's sister-in-law and her family who had moved into his house all died of the plague soon after his return.

His favorite daughter, Suor Maria Celeste, the nun of the San Matteo convent, had urged her father in the tenderest terms to confess everything to the Inquisition and thus save his life; she was ill, and wrote that she feared she would never see him again. In March, 1634, Galileo finally arrived at Arcetri, and she saw him. She took upon herself the task of reciting the penitential psalms for him, but not for long, for she died on April 2, at the age of thirty-three. The anguished father wrote after her death: "I feel that my beloved daughter is constantly calling me!" Because he believed his end was near, he did not allow his son Vincenzio to make a journey.

Meanwhile Pope Urban had punished the Roman and Florentine Inquisitors and the Master of the Sacred Palace, Riccardi, and dismissed Ciampoli, the papal secretary. He had ordered that the verdict against Galileo and his recantation be posted at all public places and that the bishops and nuncios in the whole Catholic world, and especially the university professors of mathematics and philosophy and the educated clergymen in the monasteries be informed of them. All the copies of the Dialogues that could be laid hands upon, were destroyed.

No university protested. No scientist objected. No one dared even to express himself privately on this matter. Castelli, Galileo's pupil and his friend for forty years, voiced the depth of his despair in confidential letters. The French scientists mentioned Galileo's name in their letters with embarrassed pity. Even Gassendi who had shortly before been enthusiastic over the Dialogues did not venture a word of sympathy, *"Tellement toutes choses sont chatouilleuses de ce côté là"* (so ticklish is everything connected with this question).

Descartes had completed in Holland his *Traité du Monde* containing an outline of a system of the world based on Copernican principles. Galileo's tragedy impressed Descartes a great deal: he did not publish this important work. He printed his Method only a few years later.

Galileo's influence remained confined to the natural sciences. Only Locke gave final philosophical form to his conception of the world which leads to deism.

In the spring of 1634 Galileo petitioned Rome to be allowed to receive more frequent visits from his physician; his request was harshly refused. Further petitions were strictly forbidden him in advance, otherwise, the Holy Congregation threatened, it would be compelled to consign him once more to its Roman dungeons.

Galileo fell silent. Year after year protectors and friends vainly renewed their appeals on behalf of the old scientist. Only Comte de Noailles, Richelieu's ambassador, succeeded once in obtaining a short respite for Galileo and met him at a place between Siena and Florence. Later Galileo dedicated his *Discorsi* to him; they were published "under the banner and protection" of a foreigner, because Tuscany could not or would not protect them.

Immediately after his condemnation Galileo resumed work on his second principal book. One year after his return to Arcetri he wrote to the Dominican Father Micanzio in Venice that ". . . the treatise on motion, new from beginning to end, is in good order . . . although my restless brain cannot stop brooding with great waste of time, because the new ideas that recently have occurred to me throw overboard my previous results."

Early the next year he sent the completed first parts to Father Micanzio in Venice, where he hoped to obtain permission to print his book. When Father Micanzio inquired of the Venetian Inquisitor if he might print it, the latter replied with a document that had been sent to all the Inquisitors in the world and contained the strictest prohibition of all the previously printed and future works of Galileo.

After similar experiences in Bohemia or Vienna Micanzio with great effort obtained an introduction to the famous Dutch publisher, Ludwig Elzevir. One of the Elzevir brothers came to Italy, and Galileo handed him one part of the manuscript of the *Discorsi*. He sent the rest to Holland by a circuitous route through sure friends.

Galileo, the most famous Catholic scientist, could now find only Protestant publishers in Leyden and Amsterdam. He had to give his life-work to Elzevir secretly in order to say publicly and thus protect his life, that Elzevir was a pirate who had obtained his manuscript by dishonest means.

The "Discourses on Two New Sciences" contained Galileo's theory of motion and theory of coherence. Here for the first time he completely expounded and explained the discoveries with the help of which he had created the science of mechanics, the laws of free fall, fall on the inclined plane, projectile motion, the laws of the pendulum and the theorem of the parallelogram of forces. Again we have dialogues among Salviati, Sagredo and Simplicio. They speak as though they had never been silenced by the Inquisition. This is Galileo's irony. The scene of these dialogues is the arsenal of Venice.

In 1638, when the *Discorsi* were published in Leyden, Galileo was seventy-four, blind and infirm. The year before he had lost the sight of his right eye, then that of his left eye. He comforted himself that since Adam no man had seen as much as he had. The unfortunate has the privilege of not being envied by the fortunate. At that time he made his last discovery, the daily and monthly librations of the moon.

In a letter dated January 2, 1638, he wrote to his Parisian friend, Diodati: "Ah! Your poor friend and servant is entirely and incurably blind. This heaven, this earth, this universe, that I have extended a thousand times beyond the limits of all past epochs by wonderful observation, have now shrunk to the narrow confines of my own body. Thus God likes it; so I, too, must like it!"

And Father Castelli echoed him: "The noblest eyes that nature had ever created grew dark; eyes so privileged, endowed with such rare strength that verily it may be said of them that they had seen more than all the eyes before them and that they opened the eyes of all those who came after him."

In his letter Galileo always indicated his address as "From my prison at Arcetri."

Finally the Inquisition grew more considerate toward the blind old man. The Grand Duke of Tuscany visited him several times, as well as Diodati, Gassendi and Milton. A few years later Milton, in his speech for the freedom of unlicensed printing, referred to his visit to Galileo: "a prisoner to the Inquisition for thinking in Astronomy otherwise than the Franciscan and Dominican licenses thought."

When Galileo's friends in Rome petitioned that the blind old man be finally allowed to consult his physician in Florence, Rome instructed the Florentine Inquisitor to visit Galileo with a physician and give his opinion as to whether Galileo, if granted a temporary stay in Florence for the purpose of consulting his physician, would not again try to propagate his condemned theory of the earth's motion in meetings and conversations.

So the blind and infirm star-gazer was crying for his doctor? Very well then, the Inquisitor, accompanied by its official doctor, would come to the home of the seventy-seven-year-old scientist and by order of the highest authorities check to see whether this blind man was really blind, this infirm man totally infirm. And they found him incurably blind, and totally infirm, and sleepless too, with a hundred pains haunting the head and the foot of his bed. Those who lived with him complained that out of the twenty-four hours of the day he scarcely slept one. The miserable wretch was more like a corpse than a living man. The Inquisitor wrote: "The villa is so far from the city and from all inhabited places that he can obtain the visit of a physician only with many difficulties and at great cost."

In view of the scientist's wretched condition the Inquisitor thought there was no great danger that he would talk; at any rate a vigorous admonition would suffice to keep him within bounds.

At last Galileo was granted permission—for a short time—to consult his physician in Florence, but was given meticulous instructions that he must not discuss the motion of the earth—under the penalty of excommunication and severe lifelong imprisonment.

To attend mass, once, he had to obtain a special permit from the Inquisition. Otherwise he was not allowed to leave his home or see anyone; in Florence he suffered from this seclusion even more than at Arcetri.

In 1639, the seventeen-year-old Viviani joined Galileo's "family"; in 1641, Torricelli moved into his house; later they were temporarily joined by Father Castelli, and the three formed the subsequently famous "triumvirate." The Grand Duke had sent word to Father Castelli that Galileo was old and would take much knowledge with him to his grave if someone did not have a talk with him, and that Castelli should obtain a few months' furlough from the Pope for this purpose—the Grand Duke would pay the expenses of the trip and the sojourn. When Castelli in an audience with Urban asked for a few months' furlough in Florence, Urban told him straightaway that he knew he intended to visit Galileo. Castelli admitted that he would be unable to avoid meeting him and was given permission to speak with him in the presence of an official of the Inquisition.

In the end the Inquisition also got wind of Galileo's secret dealings with the heretical Estate General of Holland concerning the correct method of determining geographical positions. A means of exactly determining latitudes at sea was greatly desired by the colonial powers. Galileo on the basis of the fairly accurate tables of the moons of Jupiter, which he had drawn up two years after discovering their existence, elaborated a method of determining latitudes on the open sea by means of the frequent eclipses of these moons; he offered his procedure first to the Spaniards, then to the Netherlanders. An academy created by Richelieu was also trying to solve this problem in Paris.

From 1635 to 1641, Galileo conducted a long scientific correspondence on this question with many European scientists. After very detailed negotiations, the Estates General sent Hortensius, an Amsterdam professor of mathematics, accompanied by a thoroughly trustworthy person, with a heavy golden chain and flattering letters to Galileo. Informed of this by his spies, the Florentine Inquisitor reported it to Rome and was told to forbid Galileo to receive the announced visitor and his gifts or to have any further relations with heretics. Thus ended the first international effort in a new science that many contemporaries compared in importance with Caesar's reform of the calendar.

This last great act of intervention by the Inquisition cut Galileo off from the world even more than before. The Florentine Inquisitor wrote to Rome: ". . . the completely blind scientist can better be described as having his head in the grave, than having his mind in the clouds of mathematical speculations." Thus the Church spoke of Galileo. At the same time Hugo Grotius praised him as the "greatest mind of all times."

"I resign myself to my misfortune," the seventy-four-year-old prisoner wrote to Diodati. He had no sooner completed his *Discorsi* than he began his work on the motions of animals, outlined instructions for making exact astronomical observations, and as late as 1641 tried to use the pendulum as a clock regulator.

In his last scientific letter, dated January 16, 1641, Galileo wrote to Liceti: "If philosophy were what is contained in Aristotle's books, Your Grace would surely be the greatest philosopher in the world, you are so much at home in him and have all his passages ready at hand. However, I think that the book of philosophy is what is constantly open before our eyes. But since it is written in different characters than those of our alphabet, it cannot be read by everyone; the letters of such a book are triangles, squares, circles, spheres, cones, pyramids and other mathematical figures that are very useful in reading it."

Galileo was dictating to his disciples, Viviani and Toricelli, his ideas about the theory of impact, when the slow fever began that was to consume him in two months.

The seventy-eight-year-old prisoner of the Inquisition died in the arms of his disciples on January 8, 1642.

When he was already blind, he wrote in one of his last letters: "I have always considered myself so unable to fathom what light is, that I would have agreed to spend my life in a dungeon with only bread and water if I could thus have gained this unattainable knowledge." But no one in all the millennia before him had said such cogent things about the nature of light as he did.

One of his favorite sayings was: "I have never met a man so ignorant that I could not learn something from him." He also wrote: "It is not worthwhile to engage in refuting a dumbbell."

He was red-headed, of more than average size and squarely built. He gave to the poor and helped the talented. He loved to see company and to work in his vineyard. His house was as full of people as an Italian farce, so hospitable was he. He was never idle and often melancholy. Quick to anger he was quickly appeased. He loved life in the country, and he loved life in the city. As a result of his habit of making nightly astronomical observations, he was inclined to sleeplessness. He had fiery eyes, was rheumatic from the age of forty, published books from the age of forty-four, was prohibited to publish from the age of fifty-two, was condemned at seventy and imprisoned after that; blind at seventy-four, he still hoped for complete freedom.

His library and wine-cellar were small, but select. He never spoke of Aristotle with contempt. He called only Archimedes "master." He compared those who read Ariosto after Tasso to those who could eat onions after melons. At court he was a courtier, to princes he wrote like a Byzantine, his wit spared none; but he paid dearly for it.

In the eyes of some of his biographers he was not courageous enough in 1633. He should have consented to be burned for their satisfaction! He chose to complete his *Discorsi,* which contains investigations made over a period of thirty years. He chose to save his main works from destruction by getting them secretly across the frontiers and publishing them in Holland. He was as little scrupulous about his oath extorted by the torturers of the Church as his persecutors, the Jesuits, were scrupulous about their means of achieving a desired end.

For the sake of science he did not spare even himself, and he did not respect even his own honor.

Galileo won his place in the history of astronomy chiefly by his telescopic discoveries. No one before him had seen so much of the universe as he.

He was the first to term the so-called "third motion" introduced by Copernicus a superfluous complication.

His worst error was his ignorance of Kepler's discoveries. In 1609

Kepler published his first and second laws, in 1619 his third law. Galileo passed over them in icy silence.

He committed his two capital errors, his theory of the tides and his theory of comets, because of his eagerness to defend the Copernican theory. He came close to the idea of universal gravitation and anticipated many important natural laws.

His greatest merit is said to be his contribution in founding the science of mechanics. He was the first to grasp clearly the idea of force as a mechanical agent. He transferred the concept of the invariability of cause and effect to the outer world.

These achievements of Galileo promoted the triumph of the Copernican system much more than his numerous arguments for the motion of the earth.

He taught that astronomical problems should be regarded as essentially mechanical problems. He popularized the idea that force derived from motion. Of Newton's three laws of motion the first was developed from Galileo's law of inertia, the second from his law of the proportionality of force and velocity. Galileo also had a presentiment of Newton's proposition that action and reaction are equal and opposite.

He swept away a whole mass of scholastic, Aristotelian and popular errors. He came at the right moment, with the necessary power for the struggle against the Aristotelians, in a field in which no one had as yet opposed them. He is regarded as one of the fathers of experimental science.

He combated the scholastic distinctions between destructible and indestructible substances; between absolute heaviness and absolute lightness; between natural and violent motions. He taught that heaviness and lightness were relative concepts; that all bodies were heavy, even invisible ones, like the air; that motion was the result of force, direct or continuous; that weight was a constant force pulling toward the center of the earth; that in a vacuum all bodies would fall with the same velocity; that the inertia of matter included both permanent motion and permanent rest. And that the substance of the heavenly bodies was as corruptible as that of the earth.

It required a powerful man and a powerful effort to explain these elementary ideas and spread them. They became sources of universal truth.

Galileo also tried to solve the problem of squaring the circle. He was one of the first to introduce infinitesimals into geometrical demonstrations. He combined experiment with calculation, knew how to deduce the abstract from the concrete, and was inexhaustibly patient in checking his results.

Did Galileo deserve his bitter fate because in regard to the great questions of civilization he turned to the people instead of to the specialists? Did not Pythagoras, Copernicus and Goethe recommend exclusiveness?

Copernicus wrote for mathematicians. Tycho remolded the Copernican system in a manner to satisfy the theologians. Kepler was absorbed in mystical dreams. All of them wrote in Latin.

Only Galileo, the greatest master of Italian prose between Machiavelli and Manzoni, told the open secrets of the sky and of physics to the people in the language of the people. In addition, he supplied tangible popular arguments for his scientific theories. This last creative mind of the Renaissance was a forerunner of the eighteenth-century enlighteners and friends of the people.

This champion of the autonomy of science fought against the authority of Aristotle and of the Church in every one of his writings. He fought against all authority. Like Socrates, he was a victim of the fatal persecution of the spirit by might. While the Athenian did not resist death, Galileo, the modern hero of common sense, managed to survive in order to be right in the end. Better to stay alive and lie publicly, when confronted with torture, than to let the truth wait! He was the sober enthusiast who in a note to Thomas Campanella, another martyr for freedom and the Copernican theory, explained: "Even to discover an unpretentious truth is more important than to discuss the highest things in detail without ascertaining any truth."

Crowds of pupils surrounded this friend of the people, in the end they almost formed a private order. Princes from many countries were his boarders even in his Padua days. Cardinals and kings boasted of his friendship. This outlaw was an authority in Europe. The mighty Pope could be easily persuaded that Galileo had called him a simpleton and ridiculed him before the entire world . . .

The poor revengeful old man in Rome! A few days after Galileo's death Urban VIII sent for Niccolini to prevent the Florentines from burying Galileo beside Michelangelo. The Florentine Inquisitor had informed the Roman Inquisitor by messenger that a large sum of money had been collected in Florence for a monument to Galileo and that the Grand Duke intended to bury his court philosopher beside the mighty sculptor. The Pope immediately informed the Grand Duke through the Inquisitors that no monument could be erected to a heretic condemned by the Church. For the Inquisition, the death of one of its victims did not make any difference. It prosecuted even corpses, especially when the heirs were well-to-do.

Niccolini described the seventy-four-year-old Urban as a living corpse whose head was so sunken in that it seemed to be on a level with his shoulders. A living corpse—but his hatred for the corpse in Florence was arch-alive! He hated Galileo as bitterly as during the first days of the trial. He cursed him and his opinions, he abused him as a disgrace to all Christendom. "And when he came to speak of individual assertions and of the answers that he himself had given Galileo and that the latter had made it known how he ridiculed a better man than he, much time was spent on that."

Like his corpse and his coffin, Galileo's memory and work remained under the ban of the Church.

Nine years after Galileo's death the Jesuit Father Riccioli published at Bologna his *Almagestum novum,* a detailed exposition of the two systems of the world, with an extensive critique of the Copernican system, and an apology of the Inquisition decree; this was the official reply to Galileo's prohibited Dialogues. At the end of his book, Riccioli tells the whole story of Galileo's trial, reprints the decrees of 1616 and 1633, the verdict and Galileo's formal recantation. For a long time obedient Catholic readers could learn of the Copernican system and get the details of the famous trial only in this book, naturally in the version of the Inquisition.

After Riccioli's death, twenty-five years after Galileo's death, the mathematician Montanari wrote to his friend Viviani: "Oh, how often have I thought with anger on how badly the Father / Riccioli / treated Galileo, and sometimes I even had the impulse to take up his defense and write his apology."

This was the only time in the seventeenth century that an Italian scientist spoke even of a fleeting impulse in favor of Galileo. He goes on to say faint-heartedly: "But this sect is all too powerful!"

A few years after Galileo's death an Inquisitor compelled a professor to change the adjective "highly famous" before Galileo's name to "generally known" in his book "On Metempsychosis, According to Pythagoras." However, in 1655/56, a selection of Galileo's writings was published with the permission of the Inquisition—naturally without the prohibited Dialogues.

Viviani's biography, the only one of consequence written in the seventeenth century, was not published until the eighteenth century. And this "last pupil" and first biographer of Galileo did not relate the first trial at all, and the second only with extreme caution and brevity. He wrote this biography as a young man. Throughout his long life he collected manuscripts, letters and reminiscences concerning Galileo, and tried with might and main to obtain the lifting of the prohibition of the Dialogues. But in 1693: "there is question of issuing general prohibitions against all the authors of modern physics, long lists are being drawn up and they are headed by Galileo, Gassendi, Descartes, etc., as most dangerous for the purity of religion."

Viviani died in 1703. In his will he asked that his body be placed beside Galileo's in the chapel, until his master's tomb should be erected near Michelangelo's, and then that his body be buried at Galileo's feet. Viviani's biography was published in 1717.

Leibniz vainly attempted to obtain the abolition of the decrees against Copernicus and Galileo in Rome.

In 1737 the remains of Galileo and Viviani were solemnly interred beside Michelangelo's tomb. In 1744 a new edition of the Dialogues was published in Italy, but accompanied by the Inquisition's decree of condemnation and a Jesuit Father's treatise on Hebrew astronomy.

Chiefly at the instigation of Boscovich, a Jesuit Father and astronomer, the Congregation of the Index resolved in 1757 to leave out the general prohibition of all books teaching the motion of the earth in the new edition of the Index of 1758. However, still explicitly prohibited as before were Copernicus' Revolutions, Kepler's Outline of the Copernican Astronomy, Foscarini's Letter, Didacus à Stunica's Commentary on Job, and Galileo's Dialogues.

Lalande, the French astronomer, tried in vain during his visit to Rome to have Galileo's Dialogues taken off the Index. The 1819 edition of the Index still contained the five forbidden titles.

Canon Guiseppe Settele, a professor in Rome, finally induced the Church to correct its own censorship instead of Copernicus. In 1820 the Inquisition had forbidden the second volume of his Textbook of Optics and Astronomy, because he presented the Copernican theory of the earth's motion not as a hypothesis, but as a scientific truth. In a detailed memorandum Settele asked the Pope for a new examination of his case by the Inquisition. His petition led to the decisions of September, 1822, which explicitly permitted the printing and publication of books dealing with the motion of the earth in accordance with the general opinion of modern astronomers.

Canon Settele wrote a diary and began it with the enumeration of his own noble deeds; at the head of these he placed his contribution to that tardy decision of the Church censorship.

In 1835 there was published the first edition of the Index Librorum

Prohibitorum that did not cite the books of Copernicus, Galileo, Foscarini, Didacus à Stunica and Johannes Kepler. Most of the great-grandsons of those pious Catholics who in 1616 had ceased reading Copernicus, Galileo, Foscarini and Didacus à Stunica, and in 1619 had ceased reading Johannes Kepler's book, now had their golden opportunity, now with good conscience they could share the sweet and intoxicating knowledge that they were living on a doubly moving earth!

Epilogue

THE GREAT TRIUMPH

Ich häufe ungeheure Zahlen,
Gebirge Millionen auf,
Ich setze Zeit auf Zeit und Welt auf Welt zu Hauf
ALBRECHT VON HALLER

Fuimus Troes
VIRGIL

Once again we have been beguiled by that arch-humorist Nature
SIR ARTHUR STANLEY EDDINGTON

AFTER Kepler and Galileo, Newton contributed most to the triumph of the Copernican theory. His law of gravitation governs the falling apple, the course of the moon around the earth, the course of the earth around the sun, and the sun, too. Thus he put an end to the fatal dualism of heaven and earth.

Isaac Newton's Principles *(Philosophiae Naturalis Principia Mathematica,* 1687, printed at the expense of Edmund Halley, his colleague) gathered all previous discoveries together and laid the foundation for all future discoveries. It is an elementary textbook of modern physics and astronomy.

Newton clarified the fundamental notions of mass, weight and force. He formulated the three laws of motion and the law of gravitation and postulated their universal validity. He was one of the fathers not only of modern astronomy, but also of modern mathematics and physics. At the same time as Leibniz, he discovered the differential and integral calculus. He discovered the spectrum by decomposing the light of the sun.

Newton went beyond Kepler's planetary laws by his discovery of the mutual disturbances of the planets as a result of gravitation. He explained the motions of the satellites and comets, the precession and the tides. He computed the form of the earth after having calculated its flattening at the poles. He computed the masses of those heavenly bodies that exert a visible effect upon the others, and their specific weight. He computed the motions of the axis of the earth and its swing (nutation).

Here are three outstanding examples of that "astronomy of the invisible" which was derived from the law of gravitation:

Edmund Halley prophesied the return of the comet named after him at the end of seventy-five years. Clairaut, on the basis of disturbances of the comet by Jupiter and Saturn, calculated a more exact period of about seventy-six years. The comet actually did reappear at about the time calculated by Clairaut, on March 12, 1759.

In 1845, Urbain J. J. Leverrier of Paris, on the basis of the disturbances in the course of the planet Uranus, computed the size and course of an unknown planet. He sent his computations to the Berlin astronomer Galle, who with their aid discovered the planet Neptune in 1846.

In 1930, Dr. Percival Lowell of the Flagstaff Observatory in Arizona discovered the planet Pluto in a similar manner.

The world of Copernicus and Kepler—the planetary system—was within the sphere of the fixed stars which floated at an indefinite distance. In the center of this world rested the sun. Around it moved the planets with their satellites and moons. One of the smallest of these planets was the earth. Kepler explained the motions of these planets in his New Astronomy. The motionless fixed stars were conceived as invariable with regard to one another, but the whole firmament completed one rotation in the "Platonic" year which is equal to twenty-six thousand of our years.

Further proofs of the Copernican system were supplied by the Copenhagen astronomer Olaf Roemer (1644-1710) who discovered the velocity of light; the English astronomer Bradley (1692-1762) who studied the aberration of light, and Edmund Halley (1656-1742) who demonstrated that the fixed stars had a motion of their own. Later Friedrich W. Bessel was the first to measure the parallax of a fixed star (in 1838) and on this basis calculated its distance from the earth; and Leon Foucault (1819-1868) devised a pendulum which demonstrated the rotation of the earth (in 1851).

Copernicus enormously extended the universe, showed the smallness and subordinate position of the earth, and pointed out the gigantic distances of the stars.

Modern astronomy enlarged the universe to seemingly absurd dimensions, and developed the mechanics of the sky into the physics of the sky. William Herschel (1738-1822), the founder of stellar astronomy, made the gigantic step from the tiny and subordinate solar system to the universe of the Milky Way and the stars. Thanks to the Prague mathematician, Christian Doppler, and his Doppler principle established in 1842 (according to which the light of a white star seems bluish if it is moving closer to us, and reddish when it is moving away from us, and this with an intensity proportionate to its velocity), the astronomers were able to measure a star's velocity in the line of sight (the radial velocity) by one measurement of its spectrum. And the spectral analysis discovered in 1859 by Robert Wilhelm Bunsen and Robert Kirchhoff enabled the astronomers, in favorable cases, not only to study the chemical composition of the stars but also their physical condition, pressure, temperature, atmospheric density, their distance from us, the velocity with which this distance increases or decreases, and perhaps even the weight of the stars and the velocities with which they move in their orbits. Thanks to astrospectroscopy, positional astronomy today often appears to be only a branch of astrophysics.

Photography opened up a new era in astronomy. The connection of the photographic plate with the telescope, by the end of the nineteenth century, enlarged the perceivable world as tremendously as only the telescope had done before. Then began the great period of precise positional astronomy.

The most comprehensive catalogues of the positions of the stars obtained before the invention of photography were the Bonner Durchmusterung (1859-1862) of more than 324,000 stars down to the ninth magnitude of the northern skies, and its complement for the southern skies, Gould's Cordoba catalogue. Catalogues of nebulae were also made, the first of these by W. Herschel (2,509 star clusters and nebulae), the second, by Dreyer (in 1888, listing 13,223 nebulae), etc. Sir David Gill began to establish photographic maps of the firmament. In 1900, Professor J. C. Kapteyn at Groningen, on the basis of photographic pictures taken at the Cape Observatory, determined the positions of more than 450,000 stars (in the Cape Photographie Durchmusterung). Also the two fundamental catalogues were made, the Berlin FK 3, and the American catalogue of Boss.

If until then astronomy had been the geometry of light rays, now measurements of intensity gained significance. By the turn of the century of photometric classifications of the stars according to their relative brilliance were made, as, for instance, the Harvard Photometry, which measured the brightness of 9,110 stars above the 6.5 magnitude. The nine volumes of the Henry Draper Catalogue of the Harvard Observatory classified the spectra of about 225,000 stars. It was found that the chemical composition of the stars was largely identical.

As compared to the Copernican picture of the world in the sixteenth and seventeenth centuries, today, after the revolution in physics, the world looks more or less as follows:

Millions of stellar systems are distributed over a space that is measured by hundreds of millions of light years. The planet closest to us, Venus, at its perigee is 26 million miles from the earth; the Proxima Centauri, the closest star, is 25 billion miles from the earth.

The closest stellar systems—such as the great nebula in the Andromeda—seem to the naked eye only weak spots of light; in the largest mirror telescopes they disintegrate into individual stars. The most distant stellar systems leave only barely recognizable traces on the photographic plate after hours of exposure.

Through the great 100-inch telescope of Mount Wilson, 2 million extra-galactic nebulae are visible; their average distance is 15 hundred thousand light years; the most distant is about 100 million light years away.

Each of these stellar systems with diameters from 10 thousand to 100 thousand light years is an accumulation of several billion shining suns, some of which are joined together in couples, threes, or larger groups in a smaller space; as double stars or multiple stellar systems they move in their courses, obviously following the same laws as the planetary system. In between, there are star clusters, looser groupings like the Pleiades or the Hyads, spheroid star clusters formed of hundreds of thousands of gigantic suns, luminous or dark inconceivably thinned gaseous masses, non-luminous matter in solid particles from the tiniest dust to fist-size stones, "cosmic dust."

The Copernican system is situated somewhere in the outside regions of such a galactic system. There the sun proceeds in its course, with its appendage of planets, moons and smaller bodies, a dwarf star distinguished in nothing from millions of other stars.

The growing range of the telescope has discovered ever-growing stellar spaces. Our most refined telescopes, it is said, show us only one millionth of our universe.

Our Milky Way alone perhaps contains 200,000 million stars. According to Pieter Johannes von Rhijn, our sun is a tiny star among the 30,000 millions of stars in its stellar system; and our stellar system is only one of 80,000 million Milky Ways.

We live on one of the satellites of the sun—insects on the surface of one of the smallest satellites of a dwarf star in a local system of one of the millions of milky ways.

And we do not know whether in the billion-fold world there are other living creatures like ourselves, trying to fathom the secret of the universe from their doubly uncomfortable position deep inside or extremely to one side. What we have found is perhaps only one local view of the universe.

According to Eddington, our sun belongs to a system containing only 3,000 million other stars. The stars are globes of about the same size as the sun, with diameters of about one million miles. According to him, the universe is not so much wasteful with stars as with the space between the stars. What characterizes the modern universe is not the immense number of stars, but the desolate emptiness between the stars, the inconceivable vast desert, where a star is a grain of sand. If stars were equal in size of a grain of dust, the average distance between one star and another would be, according to James Jeans, about eighty miles.

If there were only thirty cricket balls within the earth, Eddington explains, the space occupied by these cricket balls would correspond to the space occupied by the stars in the universe; and the risk of their colliding with one another is as small as the risk would be of thirty cricket balls distributed over our entire planet colliding with each other.

One drop of water, says Eddington, contains several thousand millions of millions of millions of atoms. The diameter of an atom is about one hundred-millionth of an inch. Within the atom, immeasurably smaller electrons follow orbits like planets around the sun, in a space that is not less vast relatively to their size than the solar system.

Almost in the middle between the atom and the star, says Eddington, there is no less wonderful structure—the human body. About 10^{27} atoms form a human body; about 10^{28} human bodies would supply enough matter to form a star. In terms of time, too, the lifespan of a human being is somewhere between that of an "excited atom" and a star. Eddington himself calls this idea only a fantasy with a serious moral: "We shall have to consider periods of time which appall our imagination. We fear to make such drafts on eternity. And yet the vastness of the time-scale of stellar evolution is *less* remote from the scale of human experience than is the minuteness of the time-scale of the processes studied in the atom."

Certain modern astronomers think they have discovered distinct traces of a law of motion within the spatial order of the universe. All existing spectrographic studies of the galactic systems show a red displacement of the spectral lines which, according to the Doppler principle, leads to the conclusion that the entire universe is in process of expansion. De Sitter, a Dutchman, advanced such a cosmology in 1917.

Are there frontiers of the universe? Is it expanding or exploding?

According to Einstein's theory of relativity, space, although unlimited, is finite in extent. Thus, as a result of its curvature, the earth's surface, although unlimited, is finite in extent. Similarly, the total volume of the space in the universe is limited in mass, because the universe bends back on itself and closes up. According to Einstein's cosmology the dimensions of space are determined by the mass of matter contained in it or by its average density. This is estimated at about 10^{-30} of that of water; the radius of the universe is estimated to be 32,000 million light years or 300 times the distance of the remotest nebula visible today. Einstein's universe stood still in static space. The objects in it moved only relatively to one another.

On the basis of the measurement of electrons, Eddington tried to estimate the mass of the universe, and obtained that it was equal to 1.08×10^{22} suns; this would give an Einstein universe a radius of 1,068 million light years. By assuming that the universe began as the Einstein universe and would end as the Sitter universe, Eddington obtained that the density of matter has so far diminished one thousand times, and that the radius of the present universe is 10,000 million light years; but according to De Sitter it measures only 1,000 million light years. And according to Eddington's theory of the expanding universe, its age is 100,000 million years. But from geological and atomistic-physical data it has been estimated that the universe is 5 to 10 billion years old. *So there are several contradictions here.*

In Professor A. E. Milne's cosmology the universe behaves like an exploding grenade; the different splinters, each equivalent to a galactic system composed of billions of suns, are hurled away from the place of explosion with velocities ranging from one hundred to tens of thousands kilometers. According to Milne, all the nebulae are moving in a non-curved space identical with the space of our everyday experience.

In addition to the exploding universe De Sitter also considered one that begins in expanded form, contracts to a minimum and then again expands limitlessly; or the oscillating universe in which expansions and contractions follow one another regularly.

All these hypotheses, however, are only several of the many possible interpretations of the observed displacement of the spectral lines. Upon the correctness of the interpretation of this displacement depends the whole thesis of an "expanding world" and all its consequences.

Some modern astronomers also fear the absolute end of the universe, just as Buffon foresaw the end of the earth. According to them, the solid substance of the universe is constantly disintegrating in imperceptible radiation. Yesterday, the sun weighed 360,000 million tons more than it does today: the difference corresponds to the weight of its radiation in twenty-four hours. The same transformation of weight into radiation is going on in all the stars (to a smaller extent in the earth too, where complex atoms like those of Uranium constantly transform themselves into simpler ones, like those of helium, and in the process release radiation; but the earth loses only 90 pounds a day).

Because energy must in the end lose all capacity for transformation, the absolute end of the universe seems inevitable. However, the modern astronomers promise our universe billions and billions of years of life, while the chiliasts of 999 A.D. announced the end of the world for the year that followed. Many of these pessimistic astronomers grant that, of course, in the meantime the laws of nature may change, not to mention the theories of the astronomers, mathematicians and physicists.

. . . . .

Are you dizzy, dear reader? Do you distrust the exaltation of the mathematicians, the physicists and the astronomers, their machines, telescopes, spectroscopes, microscopes and photographic plates?

Copernicus' neighbors refused to feel dizzy. They made a carnival farce out of his theory that our good, solid, enormous motionless, centrally situated earth was rushed around itself and around the sun in double (or even triple) motion, at a heady speed. But the powers-that-be sensed Copernicus' revolutionary implications and began their life-and-death struggle against his theory. Under many names, in many fields and on many levels, this immense struggle between the world-revolution and world-obscurantism continues.

Copernicus triumphed everywhere long ago; even his enemies call themselves Copernicans today—and continue to combat him.

But the revolution initiated by Copernicus is still going on too. This "sceptic Copernicus," as one of the advocates of "orthodoxy" called him, was the quietest noise-maker in the world.

. . . And was he not perhaps the mightiest revolutionary of our epoch?

Galileo, _Dialogues_, 379 f.

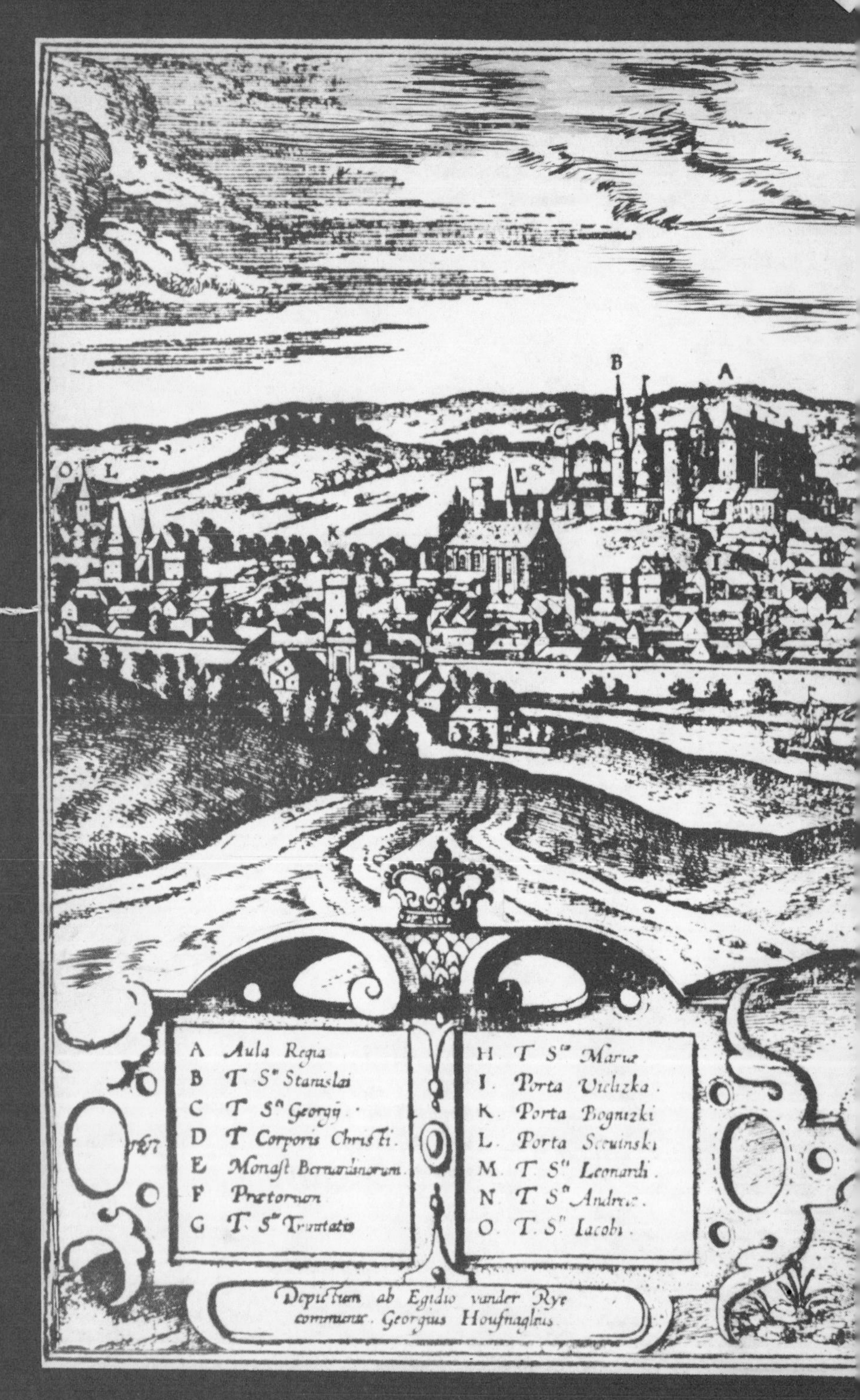

VIEW OF CRACOW
After an old copper engraving by Jerzy Braun—1572